From Then to Now

From Then to Now

The Remarkable Story of Ohio Northern University's
Raabe College of Pharmacy

Thomas A. Gossel, BS Pharm, MS, PhD

Professor of Pharmacology Emeritus
Ohio Northern University
Raabe College of Pharmacy
Ada, Ohio

ORANGE *frazer* PRESS
Wilmington, Ohio

ISBN 978-1939710-369
Copyright©2016 Ohio Northern University
Ohio Northern University
525 S. Main Street
Ada, Ohio 45810
All Rights Reserved

OHIO NORTHERN UNIVERSITY

Published for Ohio Northern University by:
Orange Frazer Press
P.O. Box 214
Wilmington, OH 45177

Telephone: 937.382.3196 for price and shipping information.
Website: www.orangefrazer.com

Top front cover photo: Pharmacy Students Circa 1890

Book and cover design: Alyson Rua and Orange Frazer Press

Library of Congress Control Number: 2015952334

Printed in China

This work is dedicated to the memory of
Dr. Charles Oren Lee (1883–1980)

A pharmacy historian and good friend,
Dr. Lee was Professor of Pharmacy at Ohio Northern
University from 1954–1971 and served the College
of Pharmacy as its interim dean between 1962–1963.

ACKNOWLEDGMENTS

This work was made possible because of numerous dedicated women and men—faculty, staff and administrators—who served Ohio Northern University's College of Pharmacy since its founding in 1884, and to thousands of students across my thirty years of teaching. To all of them, I extend my heartfelt thanks for their dedication and hard work that has made our college what it is today. I thank the students especially because they taught me so much more than I could ever teach them.

I also thank the following individuals: Scott Wills, director of development for the college, perked my interest to write a brief history for the college's 125th anniversary celebration, then encouraged me to elaborate further on the project. Anita Stanley, manager of ONU's printing services, was especially helpful in layout design and other particulars associated with assuring that my grammatical and punctuation errors were kept to a minimum. Paul Logsdon, former director of the Heterick Memorial Library and now ONU archivist, opened the institution's library of photos and news releases for my use and was never too busy to assist me tracking down a particular item of interest.

Additionally, Dr. Robert McCurdy, a close friend and fellow ONU pharmacy alumnus, was an outstanding promoter of the project through his many uplifting and encouraging stories and careful review of the manuscript. The college's former interim dean, Dr. Thomas Kier, and current dean Dr. Steven Martin, offered current data relevant to the college operation that was especially helpful. ONU president Dr. Dan DiBiasio and Chris Burns-DiBiasio were very supportive of the project and provided continued encouragement throughout its development. Marcy Hawley, publisher at Orange Frazer Press, provided valuable guidance for manuscript content. And, to my fellow pharmacist alumni and other friends of the college, I am appreciative of their support for this project, as well as for the college and its mission in general.

Dr. Ervin Pierstorf at his 99th Birthday Luncheon, July 11, 2015.

There is a very special individual and close friend who is responsible for keeping history alive at Ohio Northern for thousands of students and alumni, faculty and other friends. Dr. Ervin (Erv) Pierstorf, along with his late wife Florence and late brother Clarence, founded the Pierstorf Family Pharmacy Museum that forms a major part of the college's facility. The Pierstorfs then donated many supplies, equipment, and furnishings from their pharmacy that represented their lifetimes of work. The Pierstorf family also endowed the Pierstorf Scholarship Loan Fund established to help qualified pharmacy students who require financial assistance during their period of study to complete their program.

I am most appreciative of a very special group of dedicated individuals, my many professors, who taught in the College of Pharmacy or College of Liberal Arts during my student years at ONU, 1959–1963. Yes, I am one of those remaining dinosaurs of our profession—a four-year graduate of ONU's College of Pharmacy. These women and men inspired me in many ways, ways that stimulated me to love pharmacy enough to devote my entire professional life to it. Even now, more than thirteen years following retirement, I'm still at it. They are the ones who led me to eventually pursue graduate study, earning the degrees that qualified me to return to my beloved alma mater as a faculty member where I was able to live out my dreams.

I extend very special thanks to Phyllis, my wife of more than fifty-three years, whom I first encountered in our 8:00 a.m. freshman English class at ONU in September, 1959. She was simply too much to ignore. As bashful as I was, I still found the courage to ask her out. I must have made an impression on her because she accepted. That early encounter encouraged me to pursue other outings and we were married three years later between our junior and senior years. Phyllis has mercifully put up with me over the years in spite of all my quirks. She has, also, endured my many absences from home during my endless hours at the library or while sitting at my computer checking on endless specifics for this book. All the while I was able to ignore my many household chores, putting them off to another…then to yet another day. For that alone, I am quite thankful.

Finally, there was a group of individuals who gave generously to help underwrite costs associated with publication of this work. In addition to those persons who gave anonymously, the group included:

Peter Apone

Bruce Bouts

Mark Butler

Shawn Eaton

Verne Haugen

George Hill

J. Michael and Janet Hoopes

Kathy Karas

Rick and Jennifer Keyes

Paul Kocis

Ronda Lehman

Phil and Susan Lettrich

Jim Mannion

Steve Martin

Bob and Myrna McCurdy

Phil and Mary Oleson

Tip Parker

Bob Parsons

Erv Pierstorf

Bill and Gretchen Robinson

Todd Sega

Michael Storey

Vaiyapuri Subramaniam

Tim and Amy Tannert

Hanley and Mary Wheeler

Tom Wiechart

Scott and Jamie Wills

Suzanne Eastman-Wuest

J. Richard Wuest

It is with deep-felt appreciation that I recognize and sincerely thank each of these close friends for helping to bring this project to fruition.

CONTENTS

PREFACE

This historical account of the Rudolph H. Raabe College of Pharmacy at Ohio Northern University is presented for all who are interested in the college's long and rich history. It is not intended to be a detailed, definitive account of the entire history of the college but rather is offered to summarize some of the major influences that have made it what it is today. History lessons are oftentimes, well, boring. In relating the facts of what has happened to get us to where we are today, we may read something to the effect…"In such a year this happened, then in the next year this happened. This was followed in the next year by 'such and such.'" And so on it goes, on and on and on.

This book is written in a conversational style so that it can be understood and appreciated by individuals at all levels, not just professional historians although they are certainly encouraged to read and learn from it. Personal reflections are included as appropriate. Material is referenced not to impress, but to be used as a stimulus to enable the reader to dig further into the topics. Many of the references that pertain to the institution are now available online at *www.onu.edu/library/onuhistory/index.htm* and following the prompts. I urge all readers to check out what is available, and thus expand their knowledge about the college's heritage well beyond what is presented herein.

Ada and Ohio Northern University

The village of Ada in the 1880s may have seemed a most unlikely site to start a college of pharmacy. The tiny close-knit community of less than a thousand individuals with its dirt streets and modest frame homes, even log cabins, certainly did not reflect the cosmopolitan lifestyle and modern enterprises available in many larger towns and cities around the state. (Various sources list Ada's population in the 1880s as ranging over a wide continuum. Consensus seems to agree that a figure less than 1,000 was closest to the truth.) In retrospect, however, Ada was actually the perfect site to host a college of pharmacy. Situated on a major rail line connecting Pittsburgh and Chicago, the village was but a two-hour train ride west from Crestline, east from Fort Wayne, north from Columbus and south from Toledo or Sandusky. Ada thus had easy access from all directions. Of even greater importance, Ada's citizens welcomed the college's students with opened arms, housing and feeding them, and providing for many of their personal needs. It is because of this close association between pharmacy students and the village and its citizens throughout the years that information relevant to both groups is presented along the way.

In the earliest days of the college, students attended classes in the basement of the original ONU campus building. Their professional work was taught by a single faculty member whose full-time employment was as a pharmacist in one of the village's drugstores. Today, the College of Pharmacy is housed in a modern building and beginning academic year 2015–16, the faculty includes thirty-four full-time equivalents, along with twenty-eight shared clinical faculty assigned to sites across the state. The college's teaching sites are not limited to the Ada campus. Students can complete their rotations in all fifty states and in Africa.

It is hard to imagine how anyone who attended Ohio Northern University could not have heard about its founding. Indeed, that is one of the memorable stories I heard numerous times, starting with my early student days at ONU that began in September, 1959. As often I heard the command to "Button, frosh!" I also heard the details about how Henry Solomon Lehr overcame overwhelming personal hardship during the early days of his founding of the institution. What I heard only as bits and pieces of the story, however, was how the College of Pharmacy got its start.

During the period spanning 1961 to 1966, one of the college's most beloved and respected faculty members, Dr. Charles O. Lee, compiled a five-part historical summary of the early years of the ONU College of Pharmacy through 1959, publishing them in the college's newsletter, *The Ampul.* The pieces were prepared from information he had gathered and presented before the Historical Section of the American Pharmaceutical Association (now the American Pharmacists Association—APhA) at its annual meetings. I recall reading these accounts when first published and remember being excited as well as moved by the overwhelming personal commitment displayed by Dr. Lehr, Deans Raabe and Smith, and dozens of other women and men who, through the years, kept the college vibrant during some of the darkest periods in its existence. I also remembered Dr. Lee's final sentence in his series: "It is hoped that some person of the future will be inspired to prepare a glowing account of this College of Pharmacy, its purpose and usefulness." Dr. Lee was without doubt one of my most respected professors. He served as interim dean during my senior year and signed my diploma. I therefore decided that I would be that person of the future and accept Dr. Lee's challenge to continue his project and prepare an historical account of the college's purpose and usefulness. And so I humbly say, "Dr. Lee, This one's for you!"

What is presented herein is not intended to replace Dr. Lee's original comments. Rather, it is hoped that it will enhance his work and help the reader to intensify even greater interest in the history of the college from its origin to the present. I had the great benefit of having considerably more library resources available than did Dr. Lee some fifty-plus years ago. Dr. Lee also had limited space in *The Ampul* publications that my editors have assured me I do not have to be concerned with today.

Dr. Lee was a man of small stature, probably not exceeding five feet, more or less. But he was a giant of a man in my mind. I can still picture him standing in front of us in his pharmacy history class, always attired in a clean white laboratory coat with his arms often folded over his chest while he passed on the wisdom of his many life lessons to all of us, making history come alive. After all, Dr. Lee had lived through much of the pharmacy history he was teaching us. He was born one year prior to the founding date of this College of Pharmacy. "To know pharmacy's history is to appreciate it as a profession," he often told us. Then he would continue: "Pharmacy needs the guidance of historical knowledge more than any other profession because it is composed of parts of many sciences. It is truly sad to think of the many thousands who have graduated from the nation's pharmacy programs without any exposure to the profession's history."[1]

One point that Dr. Lee and I shared in our research for facts is that dates listed for various events often differ depending on their source. Instead of reading and then believing that a particular past event occurred in a particular year, it can be justified to imagine the noted time as an era rather than absolute year. Also, no matter how many times this manuscript was read and re-read during its preparation, and I long ago lost count, I am confident that some gremlins have likely snuck into the text. I apologize in advance for them and beg your forgiveness for my oversights, and I ask for your assistance in bringing them to my attention.

Generally, I have not gone into detail about professional matters ongoing at the state or national levels. When appropriate, however, I have included selected topics in order that the reader might have a better understanding of the forces that were influencing some of the activity ongoing at Ohio Northern's College of Pharmacy. Other times, I included some points in order to emphasize that this college was really up-to-date with the times. This is especially true as it pertains to how the college fit into the work of the greater institution, and how students reacted to the village of Ada. An Ohio Northern situated anywhere else in the world but Ada simply would not be the same. Yes, the college and university have been good to Ada, but Ada has been mighty good to them as well.

Speaking now as an alumnus of the Raabe College of Pharmacy after having spent thirty of my most memorable years of life on the faculty with six of them as the college's dean, as well as advisor for Phi Delta Chi pharmacy fraternity throughout the thirty years, I would be offering a picture of activity that was less than complete if I said I remained unaware of many student-originated pranks. Not only was I well aware of many of these, I encouraged some of them, from the sidelines for most of them, of course, and participated from the front lines in others. And yes, these were accomplished both during my student era as well as during my professional years on the faculty. All of these pranks were harmless to body and property but not necessarily to the victims' pocketbook or spirit. Most were downright fun. Indeed, years later I still chuckle at many of these "deeds of endearment" and my desire to describe them in print more clearly—well, perhaps they should be left to another time. It is because of these numerous happy memories that I have included brief descriptions of some student-originated activities along the way to help get the point across that students throughout the ages have shared more than simply the joy of studying.

Finally, I wish to share one additional reflection, one that has affected me emotionally. As I read through successive copies of the *Ohio Northern Alumnus* magazine beginning with the early years of issue through the present, a single feature hit me again and again. I would often read of an individual arriving at ONU as a faculty member or administrator, or a person who had initiated a special program or service, or accomplished something very special to the institution. In a later issue, I might read how this person was actively contributing to the mission of ONU. Continuing onward into later issues, I would then read about the person's continued accolades, and on and on it went. All too often I would eventually read an obituary in a later issue announcing that the person had died. A particularly difficult time for such examples often began in the depression years of the 1930s. With World War II approaching, I read hints of the institution's preparations for the war years and with time and escalation of the conflict, how so many of its students and faculty were leaving school to serve their country. Later, I would read the names of many of these former students or faculty whose dreams for the future had been shattered because they were now missing in action, were wounded extensively, or had been killed on the battlefield. I still think about the four new, relatively young faculty members, including myself, who joined the College of Pharmacy faculty in 1972. Now, only two of that number remain alive.

Throughout all of this, I often recall a movie from 1989 entitled *Dead Poets Society*. Set at a prestigious prep school in 1959, the teacher took his class to the school's trophy case one day to focus on the thought of *carpe diem*, Latin for "seize the day." As the students studied the photographs of many of the school's acclaimed athletes from the turn of the twentieth century, the teacher reminded them that these athletes now all shared one thing in common—they were all dead. The students were then urged to "Seize the day!" The teacher's point was that we all need to do all we can today, for tomorrow will come, then pass, all too quickly. Death statistics for every person in this and every other country are absolute: Death eventually claims every one of us.

That's the point I wish to make here—a point for all of us to remember so long as we live: Seize the day! Seize the day in all we do. We live a finite number of years. We will all be the subjects of study by tomorrow's retired pharmacy professors, or perhaps even professional historians as they write their own summaries of the people and period in which we live today.

It has been said that the best way to assess an institution's future is by studying its past—learning how our ancestors tackled the situations and problems of their day. Addressing ONU students and faculty at the university's Founders Day celebration in 1965, the Honorable John T. Connor, United States Secretary of Commerce, summed up his thoughts thusly: "The best way you can honor the past of this great institution is to look to its future. And this is what you are doing."[2] Before anyone can look to the future and try to summarize what lies ahead, he or she must first look back and study the past.

During its now greater than 130 years, ONU's Raabe College of Pharmacy has graduated nearly 9,400 women and men who have contributed in no small way to improved healthcare delivery throughout Ohio, the nation and in many other lands. More than one-fourth of all pharmacists in Ohio are Ohio Northern alumni. This has been possible because of the college's zeal for superb teaching. So long as that commitment remains its highest priority, the college can well expect to serve its constituency throughout this, and many future generations.

One valuable means to help our understanding of historical events is through viewing photographs taken at that time. While photographs taken today usually show outstanding detail and clarity, this has not always been the case with older ones. Many original photos have been lost, and other images blurred by the ravages of time. Fortunately, some were printed in pamphlets or books that still survive. Some of the pictures provided herein have been obtained from such sources and therefore may not be as crystal-clear as I would have liked. They are the best ones available.

NOTE

Throughout the eleven chapters and Epilogue of this book a third-person account was maintained for the most part. At the chapters' end, while describing the deans and their accomplishments, the more formal approach was continued. For those deans I knew personally, I then allowed my emotions to come forth in accounts added as personal reflections. The comments should not be viewed as being historically relevant, but rather as reflections or memories of the individuals as I remember them. Being my own personal memories, I humbly submit them in a first-person format. I hope you also have your personal reflections of favorite faculty and staff members and deans you remember from along the way.

From Then to Now

ONE
The Early Days

Gazing at the modern facility that today houses the Raabe College of Pharmacy, listening to in-depth lectures from its talented faculty, or examining the outcome of their high-quality research made possible by their equally effective grantsmanship efforts, or discussing current topics in pharmacotherapeutics with its students, it quickly becomes evident that this college is not a run-of-the-mill operation. Indeed, the pharmacy program at Ohio Northern University is first-rate and enjoys a rich heritage, one that all who have been associated with the college at any level can be proud of.

To understand what ONU's program has meant to the practice of pharmacy and to healthcare in Ohio, and to the greater institution as well as the village of Ada, one needs to be aware of the tremendous effort, including the trials and tribulations, that went into the founding of the North-Western Ohio Normal School and to general conditions in Ada at the time of its founding. It needs to be understood that then and now, the pharmacy program was and continues to be closely aligned not only with the mission and operation of the parent institution but also with life in and around Ada. As expressed in university catalogs spanning the ages, *Ada is a school town!*

Henry Solomon Lehr

The year was 1866. It had been raining and snowing for several days—typical March weather—when the slight and frail, but well educated, twenty-eight-year-old public school teacher Henry Solomon Lehr arrived by train in the small, swampy, backwoods village of Johnstown (later to be renamed Ada), Ohio, after spending time in several other towns along the way including Bucyrus, Upper Sandusky, Dunkirk and Forest.[1] It was less than ten months since his honorable discharge from the Union Army.[2] Not being able to connect with a representative of the school district in any of these towns, including Johnstown, he journeyed on to Lima, Delphos, and Van Wert, then continued to Monroeville and Elkhart, Indiana. Lehr then returned to Johnstown because there was something about the village that piqued his interest.[3] Never mind that there was only one main street and it was a sea of mud. His purpose in travel was to search for a town that would accept him as a teacher in its public school system. He also dreamed of eventually establishing a select school that would offer educational training at a level beyond that which was available in the public schools. Lehr envisioned opening a "normal school" that would prepare young women and men to become teachers in the public schools.[4] In the mid-century days of the 1800s, educating young people was still viewed by many as something nice to do but in most cases was not a prerequisite to making a living and raising a family. This feeling was especially prevalent among folks living in the remote rural areas of the country, particularly when describing the populace of northwestern Ohio.

The availability of qualified teachers was wanting. In order for an applicant to teach in a public elementary school in Ohio, he or she had to pass a county teachers' examination. The subjects included reading, writing, arithmetic, English, grammar and composition, geography, United States history and civil government, physiology, hygiene, alcohol and narcotics, literature, and the

Dr. Henry S. Lehr, President.

theory and practice of teaching.[2] The new school was designed to prepare prospective teachers for the ordeal of these teachers' examinations.

Lehr was especially impressed with the more liberal and broad-minded spirit of citizens of Johnstown, compared with the other sites.[5] As it turned out, his return to Johnstown was fortuitous for himself and also the local citizens. This time he met with Sanford M. Johnson, president of the board of education, who had just returned from a trip that kept him out of town during Lehr's first visit. It is told that when Johnson heard Lehr's plan for education, he remarked: "You're just the man we need."[3] The two men entered into an agreement that Lehr would teach in the local school, earning a salary of $2.75 per day, with service to begin April 9, 1866.[5] Johnson knew of Lehr's thoughts on creating a school for advanced-level learning.

Johnstown, Ohio

In the spring of 1866, Johnstown must have seemed like an unlikely location for Henry Lehr to live out his dream. It was little more than a small rural village, a typical frontier town in many respects, having a population of about 250 hearty souls.[6] The village was surrounded with dense hardwood forests filled with deer and other wildlife typical of such areas. It was located at the edge of the Scioto Marsh, which teemed with ducks and wild turkeys. Incorporated only five years earlier, the tiny village consisted of a number of modest frame dwellings and log cabins scattered haphazardly throughout the area with a grouping near the railroad depot.[5] The local economy was supported by two sawmills, a stavemill and barrel factory, a gristmill, a tannery, and an ashery.[7] There were also five saloons,[5] which Lehr likely took note of and through the years would prove to be a constant thorn in his side.[7]

A small stream bordered by prickly ash ran through the village from southwest to northeast.[6,7] The stream would plague the village for many years with severe flooding after a heavy rainfall. Johnstown and a majority of the area within Hardin County was flat, which meant that the community suffered from poor drainage.

Reminiscing about his early days in the village, Lehr described it thusly: "The question of ditching was a great problem. The people were poor and the water was plenty and the mud deep. On the west side of Main Street was a large open ditch. I have seen men…sitting on the side, fishing on a Sunday afternoon. I have seen groups of men, west of Ada, along the railroad, catch long strings of catfish, sunfish, etc."[1]

Today, one can see the visible result of massive effort around the vicinity to ditch and drain the marshland.[8] What could be described as a herculean project for the time (1860s) to drain the marsh, helped dry the land in and around the village. Still, the village streets were unpaved and routinely became a sea of mud when it rained.[1] One of the early municipal improvements within the village was the construction of a sewer system in 1872 that was formed with wood planks. This was followed by a stone conduit three years later.[9] With this in place, the village began to exhibit a newer, more modern look.[5]

The town had a newspaper, the *Ada Record.* By the 1870s, several brick buildings graced the downtown area, replacing many of the older one-story frame structures. In spite of its dirt streets and wooden sidewalks, Ada began to grow in style.[10] It was stated that these changes were "…enough to set a whirling the heads of Adaites."[5] This must have attracted a lot of attention on the outside, because the population increased over the following decades to around fifteen hundred more or less hearty souls.

One of the more interesting early efforts to improve the village's desirability for development and living was a program started roughly at the same time to maintain its streets. The village's government into the 1880s was small and underfinanced. An ordinance was passed that required all able-bodied males between the ages of 21 and 55 years to donate two days labor upon the streets and alleys or upon public roads and highways each year. College students (after the founding of ONU), as well as permanent residents, were included in this edict. Students understandably petitioned the village council for a waiver, which was constantly rejected. The story is told that one day when sixteen students were called out to work, about six hundred fellow classmates, in loud but spirited protest, appeared to the street commissioner and demanded they all be put to work at once. This act of solidarity must have seemed overwhelming to the commissioner and it appears the issue was settled quickly. Students were no longer required to "volunteer" their time to work on street maintenance and repair projects.[9]

Improvement to the village streets and alleys continued. Sidewalks were rare. When available, they consisted of wooden planks or occasionally railroad ties that didn't always offer secure footing when they were wet or covered with mud. On Christmas Eve, 1886, the first gasoline vapor street light was lit, with a total of sixty-seven lights eventually installed. They would normally remain burning until around midnight.[9] There still remained a serious downside to village life. Backyard outhouses, manure piles, trash heaps, pig pens, and chicken coups were often located close to the numerous wells that provided village residents with drinking water.

The 1876 publication, *Hardin County Directory*, listed 137 individuals along with their professional or trade descriptions. Included in this count were five physicians, two dentists, two druggists, and a Mr. Geo. S. Thomas who sold drugs, books and wallpaper.[5] By the standards of the day, Ada was considered a progressive community, and with its doctors and druggists, its citizens enjoyed at least as much attention to maintain their good health as could be expected from towns much larger.[9] In 1883, *The History of Hardin County Ohio* described Ada as remaining "…free from many of the vices so prevalent in our large cities."[8]

By 1882, the village was connected by telephone with the outside world. Residents could subscribe by purchasing tickets in multiples of fifty. Each ticket enabled the caller to talk five minutes to others as far away as Columbus or Dayton. Calls to Cincinnati had to be repeated through Springfield.[9]

Lest anyone wonder further of Johnstown's location and the public's access to it, and to what in the world Lehr was thinking when he chose it as the site for the future development of his normal school, the village was actually ideally situated for future enterprise. It boasted of an excellent transportation system via the Ohio and Indiana Railroad, which later became a division of the Pennsylvania Railroad.[9] The school's opening catalog for 1870-71 described the location as "…pleasantly situated in a rich, fertile and remarkably healthy county, on the Pittsburgh, Fort Wayne & Chicago Railway, midway between the intersections of the Toledo & Dayton Road at Lima, and the Cincinnati, Sandusky & Cleveland at Forest. It is only about a two-hour ride west from Crestline, east from Fort Wayne, north from Columbus, and south from Toledo and Sandusky, forming a grand center, easy of access from all points of the compass, and destined to become the great educational emporium of North-western Ohio."[11] Many students traveling to Johnstown (or Ada) via train in those early days could make the trip from home to campus in little more than the same length of time as students today might require in their modern automobiles.

There is an interesting story about how Ada became known by its modern name. The village was originally named Johnstown after one of its early enterprising and broad-minded citizens, Sanford M. Johnson, the same Sanford M. Johnson who hired Henry S. Lehr to teach school.[5] The name was confusing, however, to postal workers and railroad schedulers because there was also a village in Licking County with the same name. One or the other would have to be renamed. Tradition holds that when a name change was discussed for the Hardin County village the name "Sweet Liberty" was suggested. This was rejected by postal officials in Washington, D.C., who considered the proposed name too long. The department chose Ada instead, naming the village after a postal official's favorite sister.[5] It is reasonable to conclude that today, many people who live or work in Ada (okay, at least a few of us who live there) are happy that the suggestion of Sweet Liberty was rejected. The word Liberty was retained as the name of the township that today includes Ada.

Lehr's Obsession Burns Deeply

Over the ensuing years following Lehr's arrival in Johnstown, his obsession of opening a normal school continued to burn deeply within him. Through many meetings with village officials and interested citizens, Lehr proposed that the town donate a plat of land consisting of 3.5 acres and finance a building to cost no less than $6,500 of which he pledged to raise $3,500. The difference would be obtained by personal subscriptions from local citizens. Lehr was eventually successful at convincing the local citizenry that because of its fertile soil, after the marshes were drained the area would become wealthy and the people would want to educate their children. He reasoned that the village was ideally situated for easy access from all directions.[1] Moreover, there was little competition for education in northwestern Ohio—no seminaries, academies, normal schools, or colleges close by. The nearest institution was Heidelberg College at Tiffin, the nearest normal school was at Lebanon in Warren County, and the nearest institutions to the south were at Springfield and Delaware.[7] Local support for Lehr's proposal was strong since the board of education realized the potential benefit to the village if the proposed school were to grow into a regular college.[9] The money was subscribed in five days.[5] Thus, the North-Western Ohio Normal School was founded. Lehr is on record as saying that, considering the population, there were no other communities in Ohio with so many intelligent, progressive and enthusiastic citizens.[6] The contract for construction of Lehr's Normal Building was signed on April 5, 1871, and work got underway at once.

The young institution's educational philosophy was described in its first catalog: "The Normal is the result of a series of Select Terms held during the autumn months the past three years, where a large number of the teachers of the surrounding counties have received practical ideas of teaching. The patronage exceeded the accommodations. Through the liberality of the citizens of Ada and vicinity a beautiful attractive building eminence has been donated, upon which a first-class school building is in progress. It will be a commodious brick edifice, three stories above the basement, of modern style and finish, with ample accommodations for at least four hundred students."[11] Lehr's estimate that his building could contain four hundred students all at once may have been a bit exaggerated, but it could comfortably handle the student class sizes in the early days.

Opening Day

The new school formally opened on a sultry Monday morning, August 14, 1871, with Henry Lehr at its head "—for the instruction and training of teachers in the science of education, the art of teaching and the best method of governing schools."[12] Its program provided a curriculum designed to meet the needs of the students drawn to Ada.

One hundred thirty-one students from neighboring towns and surrounding country arrived in the village via train, wagon, buggy or on foot to attend classes.[13] It should be noted that some citations list the beginning headcount as 147 students. Lehr himself quoted this initial enrollment as either 131 or 147, depending on the publication. To think that a three-story brick building could be constructed in a backwoods village in such a short time when one considers the crude construction machinery available in 1871, it seems an overwhelming task. As it turned out, the Normal Building, an imposing and awe-inspiring structure, was not yet completed with the opening of the school year so the eager students met for classes throughout the village wherever rooms were available—in downtown stores' backrooms, halls and churches, in the room that housed the village's fire-fighting equipment,[6] and at the north end of the village at the public school building, then consisting of but four small rooms.[7] It is doubtful that local taverns were used due to Lehr's great opposition to the use of alcohol. By October 16, the Normal Building was far enough along to move into and classes continued in the new, modern edifice even though the structure was still incomplete.[9] The roof of the new building sagged in the center so that during a rain a deep pool of water collected at the center and leaked through into tubs set in the rooms below.[2] Townspeople were eventually able to correct the problem. That there was a great need for such instruction in that day is affirmed by the opening enrollment, regardless of which of the two numbers is the more accurate.

There was little doubt as to what instruction at the North-Western Ohio Normal School was to be all about and to whom the school recruited. The first catalog described it well: "The School-room, like the Pulpit, the Bar, the Office, must be filled by competent workers—teachers who fear not to advance modern and approved ideas. Since many of our students desire to make thorough and practical teachers, we establish each term special classes for such candidates, and drill especially for that profession.

"We aim, not only to impart the best instructions and to have our students independent thinkers, but also to assist them in acquiring the best modes of communicating what they know to others. 'It is of little moment how pure and cold the water, if there be nothing at hand to draw the sparking liquid from the fountain.' We need more practical common school teachers; more efficient teachers in all classes of schools; more punctual, honest business men; men and women who will both think and act. We strive to combine the practical with the theoretical. In our Normal Classes, students are called upon to take charge of classes and drill them as they would the tyro. It is surprising how soon the novice becomes adept in the profession and is able to instruct in the various methods."[11]

Students were promised that various interesting topics would be offered throughout the term by practical educators and orators, and no political or sectarian principles would be taught. They were also expected to be present, unless otherwise excused, at chapel services held each school day morning. This expectation was a direct result of Lehr's strong Christian commitment.[2] Although his beliefs were important to him, Lehr avoided tying the school to a particular church denomination.[11] Later he would relent when facing a serious cash shortage and to keep the school afloat, sold the school to the Methodist Episcopal Church. Textbooks were rare and students were advised to bring with them as many different books as they could transport for reference.

The academic year was divided into four terms—a fall term of fourteen weeks, a winter term of sixteen weeks, a spring term of twelve weeks, and a short "normal" (summer) term of six weeks. The summer term was intended for those who wished to study a particular topic and who could not attend a full term at any other season of the year. These periods would eventually be divided into different terms consisting of various lengths, catering to specific student needs. For example, a ten-

ONU Normal Building, circa early 1870s.

week winter term permitted students to study during the time when farm work was less pressing. There was also provision for students to enter the institution at any point during the year and remain for any length of time.[10] These provisions encouraged students to seek an education who might not otherwise be able to because of work or other responsibilities.

Year after year successive school catalogs repeatedly noted that a student could enter at any time and find suitable classes. This statement must seem incredible to those familiar with only the conventional programs of colleges and universities today. The normal school made it a literal fact, and it continued at Ohio Northern well into the twentieth century. It is astonishing to note how often new classes were scheduled to accommodate a handful of new students, often doing so with no more than a single student. This meant burdened instructors were expected to teach no less than six classes daily, and, in the summer term, perhaps seven or occasionally eight. This might total a weekly schedule of at least thirty-six hours in the classroom.[14] They were hardy men and women on the teaching staff in those days.

There was a strong expectation for strict discipline. Students were advised: "The government will be mild and parental, though firm. The teachers will pay especial attention to the moral welfare of both sexes. Students will be prohibited from attending those places of public resort which have a tendency to waste time and money and corrupt their morals."[11]

It should be noted that Lehr spent many years vigorously campaigning against local saloons. As an active member of the village council between 1884 and 1886, Lehr continued to promote his temperance cause, placing the saloons of Ada at the top of his list of undesirable haunts. He was not alone in his stand against sales of alcoholic beverages. On his side were a number of citizens, faculty members and, perhaps most surprisingly, a number of students who opposed the use of liquor. Local efforts to ban these sales had been underway since the early 1870s. When the Murphy movement swept the country in 1876, great meetings were held in the village, at which time hundreds from in and around Ada signed the pledge of temperance.[6] It would not be until the mid-

1880s that the temperance movement in Ada began to show positive results. Throughout the remainder of the decade the liquor question would be debated vigorously, motivated by a sincere belief in the inherent harm done by saloons and the consumption of liquor. During the periods when Ada was voted dry, the institution mentioned that fact in its publications. From the 1886–87 catalog: "Ada is free from the curse of saloons. They were voted out by the village council over a year ago. Parents can send their sons here without fear of danger from that source. We have a model town as regards morality."[15]

As expected, there still remained some who openly disagreed with the abolishment of the village's saloons. The fight was bitter at times.[13] In September, 1888, for example, two temperance supporters, one of whom was Ada's mayor, lost their barns to suspicious fires. Evidence suggested, but could not prove, the cause was arson. Three months later, a barn owned by Lehr burned, again under similarly suspicious circumstances.[9] On another occasion, Lehr was tipped off that he would be attacked on his way home and bodily injury inflicted. He took an alternate route and thus avoided the skirmish.[13] The announcement of a village-wide ban on alcohol was omitted from catalog copy when saloons were later permitted.[9]

From the very beginning, the use of tobacco in any form was strictly forbidden in any school facility. That provision would be reinforced many times during the upcoming years, although not always strictly enforced. When the newly constructed Robertson-Evans Pharmacy Building was opened in 1966, souvenir ashtrays bearing the university seal were given out as mementos of the occasion. Since then, however, the "No Smoking" rule within the pharmacy building as well as all buildings on campus has been strictly enforced.

Lehr set for himself a work schedule that seems unimaginable to even the most seasoned professor or administrator today. He began teaching as early as 4:00 a.m. and often taught thirteen classes a day in addition to overseeing his administrative obligations.[5] The strain from this load was immense and after several weeks into the first term he collapsed while conducting class. After a quick recovery, he returned to his duties.[4] Years later, he would reminisce: "…it was my purpose to found a school and conduct it according to my idea as to how a school for the people, especially the common people, should be conducted. I wanted this institution to be one that would recognize God in all its teachings, but still be non-sectarian; I believed in the co-education of the sexes; and I believed that a school could be so conducted that a student could study what he wanted, when he wanted to study it."[7]

Lehr's strong appeal was to all persons, young and old, who yearned for an education and had little or no opportunity to secure it. He created an opportunity by presenting a practical course of study at a minimal cost. It was a vision that Lehr maintained throughout his lifetime, and one that certainly played a significant role in his establishing the pharmacy program. Commenting on higher education in general, J.W. Zeller, State Commissioner of Public Schools of Ohio, later said: "There had been two obstacles that had hindered the masses in northwestern Ohio from securing an education—the high price of tuition and the inflexible curriculum of the college system. Standing head and shoulders above his fellows in vision, Mr. Lehr looked a quarter of a century ahead and leaped over college traditions and customs of a thousand years and broke the barriers that held back the masses from securing an education."[7]

Student Living Conditions

One of the contributory forces that assured the school's success was an arrangement for student housing in the many boarding houses that sprung up throughout the village. There were no comfortable dormitories or residence halls awaiting students in 1871, nor would there be for years to come. Lehr was convinced that students were better off, morally and materially, if they lived with upright families in the community rather than being housed in dormitories with uncertain supervision.[13] There was no doubt that the success of his school was very much due to a joint venture with the citizens of Ada. Lehr also wished to involve his students with community affairs as well as encourage the good citizens of the village to bring in such profits as they could from furnishing room and board to the students. Students were therefore offered room and board in private homes and in a number of buildings constructed by local residents specifically for this purpose. Many times identified solely by the names of the landladies, these enterprises supplied students with a room, meals, heating fuel and laundry services at a minimal cost in the 1870s ranging from $3.00 to $3.50 per week.[1] Some students formed clubs or associations, selecting a steward from their group who was responsible for purchasing all provisions. They then engaged a matron who prepared all the meals for the group. In this way, boarding costs could be reduced to $1.50 to $1.65 per week.[6] This cheap board gave the new institution the reputation of being a "poor man's school," a feature that no doubt helped contribute to its success in attracting students.

By the early 1880s, the school was offering bargains such as: "Anyone paying $119 in advance can attend the entire school year of 51 weeks and have tuition, good board and a neatly furnished room well cared for. For $110 paid in advance a student can have the same for the academic year of 47 weeks."[2] These offers were announced in the catalogs, and also in the Midwest farm periodicals, indicating that the appeal of the new school was especially directed to rural youth. This schedule of expenses remained virtually unchanged to the end of the century.

Throughout the remaining years of the nineteenth century and well beyond, students made their own living arrangements.[9] This was considered a healthy trait because for many years the institution boasted of that fact in its catalogs. Its 1885–86 issue, for example, stated: "One of the marked features of the Ohio Normal University is that the students are not herded together in large halls as is the custom and manner of arrangement of many other institutions. The plan is certainly not conducive to good manners, health or morality.

"It is a fact well known by all college students that the 'hall' is the place for fun and the breeder of mischief. We have avoided this by inducing the citizens to room our students. In this way they are brought into the families and are made to feel at home and comfortable. In case of sickness the lady of the house having few to care for, assists in nursing, and supplying them with those delicacies so essential to speedy recovery. It makes school life more like home life, and identifies the whole town with the interests of the school."[16]

School officials aided the process by contracting with various boarding houses for rooms to assure there would be sufficient living space for all attendees. Not only was the influx of students a source of revenue for the home owners and village businesses in general, the heavy competition from various boarding houses kept the cost to students very reasonable. In support of this system it should be noted that inflation, so prevalent and prominent today, was not a significant factor during the early years in Ada. Lehr did not make a public note of these living arrangements as being highly advantageous to the institution itself, but they most certainly were. The institution was spared the cost of constructing living facilities and of directly providing strict discipline for its students. With the low room and board costs to the students, and the minimal expenditure to the institution, it was truly a "win-win" situation for students, landladies, and Lehr.

And They Came and Came and Came...

Enrollment figures for the winter and spring terms, and for the next year, were less than expected. After that, students continued to arrive in droves each year, coming at first largely from farms in Hardin and adjacent counties. By 1884–85, the year a new pharmacy program was announced, the institution's student enrollment was reported to be 2,012. Enrollment increased in academic year 1885–86 to 2,369, and in 1886–87 to 2,434. Eleven years after the pharmacy department had started accepting students, total university enrollment was listed as 3,073.[5] It is important to understand that these figures represent the total headcount of enrollees for all four terms since some students enrolled for only a term or two, while others came for only a few weeks to brush up on a single area of interest. In other words, the headcount for the fall term plus headcount for the winter term plus that for the spring term plus the "normal" term equaled the total enrollment recorded for that academic year. At no time was the total number of students on campus for any given year equal to the enrollment reported for that period.[13] The first class consisted of eleven students who graduated from the North-Western Ohio Normal School on June 12, 1874. They were awarded certificates, not diplomas. Degrees would not be conferred or diplomas issued until after the institution was incorporated as a non-profit institution of learning in 1885.[13]

With enrollment increasing steadily, facilities in the Normal Building were taxed. In 1878, Lehr began looking for ways to finance a second structure. After some rather complex but ingenuous maneuvering, the Ada School District agreed to finance construction of a new building through a tax levy. The structure would be named the Administration Building. In return for the financial support, Lehr agreed to admit all students living within the local school district free of tuition.[13]

By the 1880s, with many of the problems attending the founding of the school behind it, the institution entered a period of rapid growth and diversification in curricular choices.[4] This was reflected in the trustees' decision in the spring of 1885 to change the name from North-Western Ohio Normal School to Ohio Normal University.[14] On May 19, 1885, the state issued a charter to the school under the name of Ohio Normal University. The change reflected the broad geographic area that the school's patronage embraced, the whole of Ohio and far beyond the state's borders.[13] Enrollment the previous year included students from twenty-one states and two foreign countries.[7] Moreover, no longer was the institution's mission limited to educating young women and men to teach in the public schools. Lehr retained the term "normal" in the name change because, as he thought, "...normal means natural, and we endeavored to follow natural methods in the teaching, organization, methods, and management of the school."[7]

The name change was also prompted by the students themselves. They wished that their alma mater would join the ranks of more prestigious institutions of higher learning, reasoning that the term "university" would elevate the school's status. Years later, while reminiscing about the change, Lehr noted his reason for changing the term school to the greater one, university: "After much consideration the word 'university' was used. At least two factors are necessary to constitute a true university; the one, a collection or combination of colleges giving instruction in many lines of learning and preparation for life; the other, special and extensive opportunities for original investigation. The Normal School at Ada in 1885 embraced a collection of colleges. We then had what we called the literary, commercial, engineering, music, fine arts, telegraphic, stenographic, law, military (and the pharmaceutical in prospect), departments—in all ten colleges in which was given instruction in their respective lines of culture. We lacked in a great measure the apparatus and laboratory equipment required for original investigation, but many of the universities of that day lacked both factors and were merely colleges and minor colleges at that."[7]

Another very important action to build the institution's esteem and ensure its long-term survival was undertaken on May 21, 1885. President Lehr had the university incorporated as an "Institution of Learning not for Profit."[9] Before that, the school could not legally grant degrees, even though the catalog of 1870–71 announced that: "All who complete the course assigned to the curriculum, or its equivalent, will be awarded diplomas."[11] As stated earlier, the "diplomas" that were promised were actually certificates that confirmed the students had completed the course of study.

From its Beginning

Ohio Northern University was founded at a time when higher education in not only the state, but nation as well, was undergoing great change. The pre-Civil War emphasis on the classical languages and religion was giving way to the sciences and to imparting a strong sense of vocationalism.[9] In other words, education that would lead to successful employment was an objective that students began to seek in earnest. That objective was at the heart of Lehr's establishing his normal school. It was certainly a driving factor in the founding of a program that would soon lead to ONU's College of Pharmacy. If it seemed like the institution in those early days was run like a business, truth is, it was. No apology is needed. At the same time, emphasis was underway to lift Ohio Normal University to the ranks of other highly esteemed institutions that continue in existence through today. It was because of this that the institution, and certainly the College of Pharmacy, survived through some extremely challenging periods and was able to eventually metamorphose into the modern institution of higher learning that it is today.

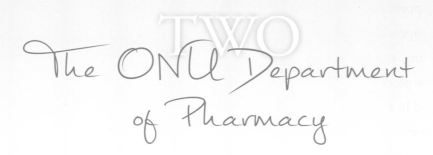

The ONU Department of Pharmacy

TWO

With today's strict standards in place for educating pharmacists, standards that include the requirement of a professional doctoral degree followed by a rigorous examination before obtaining the legal right to practice the profession, it stretches our imagination to the extreme to think that just little more than a century ago a person who wished to concoct any form of medicinal substances for the public could do so regardless of the product's therapeutic value or potential for toxicity.[1] All that was required for registration as a pharmacist was maturity to age 21, and a signed affidavit declaring that the applicant had served an apprenticeship, usually four years, working under the tutelage of another pharmacist, who himself had earned the right to practice his trade by simply serving an apprenticeship. There was no requirement for formal education or examination. There was no well-organized board of pharmacy and consequently, no inspectors to assure that the practice was forthright and honest and therefore contributed to the health and welfare of the citizenry.

A typical drugstore in the mid-1880s combined a "front end" consisting of a pharmacy work area and a general emporium that displayed a wide assortment of patent medicines, nostrums that were described as "health and beauty aids," along with other miscellaneous household items. There also was an area in the "back end" that was often out of the public's view for compounding the many scores of preparations and ingredients destined to be combined into medicines prescribed by physicians, or to be made into concoctions the druggist might personally prescribe ("counterprescribe") for his patrons after diagnosing their illnesses and recommending "just the right substance" to ease their complaints. The proprietor of the shop—the druggist (apothecary, pharmacist)—supervised a small staff of clerks (apprentices and/or other druggists) who tended to customers' needs. These people supervised most of the hard labor of measuring, sorting, grinding, sifting, macerating, and filtering extracts, spirits, and other concoctions of the crude drugs that were processed into a wide variety of remedies that may or may not have been described in the *United States Pharmacopeia*,[2]—an official publication of the U.S. government that lists established written and physical standards for drugs—or in the store's record (recipe) book of private formulations. In this manner, apprentices learned the fine art and science of pharmacy, which they in turn would later convey to others who would supervise another apprentice, and so on.[3]

It was in this environment that the Ohio legislature passed its first state law regarding the practice of pharmacy on March 1, 1884, to bring some order, and certainly much needed regulation, to the profession:

"It shall be unlawful for any person not a registered pharmacist to open or conduct any pharmacy or retail drug or chemical store, as proprietor thereof, unless he shall have in his employ and place in charge of such pharmacy or store, a registered pharmacist within the meaning of this chapter, who shall have the supervision and management of that part of the business requiring pharmaceutical skill and knowledge; or to engage in the occupation of compounding or dispensing medicines on prescriptions of physicians, or selling at retail for medicinal purposes, any drugs, chemicals, poisons or pharmaceutical preparations within this state until he has complied with the provisions of this chapter."[4]

The examination requirement of the new statute soon caught the keen entrepreneurial interest of Henry S. Lehr, president of the North-Western Ohio Normal School, which would eventually be renamed Ohio Northern University.[5] Reasoning that if pharmacy apprentices and drug clerks in the state were to be examined for their competency as pharmacists, they would certainly seek some schooling to help prepare them for the licensure examination.[3] Without delay, Lehr promptly moved to meet the anticipated demand. He announced that his school's new Department of Pharmacy would offer coursework to aid those who

Bottles with glass labels that contained liquid or solid forms of chemicals used for drug manufacture were common in most American pharmacies from the early-1860s until well into the 1940s and beyond. They are now greatly valued and widely collected for their beauty and decorative charm.

were interested in preparing for a career in pharmacy. It was too late to get this information into the 1884 catalog; the university catalog for 1885–86 was, therefore, the first to announce Lehr's intention: "The increasing demands of students wishing to engage in the study of Pharmacy have led the faculty to establish this as a distinct course. The Pharmaceutical student will be enabled to perfect himself in Theoretical Pharmacy, Theoretical and Practical Chemistry, Botany, Materia Medica, and Toxicology. Special attention will be devoted to all drugs and preparations appearing in the U.S.P."[6] The new Department of Pharmacy had been established and its program in pharmaceutical sciences was thus underway. The word "department" described the separate administrative units of the institution. Departments were later enlarged and transformed into colleges. What was at first referred to as the Department of Pharmacy evolved into the College of Pharmacy.

The requirement for successfully passing an examination to practice pharmacy in Ohio brought with it a need for professional education. The apprenticeship system continued to prevail but in many instances was found lacking in integrity. Some druggists felt they had neither time nor inclination to teach their apprentices the fine art of the profession. Druggists who did have this ability and time had no trouble in finding applicants. Often the apprentice would pay liberally for his instruction, in addition to providing service to his mentor.[1]

Moreover, this arrangement for serving an apprenticeship was not always enforceable.[7] Many stories have been told about individuals who, with little-to-no training, declared themselves capable and moved into pharmaceutical practice. Those who have seen the 1946 movie, *It's a Wonderful Life*, may recall watching 12-year old George Bailey, who, while observing Mr. Gower, the Bedford Falls druggist, about to mistakenly dispense a poisonous substance, saved the day (and perhaps an unsuspecting patient's life) when he called Gower's attention to his error. In the physical setting of this scene, which was likely during the early years of the twentieth century, the druggist (who was then well beyond middle age) could easily have been one of those self-proclaimed druggists of the day. Or he may have become registered after only a short apprenticeship without formal education because the new pharmacy law was not retroactive. If he had entered into practice in the early years following passage of the new law, he might well have had as little as twenty or thirty, perhaps forty, total weeks of schooling to prepare him for his examination. Or he may have obtained his book learning through reading one of the standard textbooks of the day such as the *United States Pharmacopeia* or Joseph Remington's *The Practice of Pharmacy*. Correspondence courses published in pharmaceutical journals flourished. One course, typified by the "National Institute of Pharmacy" and launched in 1885 by an entrepreneurial professor at the Chicago College of Pharmacy, and *The Era Course of Pharmacy* introduced in 1897 by the dean of the Scio (Ohio) Department of Pharmacy featured some of the nation's pharmaceutical scientists and educators as authors. Ohio has long been rich in educational resources that focused their teaching on the fine art of the profession (Appendix 1).

Apprentices who were not willing to endure the strict discipline set by the expanding number of correspondence courses could choose less threatening study aids typified by *A Course of Home Study for Pharmacists*, published in 1891 by the dean of the Illinois College of Pharmacy at Northwestern University. Or, they could master long lists of published questions that were commonly asked in the examination. The quiz-compendia collections of commonly asked questions in the state board examinations were strongly condemned by pharmaceutical educators and journal editors alike. Nonetheless, *A Compend of Pharmacy* (1886) enjoyed enormous popularity for more than four decades,[8] and it most likely brought a nice profit to its author(s).

The new law helped solidify the distinction between pharmacy and medicine. It stated clearly that any person who wished to serve as an apothecary must pass an examination before he or she could be licensed by the state. The act also directed the Ohio State Pharmaceutical Association to submit ten names of druggists to the governor who would appoint a five-member board of pharmacy whose duty it would be to examine all persons who desired to be registered (i.e., licensed), thus enabling them to perform specific duties associated with the profession. Provision was included to grandfather any person who was registered as a druggist prior to the law's passage, therefore excusing them from taking the examination. Needless to say, the knowledge requirements following passage of the new law were well intended to protect the citizens of the state.

The new program at Ohio Normal University—the North-Western Ohio Normal School had changed its name to Ohio Normal University in 1885— was successful from the beginning. The early curriculum was remarkably simple and easy to arrange. It most likely left very little time for hands-on laboratory experience. Courses in botany and chemistry, already taught at the institution, formed the scientific core of the curriculum and were equally suitable for students studying pharmacy. The first classes in the new Department of Pharmacy were taught in the basement of the Normal Building.[9]

The university at that time offered a preparatory curriculum in medicine, established two years previously, thus strengthening the institution's perceived capability to extend its offering of a course in pharmacy. The 1882–83 catalog stated that a demand had been met for a preparatory medical course in connection with other literary studies and touted that the facilities and work of "…this department will not be surpassed outside the medical colleges."[10] The editor of the village newspaper, the *Ada Record*, in all honesty noted that the classes in anatomy and physiology, as well as preliminary work in dissection, were of benefit in ridding the community of some stray animals. Perhaps these may have been caged with intention of using them in classroom demonstrations.[11] The institution noted that it had available a complete osseous system (human skeleton), excellent charts showing muscles and nerves, models of the ear and eye, and some valuable anatomical preparations. Students were promised: "Those desiring to fit themselves for the profession of medicine are furnished the very best opportunities in the study of Botany and Chemistry, as well as Anatomy and Physiology, and have the additional advantages of pursuing literary and other studies if they wish; also of attending the university's Literary societies."[6]

Only two additional courses (materia medica and pharmacy practice) were needed to round out the pharmacy curriculum. Area physicians were employed to teach materia medica, the forerunner of pharmacology. This was the usual case for other programs of pharmacy elsewhere in the United States. Lehr theorized that the new disciplines would also benefit students preparing for entry into a medical program so the investment in development of these two courses and procurement of faculty would pay off. All that was needed to complete the new pharmacy program was a trained pharmacist to teach the theoretical and practical aspects of pharmacy.[12] Lehr found this person in a well-liked and responsible Ada druggist, Charles S. Ashbrook.[13] Ashbrook served as instructor and department principal from 1885 to 1886, as the position that described the dean was called in those days. Although Ashbrook was listed in the 1886–87 catalog, whether he served throughout this entire year, or perhaps continued on in part-time service, is unknown.

For the new pharmaceutical program, the extent of coursework had to be estimated. Potential students read in the 1885–86 catalog that: "The exact limit of the course is not yet determined, but is expected to extend over a course of thirty weeks. Students entering this department will be expected to have a good general knowledge of the common branches."[6] The term "branches" referred to general education courses and others taught within the Department of Pharmacy or within other departments. They included botany, chemistry and physics. The catalog continued: "The different branches connected with this course will be under the direction of proficient teachers who will make it their duty to so fit students that they will be able to practice Pharmacy in those States having laws regulating this profession." Tuition for a term of ten weeks was set at fifteen dollars.[6] Those who successfully completed the program would receive the Pharmaceutical Graduate (PhG) degree.

One of the disturbing issues concerning researching facts from the early years of an institution is that accurate records of its proceedings are not always available, and some of those that are available are likely to be incomplete. Sometimes the information is undecipherable for a number of reasons including ink smudges or deteriorating paper and ink quality, or simply that the free-flowing style of penmanship so much in vogue at that time, while perhaps still pleasing to look at, is often difficult if not impossible to interpret. Then, there are the natural and other calamities that can destroy old records. This is unfortunate for Ohio Northern University since on November 4, 1913, a massive fire swept through the Administration Building and destroyed many records.[14]

An example of inaccurate records is found in the catalog for 1888–89. Mr. C.C. Sherrard is listed as Ashbrook's replacement as instructor in pharmacy.[15] Consequently, Sherrard's name has been included through the years in some university annals as having taught pharmaceutical topics and served as the department's second principal (dean).[16] This alleged association with the university was not questioned until recently. In fact, Sherrard's photo was included among those of all the other chief administrative officers of the College of Pharmacy in its "hall of deans" wall display within the current pharmacy building. The inaccuracy was uncovered in 2008 when one of Dean Raabe's articles published in 1956 was discovered. Dean Raabe wrote that he had the privilege of visiting at length with Mr. Sherrard.[13] During their conversation, Sherrard admitted that he had planned to teach at ONU during academic year 1888–89 and was under contract with the university to do so. The catalog for 1888–89, like copy for catalogs for all years, had to get to the printer well in advance of the academic year it described. It was likely prepared well ahead of the beginning of the next school year and catalogs were printed. At the last minute, however, Sherrard decided to pursue further academic study toward his degree at the University of Michigan's pharmacy department before joining the work force at Ada. As a result, he never made it to Ada. Meanwhile, President Lehr had contacted another local pharmacist, Brigham

S. Young, and arranged for him to teach during the year in which Sherrard was listed as an instructor. Near the end of that year, Sherrard and Young held a conference concerning the work in the Department of Pharmacy and mutually agreed that Young would remain and Sherrard, who was still at the University of Michigan, would go his own way. Any university correspondence or notes to this effect may well have been among those records that were subsequently lost to fire in 1913. Recently, Mr. Sherrard's photograph and citation naming him the college's second dean were removed from the hall of deans.

The new program in pharmacy was favorably received and extended to make it complete in every respect, including providing well equipped laboratories. Early university records do not specify the number of registrants in the new program. Five individuals who completed the program were listed by name in the university catalog for 1885–86. It is surmised that there were at least this number of other persons who signed up for less than the full thirty-week term, individuals who felt they had gained sufficient knowledge to pass the state examination and therefore left the program without completing the full course of study. There is little doubt that early students who attended the program for any length of time or graduates who completed the program pursued a career path other than as druggists in a retail setting.

The 1886–87 catalog made it clear that: "The favorable reception of the first announcement of this department in the catalog of 1886, and the wonderful success of its students has induced the Faculty to enlarge and greatly extend the course, making it second to none. It will be complete in every respect. The laboratories are well equipped and specially adapted to students in Pharmacy. No expense has been spared to make this department thorough; our object being to prepare students to fill positions anywhere in this country as practical pharmacists. The length of the course in Pharmacy has been fixed at forty weeks. Ladies will be admitted to the department."[17] The description continued: "For the full term of forty weeks (no less time will be counted) a fee of eighty dollars will be charged. This admits the student to all the lectures on Pharmacy and its collateral branches, besides giving him the privilege of taking any other studies he wishes in the literary department. This tuition must, in all cases, be paid in advance."

The new department was in existence for only one year but by now university officials, and certainly Professor Ashbrook, had a better handle on determining the minimum length of time required to provide a solid education in pharmacy, as well as having a better estimate of what the expanded program actually cost the institution, therefore knowing what student tuition ought to be. In that one year the program length increased from thirty to forty weeks and tuition increased from forty-five dollars (fifteen dollars for a ten-week course) to eighty dollars (twenty dollars for each ten-week period). Tuition for pharmacy proper was to be divided at the rate of forty-eight dollars paid directly to Professor Ashbrook, with the remainder (thirty-two dollars) paid to the treasurer of the literary department. This was the system employed for faculty remuneration, with the plan of teachers sharing in the tuition income remaining the policy for many years.[13] Faculty members received sixty percent of tuition in this year, at least, with the remainder paid to the institution. Other years would see different percentages paid directly to faculty members.

There was another practice of note. Operating funds were so tight in the early years that equipment required for teaching the courses was scarce. Instructors in pharmacy, chemistry and physics (also in the departments of commercial, stenographic and music) owned most of the equipment related to their work. Part of the students' fees was paid directly to the instructors for use of their equipment.[14] This practice would continue for about twenty years until the university could afford to purchase the necessary items from the professors and permit the students to use them.

Getting Along at ONU

By 1885, Ohio Normal University was well established and seemed to offer top-notch educational programs in a variety of disciplines. Institutional characteristics published in its catalog stated:

> 1. "The Institution is free from sectarian bias, but it is the constant aim of the teachers to recognize God, not only as revealed

in his word, but also in his works. To point out to the student, whenever the opportunity occurs, the wisdom and goodness of God as exhibited in nature. To inculcate lessons of morality, both by precepts and example.

2. The Institution is self-sustaining. Not having an endowment fund to rely upon, its teachers are made to feel that success and pay depend upon energetic, earnest, systematic labor. The motto is not 'How little can be done in the longest time,' but 'How much can be well done in the shortest time.'

3. The instructors are very accommodating. Kindness is not assumed, it is real. No scolds are tolerated.

4. The government is peculiar. The teachers accomplish their ends of maintaining the best of order, by putting students upon their own honor and assisting them in their efforts to do right, by parental watchfulness. A student cannot continue in wrong doing and be upheld by his fellow students, or even tolerated in society. The government being based upon reasons, and the teachers being kind and accommodating, hazing and other barbaric college tricks are unknown.

5. A leading characteristic is the sociability among the students. True merit, and not wealth and fine clothes, is the pass-word for entering into society."[6]

Student life outside the classroom wasn't ignored, and Ohio Normal University provided ample opportunity for all students to develop skills needed to assure a well-rounded educational experience. The catalog for 1885–86 explained: "About every two or three weeks the students congregate in the Literary Halls for the purpose of getting acquainted with each other, and more especially to cultivate their social nature. They spend about three hours in conversation, declamations, music, etc. These reunions afford opportunities for young men and young ladies to increase their colloquial powers, to study human nature, to appear free and easy in society, and generally to smooth and brighten by mental attrition, in the same manner as 'steel sharpeneth steel.' These reunions are in charge of one or more members of the Faculty, and are free from low jestings, and other vulgar practices, and can be participated in by the most fastidious moralists. Reunions, when well conducted, are elements of success in any school. That man is a social being, is acknowledged by all, and if the young and gay are not allowed to indulge this disposition in a proper way, all the old monastic rules of colleges and convents cannot totally prohibit the indulgence of the same in some way, and in a way which is generally to be deplored, such as is afforded by saloons, card tables and the ball room."[6] The literary societies were no doubt a valuable asset to the institution and their members. Pharmacy students, however, seldom attended the old established societies. If they met for literary enrichment, they preferred a private club.[18]

Regular written examinations were administered every four weeks. Students earning an average grade for the term exceeding seventy-five percent were promoted to the next higher class. Students were told that they or their "…parents who desire a full report of the department, scholarship, and class standing, can have the same by calling on the Secretary of the Faculty."[6]

The institution responded positively to what was definitely a significant problem at the time—a shortage of spending money. The university helped its students get around the dilemma of having to purchase the high-priced textbooks of the day by offering to rent the popular textbooks for from ten to twenty-five cents a volume, per term.[19] Persons renting books needed to deposit the value of the books, which was then paid back when the books were returned.[6] All students were advised to bring along with them from home whatever textbooks they owned or could borrow on the various courses they desired to study.

Requirements for graduation were straightforward: "The candidate…must have attained the age of eighteen, be of good moral character, have a good general knowledge of the common branches, have had two years' practical experience in the drug business (the time spent in this school may be counted in). If the student has not had this practice in the store, he will be furnished with a certificate of proficiency, and upon his completing the required course, will be granted a diploma."[17]

Students may have been enticed to study harder because of competition and a chance to win a special prize. From the 1886–87 catalog we read: "The instructor in Pharmacy and Materia Medica offers, with the consent of the Faculty, a gold medal, to the student passing the best final examination in these two branches."[17] By 1889–90, the description had been enlarged such that: "To the student who presents the best cabinet of original pharmaceutical preparations will be presented an elegant gold metal. The cabinets entered for the prize to become the property of the department."[20] Students, being as competitive as they were (and still are), and the institution itself, must have benefited greatly—students for the prize, and the institution for the display of pharmaceutical preparations. Today, nothing is known about the size, shape, or message on these metals, or even how many, if any, were awarded.

The catalogs for many years asked for donations of all sorts: "All persons interested in the cause of education, and especially in building up an institution of learning in Northwestern Ohio, are kindly invited to make donations of any specimens, geological, mineralogical, zoological, botanical, historical, Indian relics, or any curiosity of any value or kind whatever, they may feel disposed to present to the Institution. The names of all donors are preserved in the archives of the Institution."[17] This willingness to accept donations of materials that may be of interest to others continues today. Pharmacists and friends of the college are still asked to consider donating personal mementos or other items of pharmaceutical interest that are descriptive of earlier eras, which will be displayed in its Pierstorf Family Pharmacy Museum.

For some reason, the Department of Pharmacy is not mentioned in the catalog for 1887–88, although the catalog lists the then current students and alumni from the program. No reason is given for this omission. Information reappeared in the catalog for 1888–89, but its content was abbreviated over the 1886–87 issue. Students were still permitted to enroll at the beginning of any term.

Within ten years of its founding, the Department of Pharmacy had grown such that a new facility was needed to serve this burgeoning program. The campus of Ohio Normal University by now sported three buildings. The Normal Building, erected in 1871, was a large three-story brick structure. In 1878–79 another large brick structure, the Administration Building, was built to accommodate the increased patronage. In 1883, a modest two-story frame structure was erected on Gilbert Street southwest of the Normal Building. It contained two recitation rooms on each floor. An homely-looking, rectangular-shaped, wooden structure, it quickly earned the informal moniker of the "Sheep Shed."[11] It was still necessary, however, to rent additional meeting rooms and a hall from private individuals to accommodate all students. Space limitations for the pharmacy program needed to be addressed very soon.

Until this time, pharmacy classes and laboratory instruction were scattered among the three buildings on campus. The school's progress in providing pharmaceutical education was indicated by the 1892–93 announcement: "The rapid growth of this department within the past year, and the growing demand for practical pharmaceutical work, have caused us to remove this laboratory to larger and more commodious quarters. It is now complete in its appointments. Each table is supplied with an entire outfit of apparatus (with storing closet), and each student receives full instruction in the manufacture of Waters, Spirits, Tinctures, Syrups, Liquors, Extracts, Fluid-extracts, Abstracts, Infusions, Decoctions, Oleates, Ointments, Cerates, Plasters, Papers, Suppositories, Emulsions, Collodions, Elixirs, Mucilages, and the more important Galenical preparations, etc, etc."

The announcement continued with: "This work embodies all the processes of Weighing, Measuring, Ignition, Calcination, Terrifaction, Incineration, Sublimation, Evaporation, Distillation, Desiccation, Exiccation, Granulation, Crystallization, Precipitation, Dialysis, Filtration, Clarification, Decoloration, Extraction, Percolation, etc, etc."[21]

To accommodate the growing pharmacy program, a modest two-story frame building was therefore constructed on Gilbert Street southwest of the Normal Building, at the southwest corner of the present Lehr Building, just steps away from the "Sheep Shed." This was the fourth building of the Lehr era. University publications described the new facility: "The building is well arranged for light and ventilation, is heated throughout by hot air, and provided with all the conveniences necessary to the comfort of the student."[22] The first floor was used exclusively by pharmacy with the second story providing a meeting place for the Adelphian Literary Society.[18,23] While generally called "Pharmacy Hall," the building was sometimes referred to as "Adelphian Hall,"[24] and in some publications as "Pharmaceutical Hall." The new edifice was occupied in August, 1894. It should also be noted that it was unusual in those days for departments or colleges of pharmacy at other institutions to occupy their own building. Notwithstanding its unpretentious appearance, Pharmacy Hall at Ohio Normal University created a very favorable impression to students and faculty alike.[12] The means for financing construction of the new building, as with expenses for building the "Sheep Shed," remain unclear. Financing for construction of the Normal Building and Administration Building was accomplished through assistance by Ada's citizens. Apparently none of the repeated appeals to village citizens were successful for completing Pharmacy Hall.

Lecture rooms were equipped with apparatus adequate for the experiments and demonstrations used in teaching. Heat, light and ventilation were sufficient for the comfort and convenience of both the teachers and students. "By the floor arrangement, the various laboratories, scale room, herbarium and quiz rooms are connected with the lecture room, and each will be found complete in its equipment."[25]

It was also noted that the laboratory fee had been increased from $1.00 to $1.50 per term. For the first time, junior and senior courses in chemistry were included. This indicates that strong effort was made to provide more complete instruction in this important area. Advantages of the pharmacy program for 1894–95 bragged:

ONU, circa 1895 (looking west from Main Street). Pictured left to right: "Sheep Shed," Pharmacy Hall, Normal Building, Administration Building.

Pharmacy lecture room, circa 1894.

- "The Pharmacy students also have the privilege of taking Latin or any of the literary studies without extra charge. Botany is included in the regular course of Pharmacy.

- There is no large laboratory fee to pay.

- You can enter at any time and complete the entire course or any part of it.

- New classes are formed every ten weeks.

- We offer superior advantages to Reg. 'Assistants' who wish to review for examination as 'Pharmacists.'

- Our diploma is accepted in lieu of the first year's lectures by the leading medical colleges.

- Our course as arranged insures student recitations and laboratory work every school day (except Saturday) and not twice a week as in nearly all schools.

- Our reading room receives all the leading Journals of Pharmacy, and our libraries will be found to contain all books needed for reference.

- We guarantee at least 700 hours in practical laboratory work in our course."[26]

Junior pharmacy laboratory, circa 1894.

The Program

The synopsis of the course in pharmacy was outlined thusly:

"First term (ten weeks): Practice of Pharmacy, Elementary Chemistry, Botany, Materia Medica, Chemical and Pharmacal Laboratories

Second term (ten weeks): Study of Inorganic Pharmacals, Materia Medica, Organic Chemistry, Chemical and Pharmacal Laboratories

Third term (ten weeks): Study of Organic Pharmacals, Pharmacal Chemistry, Materia Medica and Pharmacal Laboratory

Fourth term (ten weeks): Magistral Pharmacy, Organic Chemistry with Volumetric and Gravimetric Analysis, Prescription Writing and Compounding, Urinary Analysis."[25]

For students wishing to earn college credit for their efforts, they were required to pass an examination at the end of each term and a final examination upon the entire course. Deviations from this rule were not permitted. Under no circumstance

were seniors permitted to leave before the final examinations were concluded.

Mention was made for the first time of a second degree. It was stated that: "Students wishing to pursue our extended course of two years for the degree of Pharmaceutical Chemist (PhC) will first complete the course for the degree of PhG [Pharmaceutical Graduate], after which the work will be extended. Students who may have graduated from schools *requiring an equal amount of laboratory work* will be admitted to the second year on presentation of proper credentials."[25] It was explained that the second forty-week year could be divided into two terms of twenty weeks each and that much of the second year's work would consist of elective courses. The PhC degree gradually became widely popular at schools of pharmacy across the

Cachets (shown in foreground) were rice flower shells that held ill-tasting solid dosage forms of drugs. Immediately prior to placing in the mouth, they were dipped in water that caused them to collapse to make swallowing easier. Used in U.S. after 1850 until gelatin capsules became widely available. Shown are supplies druggists used for filling and sealing the cachets.

country, and was especially appropriate at Ohio Normal University for the three-year curriculum in pharmacy that came into vogue in the twentieth century. The PhC degree would continue to be awarded at ONU until 1935, becoming obsolete when the four-year Bachelor of Science (BS) degree became the standard for graduates in pharmacy.

It is interesting that each of the teachers and special lecturers listed in the 1894–95 catalog was identified by name except for the individual who held the position of assistant professor of pharmacy and director of pharmacy laboratories. This position was listed as "To be supplied." It is interesting because apparently well qualified teachers of pharmacy were scarce in the early days, just as they are today. The statement continued through the 1905–06 catalog. It is assumed that, as is often the case today, other instructors combined their talents to take up the slack and *temporarily* fill the vacancy.

The catalog for 1895–96 described the pharmacy department about the same way as in the previous year, but listed several new ideas.[26] Most notable was the inclusion of photographs of laboratories and lecture rooms used for pharmacy and chemistry instruction. Provision of these photos in a catalog of that era for pharmacy emphasized the growth and progress that was well underway.

Under the description of pharmaceutical and dispensing laboratories, the following was included: "The laboratories are open at all hours, and there is no limit placed upon the time that the student may desire to devote to this work, the minimum hours required being three hours *each school day.*"[26] There was no further comment as to the merit of this after-hours privilege; moreover, no explanation was provided to note whether the extra hours were supervised and if so, by whom.

Junior and senior chemistry courses were described at length, each course comprising twenty weeks. For the junior course it was noted that: "The laboratory is open at all hours, and is under the personal attention of the professor of chemistry and an able assistant. A graded course will be pursued, and the instructions given will be carefully adapted to the proficiency of the student." In this regard it was also stated that: "The greatest care is taken to inculcate a thorough and comprehensive knowledge of characteristic chemical reactions, thus enabling our students the more readily to determine the purity of their drugs and chemicals."[26]

For the senior course, the catalog bragged that the "…course will consist of a thorough study of the chemistry of the various U.S.P. products, with equation writing and problems, embracing every form of chemical mathematics. Particular attention is given to volumetric and gravimetric methods of analysis. Our method of combining the lectures with thorough laboratory drill insures our graduates a comprehensive knowledge of analytical methods, such as can be had in no other school of pharmacy."

Extensive discussion was also provided about botany and materia medica. The same catalog stated: "The first part of this work is devoted to the study of Elementary Botany."[26] In those days, every pharmacy curriculum across the country offered a course in materia medica, which customarily included the classification of vegetable and animal drugs, their specific names, proprietary uses, doses, chief constituents and methods of isolating them, synergists, incompatibilities, and adulterants. Moreover, "A complete cabinet of organic and animal drugs is provided for the use of students free of charge. Particular attention is given to prescription writing, and the analysis and compounding of prescriptions, *presenting practical difficulties and the best methods of overcoming them.*"

Catalogs for years 1896–97 through 1899–1900 devoted about the same amount of space to the pharmacy program including listing faculty, providing course descriptions and other pertinent information, and providing pictures of the laboratories and classrooms. It appears that the pharmacy faculty in cooperation with university officials made every effort to assure their program in pharmacy provided an education that was, in their minds at least, second to none in the country.

An interesting change in course scheduling appeared beginning with the 1897–98 academic year. Instead of the four ten-week terms as had been the case, the curriculum now consisted of two terms of five months each, termed junior and senior courses. The synopsis of coursework in pharmacy was as follows:

"Junior Course (20 weeks): Practice of Pharmacy, Elementary Chemistry, Botany, Materia Medica, Chemical and Pharmacal Laboratories.

Study of Inorganic Pharmacals, Materia Medica, Organic Chemistry, Chemical and Pharmacal Laboratories.

Senior Course (20 weeks): Study of Organic Pharmacals, Pharmacal Chemistry, Materia Medica and Pharmacal Laboratory.

Magistral Pharmacy, Organic Chemistry with Volumetric and Gravimetric Analysis, Prescription Writing and Compounding, Urinary Analysis and Laboratory."[27]

No word was given as to the reason for the scheduling change. In time, the Ohio Pharmacy Board would require that coursework be extended over two calendar years with a prescribed school-free period between the terms. The purpose of this open period was to provide time for students to acquire practical experience by working in a pharmacy between terms. It is surmised that Dean Young knew of this forthcoming rule and decided to move his program into the forefront to be in compliance with the revised scheduling.

Outside the Classroom

Students studying pharmacy at Ohio Normal University near the close of the nineteenth century adhered to the same strict standards of discipline and moral culture as did students pursuing other courses of study. The catalog for 1885–86 was quite clear: "The government is lenient and parental, yet firm. The moral interests of the students receive special attention. Religious influences are so wielded that all inclination to vice and evil are discouraged. The different Churches and Sabbath Schools are regularly attended by the students. Each student is required to render cheerful obedience to the few rules that are necessary for the government of the school. Students are not permitted to attend places of public resort which have a tendency to waste their time and money, and corrupt their morals. The teachers are connected with the different religious denominations, which avoids sectarianism, but all work together for the advancement of true Christianity. The students have organized a students' prayer meeting, which has been the instrument of accomplishing much good. The various Churches and Sabbath Schools of town welcome all to their meetings and exercises, and most of the teachers and officers in the Sabbath Schools are students of the Normal School. There are in connection with the institution, a Y.M.C.A., and a Y.W.C.A., which are largely attended. They have been the instruments in God's love, of converting many to Christ. There are also Bible readings in which a few meet to study God's word under supervision of one of the teachers or an advanced Bible student. Moral culture is not neglected."[6]

Early pharmacy students, circa 1890. Note two female students, second row, far right.

Pharmacy student group photo shown in relaxed mode, 1899.

By the following year, another line had been added to the discussion: "Ada is free from the curse of saloons. They were voted out by the village council over a year ago. Parents can send their sons here without fear of danger from that source. We have a model town as regards morality."[17] Added to this was the feeling that "Ada…is comparatively free from the evils of aristocracy, and the vices so common in larger towns and cities. Its people are moral, kind and courteous toward the students, and take great pains in making their stay at the Normal both pleasant and profitable."[6]

Students and their parents continued to be reminded that: "Ada is a school town and the majority of the families are engaged in boarding and rooming students, and this is why expenses are low. The competition is sharp; hence prices are low and board good. We could furnish board at $1.00 per week, as is advertised at some institutions, but we prefer to charge enough so as to furnish good, wholesome food. Food must be nutritious to supply brain nutriment. Further, we furnish napkins for the tables, and our rooms are carpeted, towels are furnished, and all the bedding is supplied that may be needed. Students should remember that when these incidentals must be furnished by themselves, if they neglect to bring them along, they must pay what is asked when no price is named in the printed matter. Again, we do not only supply all these things, but keep them clean and in good order. When students furnish them they must also pay for the washing. These extras frequently cost more than the published price list."[6]

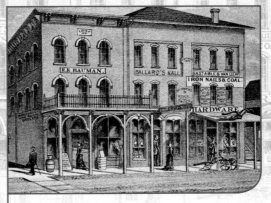

Downtown Ada, 1880s.

Then, there was another expense. In the catalog for 1888–89, the following notice was included: "Gas, in large quantities, has recently been discovered in the vicinity of Ada which affords cheap fuel. But what is of greater moment to the student than cheapness, is the convenience and cleanliness. A fire is easily started, no kindling is needed, no ashes are to be carried out. The temperature of the room is easily regulated and without extra cost the room can be kept warm both day and night. Coal and wood fires need to be replenished frequently, where gas is used, this is not the case, thus saving much time and annoyance. It is safe, convenient, cheap."[15]

By 1893–94, the catalog copy for fuel no longer touted the merits of natural gas as fuel for heating. Four years later, the reference to gas was eliminated and replaced with "…coal and wood are used as fuel." Either way, during this span, the average cost to each student for fuel and light, for the entire year was about $10.00.

Admittedly, students today might scoff at the thought of having to deal with such inconveniences and restrictions upon their living arrangements which, obviously, somewhat restricted what they could and could not do in their personal time. In those early days, however, students accepted the restrictions for the most part and continued to make Ohio Normal University their port of call for earning a top-notch education that prepared them for their life's work. Of course, they, like young people through all the ages, also believed the old saw that "all work and no play makes Jack a dull boy."

The university's students from the very beginning were an "adventurous" group, enjoying pranks, mostly innocuous, but certainly spirited, physical, and sometimes bloody.[14] Pharmacy students were no exception. In 1900, the junior and senior classes staged a joint parade through Ada while dressed in their nightshirts. Each class posted humorous placards about the other throughout the village. The juniors then invited the seniors to a roast.[11] An article in the *Ada Review* stated: "Upon the whole the conception and execution of the cartoons and program was good and wholesome fun, barring one of the cartoons left at Kemp's [drugstore] and included some good take-offs on the quips and quirks, the shortcomings and peculiarities of some of the teachers and Seniors."[28]

Perhaps more notable than the competitive fun between the two classes were the regular scrimmages between the pharmics and engineers. What started as a friendly rivalry soon turned into periodic riots. In 1902, a class scrimmage between the two students groups turned into a bloody mess because of flying missiles.[29] More will be said relative to the frolicking merriment of ONU's pharmacy students in the following chapter.

A significant event for the institution was recorded for 1898. As mentioned before, since its early years, the university suffered from significant budgetary woes. With no endowment from which to pull funds, along with an extremely low tuition base, serious trouble loomed ahead. The two major buildings on campus, constructed in 1871 and 1879, and the more recent "Sheep Shed," were by now outdated and in need of extensive repair. Pharmacy Hall already had space limitations. There was no prospect for financial assistance from any off-campus source. Looming just over the horizon was the termination of the thirty-

Pharmacy students with Dean Young (second row from bottom, fourth from left).

year contract between the Ada school district and the university. In 1879 the Ada taxpayers had erected the large, imposing Administration Building and leased it to the institution in return for free tuition for Ada students. Under the terms of the contract, which had only nine more years to run, the land on which the building stood would revert back to the local school district. A sponsor with deep pockets and prestige needed to be identified as soon as possible if the institution was to survive into the twentieth century.

At the September, 1898 meeting of the Central Ohio Conference of the Methodist Episcopal Church (now known as the West Ohio Conference of the United Methodist Church) held in Sidney, Ohio, the university trustees sold the real estate and personal property belonging to the university to that conference. President Lehr had intentionally avoided affiliating the institution with any specific church group for so many years. He now reasoned that the move was necessary to place the increasingly popular institution for higher education on a solid foundation and to insure its permanency by guaranteeing to it the support and cooperation of a progressive, wealthy and influential religious body. Many of the institution's former students were ministers in the Methodist church and supported the church's purchase of their alma mater.[23] Not everyone was supportive of this suggestion, however, voicing their opinion that it would be sinful to teach the professional courses such as engineering, pharmacy or law in a school endowed by a church.[24] The church could certainly provide the buildings and equipment so badly needed. Proponents won out, however. The transfer of property took place on August 2, 1899.

Dr. Lehr retired as university president in August, 1902, and was replaced by Dr. LeRoy Belt, a Methodist minister. In the course of Belt's administration, as fast as existing faculty contracts permitted, came a change in the relationship of the several departmental schools with the main institution. These heretofore semi-independent units, including pharmacy, were reorganized under one management and control. Deans and faculty were placed on salary instead of commission, with all tuition funds being sent directly to the treasurer who then paid individual professors a stipulated salary.[11]

During this era another event was underway that would become an important part of the institution's pharmacy program. On April 16, 1901, university trustees formed a committee to examine the need for a new building. In January, 1902, the institution received a gift of $10,000 from Lewis Dukes, a prosperous Hancock County farmer and president of the university's board of trustees, to finance the project.[14,30] Following a subsequent gift from Dukes, excavation for the new building began in June, 1902. On July 27, an impressive ceremony marked the placement of the cornerstone,[31] and by April, 1903, Dukes Memorial was occupied and in use. When completed, the building was the finest structure on campus. It contained eight spaceous classrooms with an office space for each room.[32] The handsome structure would initially house the departments of chemistry and mathematics, and the College of Engineering. Thirty years later, it would be occupied by the College of Pharmacy, leading to a true student and faculty "love-hate" relationship that held until 1966, when the college moved into its new facility on the West Campus.

At the July 28, 1903, meeting of the university trustees, the name of the institution was changed from Ohio Normal University to Ohio Northern

University. Tradition holds that a group of engineering students petitioned for the change. They felt that as members of a professional program, the value of their diploma was lessened by their receiving a degree from a mere *normal school*, and that the new name would more accurately reflect the true character of the institution.[14] President Belt was sympathetic to the suggestion and later explained: "The word 'normal' being expressive of but one specific function performed by the institution, [it] was thought to be incompatible with the idea of the university, and, though performing the function of normal teaching, this school was judged by the status of other poorer normal schools."[33] The name change was well received by all parties, including pharmacy students, and also had another advantage, the additional benefit of preserving the school's traditional "ONU" identity.

Medical Education

A preparatory course in medicine had been available at the time of the founding of the Department of Pharmacy, and this, along with the institution's sound science program, may have greatly influenced Lehr's announcement of the new pharmacy program. The preparatory course, along with other departments, suffered from the school's chronic shortage of funds and the medical course was dropped shortly after the new pharmacy program was begun.

In April, 1904, however, the idea of a medical department was revisited. An affiliation was struck with the Fort Wayne College of Medicine in Indiana, a college that had been in existence since 1878 and was located just approximately eighty miles from Ada. The terms of this arrangement stated that the medical college would constitute a department of the Ohio Northern University and that university publications would refer to it thusly. The Fort Wayne College of Medicine would list its medical school as a department of Ohio Northern University in all publications, and recommend to its students and to all other persons who may desire a general education that they attend and receive such coursework from Ohio Northern.[34] Students applying to the Fort Wayne College of Medicine, whose general education was insufficient for studying medicine, were encouraged to attend ONU to correct such deficiencies. They could then enroll at the Fort Wayne campus and at graduation receive diplomas signed by the secretary and president of ONU and would bear the ONU seal. Beside the obligation to encourage students to attend each other's schools, this arrangement left both institutions with complete autonomy. Neither assumed any financial obligations of the other, nor was any means intended for sharing tuition income. Each retained total control over its respective curricula.[35]

This arrangement had great potential for raising the esteem and providing extra tuition dollars for Ohio Northern University and the arrangement made good sense as a means to augment the pharmacy program. But, it proved to be short lived. The ONU catalog for 1904–05 ran a glowing promotion of the project including publishing a photograph of a very stately and impressive-looking building labeled as the "Fort Wayne College of Medicine" next to the pharmacy write-up.[22] This image was embellished the following year with additional photos, appearing even more impressive than those from the previous year. One was labeled "Hope Hospital, College of Medicine, Ohio Northern University;" and another, "St. Joseph Hospital, College of Medicine, Ohio Northern University."[36] It doesn't need to be stated that such an affiliation and the wording to describe it was of definite advantage to the Ada school for attracting students. Further mention of the arrangement was subsequently dropped without comment, however. In October, 1905, the Fort Wayne College of Medicine merged with the Indiana College of Medicine to form the School of Medicine at Purdue University.[37]

THE DEANS

Two men served as dean (or principal) throughout the period of this chapter: Charles S. Ashbrook and Brigham S. Young. As discussed earlier, C.C. Sherrard is still mistakenly listed in some references although he neither taught in the Department of Pharmacy nor served as its dean.

Charles S. Ashbrook

Charles S. Ashbrook was born in Pleasantville, Ohio, on April 27, 1861. He was a pharmacist in Ada working at Kemp's Drugs, the site of what would become Gardner's Drug Store, when tapped to teach a new curriculum in pharmacy at Ohio Normal University beginning in 1885, and to become the first dean in the new Department of Pharmacy. Professor Ashbrook taught practical pharmacy and materia medica courses for two or more years,[38] and was reported to be highly loved and revered by all who knew him including members of the Ohio State Pharmaceutical Association, of which he was an active member.[9] Ashbrook later was appointed chairman of the committee that formulated the pharmacist's code of ethics for the state of Ohio.[13] Under his leadership, the curriculum had evolved into a forty-week program, divided into four, ten-week terms.

In 1889, with borrowed money, Ashbrook purchased Ada's Mahan Drug Store. This was to eventually evolve into Peper Drugs.[38] After awhile he sold the establishment to his clerk and in 1895 moved to Mansfield, Ohio, where he purchased the pharmacy owned by Charles L. Irwin. In his new position, as well as in later practice sites in Findlay and Ashland (and perhaps elsewhere), he gained the reputation of being a progressive and thoroughly reliable businessman.[39] The 1930 census report listed him as a resident of Elyria, Ohio.

Charles Ashbrook died in Warren, Ohio, on March 6, 1944,[40] and is believed to be buried in Findlay. His wife Ella preceded him in death in 1931. The Ashbrooks were the parents of seven children.

Charles S. Ashbrook, Dean 1885–1888.

Brigham S. Young

Brigham (Brig) Scott Young was a native of Ada, born October 30, 1858. He graduated from Ohio Normal University with a degree in music. After Dr. Lehr suggested in 1889 that he study pharmacy, Young pursued the PhG degree, earning it in 1890. While studying pharmacy, he was known as a brilliant scholar.[41]

During his service to the college, which ran from 1890–1905, Young was able to bring a measure of much needed stability to the pharmacy program. As its second dean, he helped enrollment grow steadily such that by 1894, a new building was needed to accommodate the growing pharmacy program. In 1905, his final year of teaching and service as dean, the college's graduates numbered ninety-four. Many more students attended classes in order to take the licensing examination, but chose not to pursue a formal degree. Former students remembered Professor Young as an enthusiastic, vigorous, highly energetic, very fluent speaker, and intellectual and inspiring teacher.[9] He was well liked by his students. Dr. Lehr described Young during his student years as a "jolly pharmic senior."[24]

Brigham S. Young, Dean 1890-1905.

Brigham Young remained as head of the college until 1905, although much of the work during his last couple years was delegated to others. His resignation was due in part to a salary dispute. While Dr. Lehr was president, Young received ninety percent of the tuition paid by his students with the institution receiving the remainder. After Dr. Belt assumed the presidency, the proportion of tuition income was revised downward, such that Young received fifty percent with the school receiving an equal portion.[13]

Being a native of Ada, Brig Young was very involved in civic affairs. He played the organ at Ada's First Presbyterian Church and also played the coronet and a variety of other musical instruments. He belonged to the Knights of Pythias of Ohio, and later was appointed Supreme Chancellor Commander of the Knights of Pythias of the World. He inherited the Young Hotel (located on North Main Street) in downtown Ada that his father had built, which later would be named the Arbogast Hotel. In addition, Young served as Ohio's state chemist for fourteen years.

During his more senior years, Brig Young lived in Washington, D.C., where he served as an assistant director of the Veterans Bureau. He remained there until his death, April 26, 1924.[42] Newspaper obituaries reported that he is buried alongside his wife in Ada's Woodlawn Cemetery. However, a walking tour of the cemetery in 2013 failed to locate his grave. Moreover, Woodlawn Cemetery records do not affirm his presence there.

THREE
A New Century

With the new century well underway, ONU's pharmacy program continued to operate true to Lehr's original vision of providing practical instruction at minimum cost. Tuition for a twenty-six-week term in pharmacy remained at $40.00. A deposit of $4.00 a term was required in the chemical laboratory and a fee of $2.00 a term in the physical laboratory to cover the expense of desk rent, material used and breakage,[1] with an additional $1.50 per term laboratory fee. Students could enter any of ONU's colleges, including pharmacy, at any time and remain as long as they wished to accomplish their goal of learning as little or as much as they desired. Graduation fees for those who completed the entire course in pharmacy were $3.00.[2]

So, What's New in Ada?

While traveling throughout the country over the years, ONU alumni and other people familiar with the village have asked me many times: "So, what's new in Ada?" Something new in Ada—hardly. But, Ada is Ada, after all. Actually, Ada has always been fortunate to have Ohio Northern University within her boundaries and Ada continues to thrive (in 2015, still as a village) largely because of its relationship with the university. At present, ONU is Ada's largest enterprise. A book titled *A Twentieth Century History of Hardin County Ohio* published in 1910, provides a good look at what pharmacy students in the village of Ada early in the twentieth century faced.

"The first efforts at lighting the streets of Ada at public expense was by a gasoline vapor system put in use in 1887. In January, 1899, an electric light plant, backed by local capitalists, was put in operation, using twenty-five arc lights for the streets and incandescent lights for commercial and residential use. The number of street lights has been increased to thirty and all-day service is furnished for power and incandescent lighting. In connection with this plant a fine water works system is operated which was installed in 1902. The water supply is obtained from four six-inch diameter wells drilled into the limestone rock to a depth of 250 feet. Five free public drinking fountains, located at different points along Main street and one on Buckeye, furnish man and beast a constant supply of pure water. The water company also operates a Yaryan heating system, whereby hot water is forced through pipes under the street, encased in non-conducting conduits, and through the radiators of the customers, making an ideal system of heating without any attention whatever from the patron. The heat is turned on October 1st and the contract calls for cessation of service on April 1st, but if the weather is unfavorable it is continued.

"In 1905 a fire alarm system was installed by means of which alarms can be sent in from any of the twelve public boxes, and in addition to this, the users of any of the three hundred telephones in use in the village can send in an alarm from his phone, on the box of which is a label giving the number of the fire district in which that particular phone is located. A call to central, giving this number, is instantaneously followed by a public alarm by means of a mechanism connecting the phone station with the fire alarm mechanism bell. This fine system, together with the water works system and a live volunteer fire department, has made the annual fire loss practically nothing, and the pure water has made the death rate phenomenally low."[3]

The description continued: "In 1905 improvement of the streets began by paving Main its entire length, one mile, and Buckeye a half mile. In 1908 Johnson street was paved south of the railroad, a distance of a half mile, and two blocks were paved on East Montfort. In 1909 Gilbert was paved nearly its entire length, adding another mile, while Highland Avenue (name changed this

Early 20th century drug store, Ada, Ohio, circa 1900.

Main Street in Ada looking south, 1907.

year from Hoosier) was paved for a half mile. A block was also paved on Lincoln Ave., formerly Mill street, from Main to Johnson, and the remainder of that street to the east corporation line curbed and macadamized, making a total of two miles of improved streets for that year."[3]

A macadamized road was constructed by compacting a solid mass of finely crushed stone into a convex (higher in the middle than on the sides), well-drained roadbed. The stone was limestone obtained from the nearby creek beds, and crushed by steam power.

At this point, the population of Ada was reported to be close to three thousand, exclusive of students.[3] That number appears to be overestimated since numerous other references state much lower figures.

College Life

The university catalog for 1905–06 stressed that "…the bulk of our students are mature young people who depend mainly upon their own resources to carry them through college. They come from every walk of life and know the worth of hard labor and true economy. They come. They are not sent to college."[2] The catalog also described the school's concern for its students while strongly stressing the many advantages of Ohio Northern when compared to similar institutions.

The university trustees' feeling about student housing continued from the earliest days. There remained a strong feeling of disrespect in general for dormitory living. It remains difficult to distinguish whether that feeling still emphasized Lehr's thoughts that such living arrangements were bad for student morals, or that the school simply didn't have the cash to spend on building dormitories. Today, of course, emphasis is upon adding additional housing units to handle the institution's increasing number of students and providing them with the amenities that, in some cases at least, exceed what they are accustomed to at home.

In earlier times, however, students continued for the most part to be housed, fed, and cared for by the citizens of Ada. University administrators at the turn of the century continued to feel that this arrangement was conducive to promoting good manners and good study habits, and the most efficient means to maximize students' health and morality. This plan for providing room and board, while very popular early in the twentieth century, has certainly gone out of fashion and would most likely not be appreciated by college students today.

There was another important point, one that continues through today. The philosophy at Ohio Northern University was that: "There can be no true education where the moral and religious natures of the students are neglected. The management feels it a paramount duty to give large attention to this department of culture. The University is owned and controlled by the Methodist Episcopal Church, but is in no sense sectarian. Students of all religious denominations are received on equal terms and treated with equal courtesy."[4] President Lehr and his successors had a strong Christian heritage and throughout their lifetimes sought to inculcate their personal beliefs on the students. Daily attendance at chapel service each morning continued to be expected but was not compulsory. The description continued: "Much importance is given to the moral and religious life among the students. Prayer meetings are held twice each week—Tuesday and Saturday evenings. The Young Men's and Young Women's Christian Associations in connection with the college, wield a most wholesome religious influence upon the lives and habits of the students. All are invited to join these Associations. To further this work, classes are organized each term in Bible studies."[4] There are no records that detail whether pharmacy students of the era endorsed the expectation to actively participate in the university's religious life program.

All this is mentioned as regards student life at Ohio Northern University because it would appear that serious attention and concern was given in those early days to the cultural, as well as educational welfare of the students.[5] This was expressed very clearly under the subject of student government: "The university publishes no stereotyped rules of conduct for its patrons. Each student is placed on his honor. While students are assisted in forming correct habits, this is not a reform school. Persons who cannot govern themselves are not wanted…all are treated as ladies and gentlemen until they prove themselves otherwise."[4]

It is obvious that students, pharmics included, who attended ONU during the early years of the twentieth century were quite lively and imaginative, even sometimes muscular, in their pursuit of adventure, in some respects perhaps even more so than in recent times. Given the circumstances of college life during that period, it is no wonder that pharmacy students were both the giver and receiver of pranks and/or fights as they worked off their youthful energy. Even with its enterprising growth since its founding, Ada still remained a small village at the turn of the century with limited resources for providing appropriate amusement. Means for travel into Lima, Findlay, or Kenton, or into one of the larger cities at farther distance was both difficult and uncomfortable even with suitable railroad service, and very few students had access to an automobile. Students therefore sought relief from their pent-up energy any way and any time they could.

For example, Dukes Memorial, the home of the College of Engineering and departments of chemistry and mathematics at the time, was the site of two memorable battles between the junior and senior classes, and the two largest departments of the school, the colleges of pharmacy and engineering. The first occurrence was on July 5, 1905. The senior class "seized control" of Dukes and claimed victory as it flew its class colors from the building's rooftop. The juniors attempted to capture the flag, thereby ripping holes in the building's inside walls and ceiling to gain entrance. A senior student was seriously injured during the fracas when, while trying to save his class flag, he tucked it under his coat and then leapt to the ground from a third-story window.[6]

Another encounter was reported in the *University Herald* of December 8, 1905. During the night, the emblem of the College of Pharmacy (at that time, Skull & Crossbones) had been painted on the roof of the facility where engineering students met for classes.[7] Dr. Albert E. Smith, the university president (and a Methodist minister) ordered the building site to be repainted immediately and threatened to expel any student caught scaling it.[8] As best as can be determined, the perpetrator(s) was/were never apprehended. Think about this. Who other than enterprising pharmics would care to share the esteemed College of Pharmacy's emblem with anyone outside the college itself? The next evening, students of both colleges staged a noisy parade and assembled on the campus lawn. They set several cords of wood ablaze, lighting up the area for several blocks around. Again, no action was brought against any student, largely because the guilty one(s) was/were never caught. Pharmics were, and still are, ingenious at covering their tracks.

There were other rules that no doubt ruffled students' feathers. For example, dancing was not permitted for students, on or off campus. Any university student group who organized a dance or any student caught dancing would have been subject to swift retribution. At a chapel service in 1906, students were warned by a sternly-sounding president that such infringement of university rules would subject the guilty party or persons to immediate expulsion.[8]

Watching motion pictures was also included in the president's hit list of unsuitable pastimes. Referring to their influence on student culture and growth, the president maintained: "All the impact of the sensuous movie is on your age with its suggestion and looseness, in caricature of true love, and the true home, and true religion, making it the paramount curse of our time."[9]

ONU Class of 1905 showing pharmacy students in lower left corner. Buildings in background include (left to right) Dukes Memorial, Pharmacy Hall, and the Normal Building.

As mentioned in Chapter Two, saloons had been voted out of Ada by the village council. Soon, the entire county would become "dry" under Ohio's Rose Local Option Law.[10] In the fall of 1905, cigarettes and pipes were banned from campus. Curiously, cigars continued to be acceptable. The ban applied only to the campus, but the door was left open to the possibility of inspections of boarding houses and elsewhere where students and faculty lived or assembled.[11]

University officials also began to sound out the boarding house landladies on limiting each dwelling to members of a single gender.[12] To say that attempts at "irregularities" had not been made prior to this time would be foolhardy. At the same time, one can surmise that the presence of a stern proprietress kept this at a minimum. Still, by the 1912–13 academic year, female students arriving from outside Ada were required to live in rooming houses managed exclusively for women.[11] To set the record straight, there is no documented evidence that any pharmacy student of the era was to ever break any of President Smith's strict rules involving alcohol or tobacco abuse, or violate the separate-gender living conditions. Wow! How the times have changed. Regular skirmishes, including

Burying the hatchet cartoon from ONU yearbook.

fistfights, between students in the colleges of pharmacy and engineering continued to agitate President Smith. Unlike the ongoing conflicts between the junior and senior classes, the pharmacy/engineering clashes, except in a few instances, did not appear to result in major injuries or structural damage to university property.[11] At the same time, the sternly-sounding president let it be known that all "student high spirits" needed to cease at once.

In 1911, a joint committee representing both colleges decided that the best substitute for the annual fight between the two colleges was a final and complete abandonment of the conflict. As a final chapter, the committee decided that a hatchet burial ceremony was in order.[13] No thought was ever given at the time that the ceremony would be continued beyond the first year, but the "spirit" of the ceremony would not be squelched. Here is a description of the ceremony as reported in the *Northern Alumnus*.[14] The event was celebrated on the last Friday before Thanksgiving in 1911.

"Chapel was ordered dispensed with by common consent of the students of the two departments, with police committees of both departments guarding the doors in compliance with that order; the chapel bell was tolled from seven a.m. to eight a.m. and promptly thereafter during the chapel half hour, the students of the two departments formed a great "V" on the campus, pharmacy students on one side and engineering students on the other, with other students and citizens as onlookers out on Main Street.

"Presently at 8:10 a.m. in a blinding snow storm, led by the Ohio Northern University band to the strains of *Lead Kindly Light, Nearer My God to Thee,* and *God be With You Till We Meet Again*, the procession moved slowly up Main Street with bared heads to the point of the "V," followed by the pallbearers carrying the blood-stained stretcher, upon which reposed a bright red wooden hatchet. At this point the procession halted while an oration as a parody on Lincoln's Gettysburg speech was delivered.

"The hatchet was placed on a prepared fire at the close of the ceremony, with an Indian war dance around the same by a dozen students, half pharmics and half engineers. After this a speech of approval and blessing by President Smith was heard,

"Burying the Hatchet" celebration between pharmacy and engineering students, circa 1920s.

as well as statements by Deans Mohler and Smull of the two departments accepting the new order, and ensued a joint pharmic–engineer parade all over town with a consequent closing of all classes in each department that day."

These celebrations between the two largest colleges on the ONU campus would continue annually into the 1920s, on the last Friday before Thanksgiving, with burying a metal hatchet in the campus lawn on Main Street. By then, Dean Raabe of the pharmacy college and Dean Needy of the engineering college questioned the appropriateness of what had by then become a rowdy campus tradition. Both deans clearly outlined their displeasure in articles published in the student newspaper in 1928.[13] Note: There is convincing evidence that Dean Raabe actually believed the tradition was amusing, but felt he could not say so publicly. The final "burying of the hatchet" occurred in November, 1929. The stock market crash only a few weeks earlier and the resulting sobering in the campus mood probably played as great a role as did administrative disapproval, in ending this tradition.[11]

As a side issue, in digging around campus several of these hatchets have been recovered.[15] In June, 1957, workers on the ONU campus dug up the rusty remains of what was believed at the time to have been the original metal hatchet head buried more than forty years earlier.[16] Whether this was the actual head from the hatchet that started the tradition, and where it is today, remain a mystery.

In 1929, a new custom between the two rival colleges of pharmacy and engineering would be initiated, this time with much less anger and exchange of blows by its members.[17] The custom would be an annual football game with the winning team gaining possession of the ball used during the game. It is not recorded

FROM THEN TO NOW

The Blinkensderfer typewriter with keys containing many common symbols for patient instructions (teaspoonful, ounce, etc.). The unit may have been used in pharmacy in the early-1900s to type instructions on a prescription label. More likely, however, patients' dosing instructions were usually handwritten with pen and ink.

how many games were played; however, it is known that the pharmics lost the first game as a result of a fumble. Football was later exchanged for baseball. Today, the college's Pierstorf Family Pharmacy Museum has four softballs on display—two from pharmacy–engineering games of 1932 and 1934, and two from pharmacy–law games of 1939 and 1940. The 1934 ball lists Dean Raabe as "BB," a familiar abbreviation for bat boy.

Pharmacy Education at the Turn of the Century

At the onset of the twentieth century, the typical curriculum for completion of a degree required two years. This included the program at ONU. Three- and four-year programs were available at some schools. The school year varied across institutions from twenty-three to forty-two weeks; most colleges were day schools, but evening sessions were not uncommon. Admission requirements ranged from no specified educational requirements to high school graduation, with most colleges requiring only the completion of an elementary or grammar school education. Most colleges conferred the PhG degree, but others awarded the PhC degree, the BS, or the Pharm D degree for advanced work. At this point, both the PhG and PhC degrees were available at Ohio Northern University. Some other colleges required a specified amount of practical experience for one or more of their degrees, others imposed no such requirements. Students at ONU could choose the degree they wished to receive.[18]

The move to require graduation from a school or college of pharmacy as a condition to sit for a pharmacy licensure examination began at the 1891 meeting of the American Pharmaceutical Association's Section on Education and Legislation. The motion was soundly defeated by board members who felt that the profession was not ready to take such an advanced step. What could not be accomplished at the national level was pursued by state pharmaceutical associations in the form of so-called "prerequisite legislation." In 1905, the New York State Pharmaceutical Association ushered a bill through its state legislature that required applicants for licensure to be 21 years of age, have four years of practical experience, and pass an entrance examination covering twelve specific high school credits. Institutions were required to register with the board of regents, teach a two-year course, and maintain a "proper pharmacy standard."[18]

Ohio Board Recognition of ONU's College of Pharmacy

Catalog copy for 1905–06 reported for the first time that the college of pharmacy was recognized as in good standing by the Ohio Board of Pharmacy. Certain pertinent stipulations were as follow:

> "Requirements for admission to schools and colleges of pharmacy: *Resolved*, That on and after July 1, 1905, no school or college of pharmacy shall be recognized as in good standing by the Ohio Board

of Pharmacy which does not require of all applicants as a minimum condition of admission, a common high school education or the equivalent thereof, which shall include one year in a high school of first grade (Ohio), or an academy, legally constituted, providing a course of study of not less than four years.

"*Provided,* That nothing in this resolution shall apply to students who have matriculated previous to November 1, 1904, in any school or college of pharmacy heretofore recognized as in good standing by the Ohio Board of Pharmacy.

"Requirements demanded of schools or colleges of pharmacy: *Resolved,* That on and after July 1, 1905, every school or college of pharmacy shall comply with the following requirements as a condition of being recognized as in good standing by the Ohio Board of Pharmacy.

1. It shall exact the requirements for admission to schools and colleges of pharmacy adopted by the Ohio Board of Pharmacy (October 13, 1904).

2. It shall possess an adequate equipment for teaching pharmacy in all its branches, including laboratory facilities and apparatus.

3. It shall have an adequate and competent faculty for instruction in the following branches: Pharmacy, Chemistry, Materia Medica, Microscopy, Physiology and Botany.

4. It shall require an attendance of 80 percent, upon two graded courses of instruction in branches specified (in Article 3) of not less than 28 weeks each, excluding holidays, in two separate years.

5. It shall exact an average grade of 75 percent, on examination as a condition of graduation.

6. It shall admit students within thirty days after the opening of any school year, and it shall confer degrees in pharmacy only at the close of each school year upon completion of the prescribed course of study.

7. Any college may honor official credentials issued by other colleges of pharmacy in good standing as determined by this board, so far as the work offered is the equivalent of or identical with the required work of the school to which credentials are presented, except in branches of study embraced in the last year of its own curriculum."[2]

These requirements were printed in the catalogs through academic year 1912–13. Beginning with the 1913–14 issue, the Ohio Pharmacy Board regulations were condensed into a single paragraph: "No school or college of pharmacy shall be recognized as in good standing by the Ohio Board of Pharmacy which does not require of all applicants as a minimum condition of admission, a common school education or the equivalent thereof, which shall include one year in high school of the first grade (Ohio) or any academy, legally constituted, providing a course of study of not less than four years."[19]

ONU's College of Pharmacy then attempted to interpret the condensed paragraph: "This means that as a minimum, the applicant must have had a year of instruction in the following: algebra, English, natural sciences, history (United States or general history) and must have reached the age of seventeen years. If he cannot present a certificate of grades in these branches an entrance examination is required before matriculation. This examination, however, is demanded of those who are candidates for the degree of Pharmaceutical Graduate. Those having had four years practical experience and desiring to prepare for state examinations, need not present certificates as above mentioned."

It was clear that while requirements for practicing pharmacy in Ohio were strengthening, a college degree was still not a requirement for taking the state licensing examination. The educational requirements, as prescribed, applied only to those individuals who expected to earn a college degree.

The thirty-sixth catalog (dated 1906–07) attempted to explain the requirement of one or two years of college work to earn a degree. It read: "The year is divided into two semesters, the first beginning October 16, 1906, the second March 12, 1907. Students may enter at the beginning of either semester, but by the requirement quoted above, no one is allowed to take up the senior work until twenty-six weeks have elapsed since his finishing the junior courses."[1] This edict essentially put into effect the plan that students should be enrolled in their academic program for only half of each year. During the months separating the two terms it was expected that students should be working, preferably in a drugstore, although this was not mandated. The two-year requirement for earning a degree was instituted to permit, even encourage, students to work and therefore earn enough money to pay their second term's tuition expenses. No doubt it was also felt that the students could gain valuable work-related experience during this time.

Claims by the University for Patronage

In order to attract students, including those who wished to study pharmacy, the institution published a list of twenty-five reasons why ONU should be considered. From the catalog for 1904–05 we read:

1. "Because students can enter at any time and find what they want.
2. Because the University receives students of all grades of scholarship.
3. Because the Common Branches receive as much attention as the Higher Branches.
4. Because the University through its Normal Department makes a specialty of fitting teachers for their work.
5. Because all of her instructors are specialists in their lines.
6. Because her instructors are kind and sympathetic, and make the welfare of the student of first importance.
7. Because of the wonderful enthusiasm everywhere manifested in recitation room and out.

8. Because the work done is practical and fits young men and women to do something after leaving her walls.

9. Because she offers thorough work in many special lines.

10. Because she invites inspection as to the work done and guarantees what she advertises.

11. Because expenses are low—so low that many find it cheaper to go to school here than to stay at home.

12. Because nowhere else can so much be gotten for so little money.

13. Because the school is the friend of the poor boys and girls, and furnishes them an opportunity to get an education they could not otherwise obtain.

14. Because of her strong intellectual and social environment, felt everywhere within her walls and in the town.

15. Because of the healthy moral and religious life felt throughout the school and town.

16. Because the citizens of the town take a deep interest in the students and try to make their stay pleasant.

17. Because the student can take just such studies as he needs and is not confined to a special curriculum of studies.

18. Because where the student is compelled to drop out of school for any reason, he does not lose his standing in his classes, but can resume his work at any time, and when he has finished his course can graduate.

19. Because the town is healthy and free from the vices so common in larger cities.

20. Because the students room and board in private families and the home life is not sacrificed by room in dormitories.

21. Because no entrance examinations are required of students before they can be admitted to full standing in the University classes.

22. Because every student is treated as a gentleman or lady. They are placed upon their honor.

23. Because our students know the true worth of hard honest work. Lazy students are not countenanced.

24. Because our students are satisfied with the work of the University and work for her. They are our best advertisements and our best advertisers.

25. Because the country has come to recognize the character of the instruction given here and the demand for our graduates to fill places of trust, honor and profit is greater than the supply."[4]

The institution provided loans to eligible students. From the catalog for 1906–07 we read: "The Board of Education of the Methodist Episcopal Church lends money to members of that church taking a regular course in school, who have been in attendance long enough to merit a recommendation from the Faculty. No interest is charged if the debt is paid within five years from the time of leaving school, but a payment of $5.00 each year must be made on the principal. No security is required other than a recommendation from a quarterly conference. Loans are made at the beginning of each term. Application should be made two weeks before the opening of the term, and no application can be received later than the close of the first week of the term. The amount that can be allowed to each applicant is generally sufficient to pay for tuition and books. Many of the best students avail themselves of this advantage…Many students in the University make their entire expenses by working as waiters, janitors, and at other occupations in the town and vicinity, and, at the same time, carry full work in their studies."[1]

A Note to Prospective Students

The following messages appeared in the catalog for 1907–08:

> *"Why Attend a School of Pharmacy?*
> No calling at the present time is in greater need of qualified men than

the Profession of Pharmacy. The novice without previous training no longer can hope to be a successful pharmacist. The times demand that he be skilled and schooled in his work. The wave of popular demand for purer foods and drugs, resulting in legislation all over the country, has created an unprecedented demand for pharmacists trained and up-to-the minute. Commercial Chemistry and Practice Pharmacy have never before played such a part in the matter of human living and the extent of their use and application is continuously enlarging. This means numberless vacancies at the present and in the future ready for men who can do things. *'What can you do, and will you do it?'* is the paramount question in commercial life today.

"Why Attend the O.N.U. College of Pharmacy?

The majority of those seeking a school of pharmacy are after a school where a practical and thorough course is offered at the least expenditure of time and money. Behold it here. Attention is respectfully called to the following pages descriptive of the facilities and work offered in the O.N.U. College of Pharmacy, and a comparison with other pharmacy schools challenged. It is believed that no where else are more complete courses offered, is more thorough work done, or is the needful expenditure of hard-earned money less than here.

"Advantages

- There is no matriculation fee.
- At least one thousand hours of practical laboratory work is required in the course.
- A diploma from this College is accepted in lieu of the first year's lectures by the leading medical colleges.
- Superior advantages are offered to registered 'Assistants' who wish to review for examination as 'Pharmacists.'

- In the reading room all the leading journals in Pharmacy may be found, and in the library hall all the books needed for reference.

- The courses are so arranged as to bring each student into recitations and laboratory work each school day, except Saturday, and not twice a week, as in nearly all other schools."[20]

Courses, Degrees and Facilities

In 1906–07 a third degree, that of the Pharmaceutical Doctor (Pharm D) was described in the catalog: "To obtain the degree of Pharm D, the candidate must be twenty-one years of age, must hold a standard high school diploma, and must have had four years of practical experience in a store where prescriptions are filled; must be a graduate of the College of Pharmacy, and must take an additional course, specializing on formulae and assaying of crude drugs. This work requires about twenty weeks for its completion."[1]

A listing of the earned degrees in pharmacy reported in the catalogs up to 1915 show that both the PhG and PhC degrees had been awarded, but the Pharm D degree apparently was not as popular. There is no confirmed record that the three-year doctorate was ever awarded. At the same time, however, the ONU's Registrar's Office has on display a copy of a diploma dated January 4, 1905, and signed by President LeRoy Belt and Dean Brigham Young. The emphasis, here, is on the word "copy." Its authenticity cannot be assured. Of interest is that the recipient named on the diploma is not included in the institution's official list of graduates for 1905. At this time, the number of Pharm D degrees granted in the early years, if any, cannot be confirmed.

The additional school time needed to complete the requirements for the advanced professional degree was probably a deterrent when one considers that doctorates, or even any college degree for that matter, were not considered essential to success in the early years of the twentieth century. Today, of course, the Doctor of Pharmacy degree is the only degree awarded by U.S. colleges of pharmacy, including Ohio Northern University, that permits graduates of an accredited pharmacy program to enter into the profession. Just think. Our profession has progressed from an era when no formal high school or college education was required, to a point when a college's academic program could be completed in thirty weeks, to today, when a minimum of 198 weeks (six years) of full-time study are required to complete the program[21], and all this has happened in just a little over a century. Who knows what the years beyond today will demand to practice pharmacy? Today, there is talk from the national level that a seven-year program, a four-year bachelor's degree plus a three-year professional curriculum, may be the eventual goal. Some schools already require that time or longer to complete their programs.

Pharmacy Hall on the Move

Two notes of interest appeared in the catalogs for 1909–10 and 1910–11. Both referred to Pharmacy Hall.

The first notice was a special announcement: "Before the opening of the new school year, as the plan now is, the Pharmacy building will be moved from its present site and enlarged to meet the needs of the growing College of Pharmacy. The entire first floor, except the Dean's office, will be refitted and used for lectures and recitations. New extensions will increase the floor space of laboratories to 10,000 square feet. Considerable expense is to be incurred in furnishing the pharmaceutical laboratories with modern equipment. Each student will be provided with an individual locker

Pharmacy Hall in process of being moved approximately one-half block north on Gilbert Street, 1909.

and outfit, and no pains will be spared to have the accommodations and appliances of the ONU College of Pharmacy equal to the best."[22]

The next year's catalog listed improvements across campus during the previous year. Relative to pharmacy, it stated: "The...great improvement of the year was the removal of the Pharmacy Building from its old situation on the campus to the northwest corner of the grounds, and its thorough remodeling into one of the most imposing buildings of the entire school. A finely finished basement was built under it, affording room for two large well-lighted laboratories; the second story has been transformed into splendid recitation

Pharmacy Hall following its move one-half block north on Gilbert Street, circa 1925.

rooms and offices, so that in this building the University has a noteworthy addition to its working outfit."[23]

Since 1894, Pharmacy Hall had served the college admirably. However, by 1909, classroom and laboratory space were at a premium. During the summer and fall of that year the frame building was moved approximately one-half block north to the southeast corner of Gilbert Street and University Avenue. A half-basement was dug and laboratories were constructed in the new space. Pharmacy Hall was remodeled with the first floor converted into recitation rooms and offices.[24]

Other renovations would follow. In 1916 a microscopical laboratory was added. In 1926 the building's second story was remodeled with the north half converted into a pharmaceutical dispensary and the south half into a large classroom.[24,25] This facility would serve the College of Pharmacy until 1934 when the college would move into Dukes Memorial.

Early catalogs continued to publicize extravagantly all the benefits of ONU's College of Pharmacy. This hype was considered suitable since similar promotion was also given by the writers of catalog copy in describing programs at other schools of pharmacy. By academic year 1913–14 the advantages list had been added to: "Since a majority of those seeking a school of pharmacy are after a school where practical and thorough courses are offered at the least expenditure of time and money attention is respectfully called to the following page's description of the facilities and work offered in the ONU College of Pharmacy, and a comparison with other pharmacy schools challenged. It is believed that nowhere else are more complete courses offered, is more thorough work done, or is the needful expenditure of hard-earned money less than here.

"The laboratories are large and an entire outfit is given to each student. He is fully equipped to make all the various preparations himself, and is thus enabled to receive the practical training desired and required by the employer."[19]

New Features for Pharmacy

Numerous innovations in pharmacy were noted during this era. The most striking were the new requirements for education by the Ohio Board of Pharmacy, mentioned previously.

The catalog for 1906–07 described a college drugstore: "The Trustees are seeking to make the College complete in every detail, and recently have added a new feature—A College Drug Store, where the student can purchase his drugs, learn how to manipulate the scales, and become acquainted with, and skilled in, the art of weighing, wrapping, typing and placing packages in the hands of other students assuming the role of customer."[1]

Also mentioned the first time in this catalog was a newly founded pharmaceutical association: "Connected with the College is a Pharmaceutical Association, to membership in which each regularly enrolled student is eligible. The membership fee is one dollar, with no dues to be paid afterwards. The fee is applied to the building up of a Pharmacy Library, and the members of the Association, as long as they remain in the school, have library privileges and free access to all the best and latest Pharmaceutical journals and periodicals."[1]

Mr. Raabe Comes to Town

One man left his mark on ONU's College of Pharmacy more so than any other and it all began during this era. Having recently earned his pharmacy degree at Ohio Northern, Rudolph Raabe was invited in 1910 to remain as instructor. This would mark the beginning of a record of service that few others in this country or world can match. It would be the beginning of a pharmacy career spanning forty-five years of devoted service in pharmacy education to Ohio Northern University that remains unmatched to this day. Dean Raabe's story follows in Chapter Four.

Tragedy Strikes

In late October, 1913, demolition began on the Normal Building, the institution's original structure.[26] The university library had been moved from the Normal to the top floor of the adjacent Administration Building. In the early morning hours of November 4, 1913, Samuel Axline, dean of the College of Law who lived on Main Street directly across from the campus, was suddenly awakened by his cat. The animal was sneezing incessantly from dense smoke originating from an unknown source. Its origin was soon determined to be the Administration Building where a fire that had started in the front part of the basement had by then engulfed the building. The local fire brigade put forth its best effort to contain the conflagration but that effort was to no avail. The structure was reduced to a shell before dawn.[11] This tragedy, along with the recent demolition of the Normal Building, left the university critically short of classroom space. It also meant double-duty for Pharmacy Hall as student meeting rooms were now critically needed.

Administration Building (front) after fire. Pharmacy Hall shown toward the rear.

There was some good news that came out from the fire: No one had been injured, and even though some of the institution's records were destroyed, approximately one-third of the library's holdings had been saved. These remaining volumes were moved into the Church of Christ Disciples across the street from the campus.

The 1913 fire in the Administration building was actually the second one of significance in the university's history, the first occurring in 1889. Even though much damage was incurred in the earlier fire, the building was saved.[27]

Shortly after the fire, the university trustees declared that a new building would be constructed on the original site of the destroyed one. Despite initial concerns about their structural integrity, the remaining brick walls of the Administration Building were incorporated into the new edifice. The third floor of the original structure was omitted from the new building, and the bell tower was truncated. Construction proceeded at a rapid pace and when completed, the building was renamed Hill Memorial in honor of the Reverend John Wesley Hill, Sr., whose son was a university trustee and substantial donor to the project.[11]

At the same time, work began on Lehr Memorial, sandwiched in between Hill Memorial on the north and Dukes Memorial on the south. Brown Hall, located in front of and to the north of the Administration Building at the southwest corner of Main Street and College Avenue, had received minor damage from the fire. Repair was undertaken and the building remained functional. Brown Hall had served over the years as a gymnasium, cafeteria, library, and general catch-all for departments awaiting new buildings. It would be demolished in 1976 and the area grassed in.[11] Hill Memorial and Lehr Memorial would both be remodeled through the years as the need dictated and today, they, along with Dukes Memorial, constitute the three buildings remaining on the original plat of Main Street, and continue to serve the needs of the institution.

College Enrollment

Appendix 2 lists the number of pharmacy students by gender who graduated from the time of the college's founding to the present. Since its founding, there were many more students enrolled than received degrees. For example, the period from 1897 through 1899 shows 1,269 students enrolled as undergraduates, with 524 receiving a degree. The first decade of the twentieth century records 909 undergraduates with 570 graduating.[5,28] These discrepant figures seem to confirm that in the early years before a college diploma was necessary to take the state board examinations, many enrolled at ONU with the sole intent to learn just enough to pass the board's licensing exam. Of those

Hill Building rebuilt after the fire.

who passed the board and earned the privilege to practice pharmacy, few, if any, returned to complete the necessary requirements for graduation.

THE DEANS

Two deans served the college during this era: Brigham S. Young and David C. Mohler. Dean Young's profile is given in Chapter Two.

David C. Mohler

David Christian Mohler was born in Henry County, Ohio, in May, 1868, the youngest son in a family of six boys.[29] He spent his boyhood days helping his father on the family farm. Following grammar school, he successfully passed the teacher's examination then entered high school, graduating in three years.

Mohler taught in the public school for several years. He then enrolled in the Chicago College of Pharmacy and spent one year there before becoming a prescription drug clerk in Chicago where he remained until January, 1893. At

David C. Mohler, Dean 1905–1917.

that time he enrolled in the Ohio Normal University's pharmacy program, earning his PhG degree, and graduated in October of the same year. He successfully passed the Ohio and Michigan pharmacy licensing examinations. While enrolled in ONU's pharmacy program he met and married Marie A. Hall of Ada.

David Mohler succeeded Brigham Young as the college's dean in 1905. During his tenure at Ohio Normal University, the College of Pharmacy continued to grow substantially, outgrowing its facility. Pharmacy Hall was moved from its original location to its new site, and its capacity for use increased during his term.

David Mohler enjoyed a wide experience in his chosen profession, having about twelve years experience as prescription clerk and manager of drugstores in various towns and cities and more than ten years in the teaching of pharmacy.

He retired at the end of the school year in 1917,[25] and later moved to the Masonic Home in Springfield, Ohio. On October 6, 1966, at ninety-eight years of age, he died of complications from a fall. David Mohler is buried alongside his wife in Ada's Woodlawn Cemetery.

{1917–1950}

FROM THEN TO NOW

FOUR
The Dean Raabe Story

A wise man once said: "An institution is the lengthened shadow of one man." Certainly it can be said without apology that the Ohio Northern College of Pharmacy is the lengthened shadow of Rudolph H. Raabe."[1] Thus shared Dr. F. Bringle McIntosh, president of the university in 1950, as the institution conferred upon this great man of pharmacy the esteemed title of dean emeritus of the College of Pharmacy. And a very long shadow it was and remains so through today. Without a doubt, Rudolph Raabe was more closely associated with the College of Pharmacy and shaped its future to greater extent than any other graduate of the college, or dean or fellow faculty member or anyone else throughout the college's more than 130 years of existence. So what was it about this giant of a man that the college would be named in his honor, and students and faculty past and present along with colleagues and friends from across the country would hold him in highest esteem? To answer that question it is necessary to delve into his life and times.

Rudolph Henry Raabe made his appearance into the world on June 8, 1881, in Ft. Jennings, Ohio, a small village in Putnam County located in the northwestern corner of Ohio, about thirty-five miles from Ada. A student at heart from his earliest days, young Rudolph was thoroughly captivated with the beauty of nature and learning and spent many hours satisfying these great passions by reading all he could find. One of his former instructors, when introducing him to a convention of teachers years later, said: "I first discovered Rudolph sitting by a shock of corn reading a book on nature study. A few weeks later I saw him, while giving his team of horses a rest, reading a new book on physical geography. He loves God's out-of-doors."[2]

Rudolph Raabe and the Ohio Normal University

The young man quickly gained a healthy respect for Ohio Normal University when he arrived on the Ada campus in July, 1900. He came as a student enrolled in the scientific course. The first person he met that day made such a strong impression on him that it forged his confidence in and love for the school. Although he could not know it at the time, it certainly helped solidify his eventual commitment for what would become his profession of choice, for the institution's College of Pharmacy, and for his beloved and adopted village of Ada as his preferred place to call home and raise a family. This person was the founder of the university himself, Dr. Henry Solomon Lehr, who cordially welcomed Rudolph to ONU. Dr. Lehr administered the institution's entrance examination and showed his concern for the new student by helping young Raabe find living accommodations and then personally escorting him to his first class. The beginning of what would be a lifelong commitment with the university was underway.[3]

An excellent student, Rudolph completed the requirements for his Bachelor of Science degree in 1903 and returned to Putnam County. There, he taught in the local school system and served as superintendent of the Cloverdale, Ohio, school for several years.[4] All the while, he was concerned about the state of healthcare in the community. He therefore served a three-year apprenticeship with Joseph E. Stephan, a local pharmacist-physician. This introduced him to pharmacy and led him into a venture that, at the time, he could never have conceived. Rudolph's life and consequently, his life's work, would soon change.

Rudolph H. Raabe, Dean 1917–1950.

Along with several other men, Raabe purchased a small, failing patent medicine store in the village of Cloverdale. The business was doing poorly and the investors were able to purchase it for little outlay of cash. "When we started, the store was worth about 20 cents on the dollar, but three years later it was worth $1.10 on the same scale," R.H. Raabe, store manager, said. "I enjoyed the purpose of pharmacy and working with medicine, and so in 1909 I returned to Northern to take pharmacy courses and such others as I was interested in."[3] He sold his interest in the store when he returned to ONU.[4]

Rudolph Raabe, Pharmacist

Back at Northern, Raabe completed the requirement for his PhG degree in October, 1910, and was asked to remain at the college as an instructor. He had passed the pharmacy board's licensing examination the year before. From that day forward to the time he retired in 1955, Rudolph Raabe remained closely tied to the university for forty-five years, a remarkable and unbroken period of service. Upon his retirement, Raabe had served the university for a longer consecutive time without vacation or sabbatical leave than any other person in the history of the institution. Much of this service was rendered during a very trying time, the university's darkest hours, the expanse of time that included the period marking America's Great Depression and World War II.

"I took the state pharmacy test in 1909 and later the president of the state board told my father that I had earned the highest grade in the state. I continued teaching at the university and asked for the privilege of using equipment and materials so that I could work on the degree of Pharmaceutical Chemist in addition to that of Graduate Pharmacist, which I had earned in 1910," Raabe noted.[3] By teaching days and studying nights and Saturdays (by his own admission he had a "full schedule") the degree of PhC was added a year later and he returned to full-time teaching.

His formal education was not yet ended, however. Raabe had met a number of faculty members from the University of Havana, Cuba, at a national pharmacy convention. They were very scholarly men, educated in Europe. Raabe noted that these men served on significant convention committees, and he thought highly of them. The University of Havana also had a very high professional standing among colleagues outside the institution.[2] So in May, 1928, he enrolled in the island university and began traveling to Havana between terms, being absent from ONU no longer than one month at a time.

"When the time came for the final examination, I learned it was really to be rigid. On the first day there were three faculty men quizzing me, on the second day two, and on the third day there were three or four."[3] The examination involved questioning on topics in chemistry, plant chemistry, medicinal herbs and problems in pharmacy. After the examinations, the work was concluded with his presentation and the institution's acceptance of a formal thesis.[5] On May 2, 1930, he was awarded the Doctor of Pharmacy degree. Despite the rigors of travel at that time and the challenging language barrier, R.H. Raabe officially became Dr. Raabe.

Rudolph Raabe, Educator

Throughout his professional career Raabe's primary focus was the education of his students. As stated earlier, in 1910, he was appointed an instructor in the College of Pharmacy. Between 1912 and 1915 he served in several divisions of the university and became an assistant in alkaloidal assaying and in the art of compounding. In 1915, the title "professor of pharmaceutical botany and pharmacognosy" was conferred.[5] Even when he was appointed dean of the College of Pharmacy in 1917, this apparently caused little more attention than shifting to another desk. Said Raabe: "I didn't even know that I had been named dean that year until the executive secretary addressed me, 'Good morning, Dean.' I asked him where he got that stuff because I thought my good friend Mr. D.C. Mohler was still the dean. But, it turned out he knew it before I did."[3]

When considering what he thought was his most important achievement Raabe stated: "It would be that I met and kept pace with the progress of pharmacy as exemplified in the laws of the state." He believed that his "...objective in teaching was to lay the basic foundation in pharmacy and to keep in mind these people came to college so that they could qualify to be registered pharmacists.

"But there were many personal satisfactions as well. At one time, I can remember that four of the five men on the state board of pharmacy were Ohio Northern men. In one year Northern had the highest grade on the state pharmacy test four times,"[3] said Raabe.

Dean Raabe was recognized as an active supporter of many of America's professional pharmacy associations. He was also a tireless worker in their activities, serving many years as a member or chairman of the Committee of Pharmaceutical Education and Science of the Ohio State Pharmaceutical Association. He also was secretary and later chairman of the Committee on Education and Legislation of the American Pharmaceutical Association,[2] and was a member of the American Association for the Advancement of Science.[6] Dean Raabe was a member of the Theta Nu Epsilon and Alpha Kappa Pi fraternities, since combined to form Alpha Sigma Phi. He was a charter member in 1920 of Gamma Delta chapter of the Kappa Psi pharmaceutical fraternity at Ohio Northern.[7] He was also a member of the Masonic Lodge and the Order of the Eastern Star, and an energetic member of the First United Methodist Church in Ada.

Dean Raabe continued as the college's chief administrator until July, 1950, at which time he requested to be relieved of his administrative responsibilities so he could devote full-time attention to teaching. He continued teaching the courses he loved until health considerations dictated his retirement in 1955.[7] When he retired he was told he had served the university for a longer consecutive time without vacation or sabbatical leave than any other person in the history of the institution.[3]

Following retirement, Dean Raabe continued to reside in his home in Ada at 316 South Gilbert Street, located about a block north of the main campus at the site of the current Dicke Hall. From there he maintained close contacts with the college and university. His days were filled with a busy schedule. His continued interest in the profession was kept alive as reflected in his incessant reading of trade journals and other literature to keep posted in what was going on in pharmacy. The interest he showed in his students throughout forty-five years of great teaching at Ohio Northern University remained with him, even after retirement.[2] He maintained a close, personal contact with many of his former students, and they with him.

Dean Raabe, With Highest Esteem

On Commencement Day, 1964, Dean Raabe was awarded an honorary Doctor of Pharmacy Administration degree by Ohio Northern. The following citation was read by Dr. F. Bringle McIntosh, president of the university:

> "Rudolph Henry Raabe, distinguished son of the State of Ohio, loyal alumnus of Ohio Northern University and the University of Havana, Cuba; for 45 years a truly great teacher in that college and 33 years Dean of the College; a man of whom it has been said… 'He has undoubtedly educated more pharmacists than any other man in America;' a teacher and administrator greatly beloved by his students, often referred to as 'Mr. Pharmacy' and the 'Grand Old Man of Ohio Northern;' recognized by and active in many of America's professional bodies. It gives me distinct pleasure and great honor to confer upon you this mark of distinction."[3]

Dean Raabe's final appearance on campus was on October 22, 1966, when he spoke to a full house of pharmacy alumni and other dignitaries at the dedication of the Robertson-Evans Pharmacy Building, the new home for the College of Pharmacy. He was in a wheelchair at the time after having a foot amputated.

Because of failing health, he moved to Toledo to live with his daughter and son-in-law. Two years later on November 12, 1968, Dean Rudolph H. Raabe passed away at age 87. His body was returned to Ada where he was laid to rest in

Ada's Woodlawn Cemetery alongside Mamie Lucille Klinger Raabe, his beloved wife and companion of fifty-one and a half years.

In 1971, the college was named the Rudolph H. Raabe College of Pharmacy in his honor.[8,9]

Dean Raabe's life was framed by a praiseworthy career that few others will ever achieve. He was well known and highly respected and dearly loved by thousands of members of his profession and many others who knew him.[10]

Writing in the first issue of the college's newsletter, *The Ampul,* in an article entitled "Honored Son of O.N.U.," Tom Smailes (BS Pharm '53) commented: "Oh, that there would be more people in this world such as Rudolph H. Raabe, who would be doers of the word and not hearers only. Many things which he has done for our Profession and for the good of other people have gone by unsaid and unrecognized....Surely Dean Emeritus Rudolph H. Raabe shall be called 'Great' and surely he shall be duly rewarded."[6]

Max Myers (BS Pharm '54) warmly described his feelings in an eulogy for his former professor and friend: "It is impossible to isolate a single human quality, milestone or achievement in a man's life which in itself merits the accolade of great. Greatness is, instead, earned by the sum of a man's life, contributions and achievements. This being so, there can be no question as to the greatness of Rudolph H. Raabe.

"In this age of superlatives, GREAT seems hardly adequate to describe Dean Raabe, and yet, to those of us who knew him, the term 'great' seems somehow pretentious when applied to someone we remember as a simple, warm, compassionate and honest man. Dean Raabe certainly did not consider himself a great man... perhaps that helped make him one."[7]

Personal Reflections

I met Dean Raabe only once. That meeting occurred during my sophomore or junior year at ONU, sometime around 1960 to 1962. A small group of us students visited with him at his home. The meeting lasted only a short while, and at this time, I can't even remember why we visited with him. I do recall him as an elderly, but gracious, host; otherwise, that's about all I remember.

With Dean Raabe as a cue for this message, I often think of other individuals I have met casually along the way, interesting people, including some special students. I never took the time to get to know them better. I guess I felt I was just "too busy" at the time. And, I think of selective faculty members I studied under while a student at ONU, people who were still alive and living in Ada when I returned to campus in 1972. Robert Bowden, Boyd Sobers, and Anna Koffler were such individuals. There was Robert Fischelis, Ronald Weber, George Henlein, and others. There have been so many of these people who are now either deceased or living far away from Ada. I had my chance to get to know each one of them much better, to learn from them, and in each case, I blew it.

I pass on these words of wisdom—as a friendly message—to all who read this. Take the time to visit, then re-visit your own acquaintances from earlier times. Get to know them better. My guess is that someday, you'll be glad you did.

FIVE
A Period of Great Transition

The period that spanned 1917 through 1929 for the College of Pharmacy at Ohio Northern University, as well as for this country and indeed the world, was rampant with many significant events. The United States was pulled into World War I early in 1917, after having long professed its isolationism status during the early period of the conflict. Pharmacy enrollment declined by more than two-thirds as students enlisted or were drafted into the war effort. Graduates in pharmacy at ONU dropped from fifty-seven in 1917 to seventeen in 1918, and ten in 1919. Many of our nation's college campuses, including ONU's Ada campus, were pressed into service as training camps to prepare young men for the war effort, an effort that no doubt greatly disrupted the educational programs.

During the winter of 1917, students had to manage as best they could with a nationwide fuel shortage. The combination of greatly increased demand for fuel by the war industries, along with diminished coal production and numerous nationwide transportation misadventures, was already hampering the economy in addition to America's ability to keep warm. The problem became so serious that in September, the federal government urged all families to reduce home temperatures by at least five degrees. Ohio Northern was expected to bear its share of the burden, as were all other educational institutions in the country. Only half of Pharmacy Hall was heated, so all pharmacy classes were scheduled to meet in that section. Other concessions were imposed for the other campus buildings and university programs. All heat to academic buildings was shut off on weekends. Evening meetings were limited to Wednesdays and Fridays. By late January, 1918, even more stringent measures were decreed. Some classes were moved from one building to another so that heat in the deserted building could be turned off completely, while in others, the heat was turned off by early afternoon. The noontime break between classes was cut in half.[1]

The war would continue until late 1918. With its termination, ONU and other academic institutions soon returned to their former order of business. By 1920, the number of pharmacy graduates had increased to twenty-four, by 1923 to forty, and in 1926, seventy-three students graduated in pharmacy.

Ohio Northern was jolted, as was the world, by World War I. As prices began to escalate, the boarding house operators were no longer able to feed hungry students for as little as $1.50 per week. The institution was forced to go into the restaurant business for itself, in self-defense. A basement was dug underneath Brown Building and a cafeteria installed.[2]

The Institution

Lehr's founding mission for the institution continued into the 1920s. As the 1920–21 catalog explained: "The Ohio Northern University invites to her privileges all worthy young men and women, especially the self-dependent who are ambitious for a liberal education. Her entire regime has in view the creation and maintenance of an atmosphere inspirational and congenial to plucky young people of both sexes whose lot in life has taught them the worth of hard labor and close economy. Jeans and broadcloth, homespun and silk have equal chance. The atmosphere is thoroughly democratic, a lead-characteristic being the marked camaraderie of the students, a majority of whom are relying mainly on their own pluck and push. Thorough practical instruction in all the departments is provided at a minimum expense to the student."[3]

The expectation for student discipline was also clearly defined: "The opportunities and advantages of the University are offered to all sincerely desiring to develop the best in themselves, and aiming at a broad culture and a thorough preparation for useful service.

"Self-government is made the key-note in discipline. All are treated as ladies and gentlemen until they prove themselves otherwise. Incorrigible and morally corrupt persons are summarily dismissed from the institution. Every possible help is afforded in the formation of right habits, but those who cannot govern themselves are not wanted. This institution does not pose as a 'reform school.'

"Regular attendance upon class work, prompt response to duty, and thoroughness in all assigned tasks are insisted on, not more for their bearing on scholarship than for their effect upon conduct and life."[3] If adherence to a strict schedule for discipline was not compatible with student life in the 1920s, an alternative thought that put things into a perspective all persons could understand was offered: "An Alumnus has figured that by completing a course in the Ohio Northern University, a student gains one year in time and one thousand dollars in money."[3]

The school's easy access and the village of Ada's charm continued to be stressed in order to attract more students: "Ada, the seat of the Ohio Northern University, is an attractive little city in Northwestern Ohio, on the Pittsburg (sic), Fort Wayne & Chicago Division at the Pennsylvania Railroad. Fifteen miles east of Lima and twenty-eight west of Upper Sandusky. Railroad connection is made at Lima with the Baltimore and Ohio and the Lake Erie & Western division of the New York Central Lines and the Erie Railroad. Connection is also made at Upper Sandusky with the Hocking Valley, at Forest, sixteen miles east, with the Big Four, and at Dunkirk, ten miles east, with the Ohio Central Lines.

"Lying on the great watershed separating the waters tributary to the Ohio and the Mississippi from flowing into the Great Lakes, Ada, with its population of three thousand, has an elevation above sea-level as high as any in the State [no falsehood, for the highest geographic point in Ohio is approximately thirty miles to the south of Ada], with healthful climate, sanitary conditions well guarded, and an abundant supply of excellent water from drilled wells. The town is unsurpassed in healthfulness and freedom from epidemics. Numberless forest trees line avenues and adorn premises, affording a delightful retreat during the warm summer months. The paved streets, cold water plant, electric light and natural gas evidence the wide-awakeness of the citizen in the matter of public utilities and city improvements."[3]

The Pharmacy Program

The period encompassing 1917 through 1929 was one of the most interesting in our country's history, as well as in pharmaceutical matters. It was a period of significant educational turbulence in many aspects of pharmacy education. Today it is still hard to think that just little more than nine decades ago, in 1917, there were no well defined educational requirements for pharmacy. During that year however, the membership of the American Conference of Pharmaceutical Faculties (its name was changed in 1925 to the American Association of Colleges of Pharmacy) voted that after 1920 a four-year high school diploma would be an educational prerequisite for entrance into schools of pharmacy. This requirement had been in effect at Ohio Northern University for some time for those who elected to take the four-year course leading to the Bachelor of Science degree.

Early in the twentieth century, the Ohio Board of Pharmacy took a close look at the preliminary education of candidates for licensure. If a student wished to enter college and could not show evidence of a common school education including one year of high school, he or she might satisfy this requirement by taking an examination over a number of stipulated subjects.[4] The Ohio board was empowered to "… appoint an Entrance Examiner who shall not be directly or indirectly connected with a school of pharmacy…who shall determine the sufficiency of the preliminary education of the applicants for admission to a school of pharmacy in good standing and to whom all applicants shall submit credentials."[5]

The preliminary education requirement was gradually increased so that by 1920, the board announced: "The following preliminary educational credentials shall be sufficient: On and after January 1, 1920, a diploma from a legally constituted high school, normal school or academy, issued after at least four years of study" would be mandated.

Moreover, "Those wishing to pursue the three-year course of study leading to the degree of Pharmaceutical Chemist (PhC) must present an entrance certificate from the State Examiner.

Porcelain invalid feeders or "sick feeders" held liquid medication that was poured directly into the opened mouth of patients.

"Persons wishing to pursue the four-year course of study leading to the degree of Bachelor of Science in Pharmacy (BS) must present an entrance certificate from the State Examiner.

"Students from other Colleges of Pharmacy will be admitted to advanced standing upon satisfactory evidence that they have met all the requirements established by this college to attain such standing."[3]

From this it was clear that the Ohio Board of Pharmacy had begun to stress the importance of pre-collegiate education not only for board candidates but for the school's applicants as well. Persons who entered the College of Pharmacy prior to January 1, 1920, were permitted to continue their course of study without obtaining another entrance certificate.

The requirements for taking the Ohio Board licensing examination advanced in 1920 from a candidate holding a high school diploma to where in 1925, candidates must have graduated from a recognized college of pharmacy. The following made that clear: "The State of Ohio requires all candidates for registration as pharmacists to be graduated from a recognized college of pharmacy before admission to its examinations except those who qualified under the laws existing prior to July 1, 1917."[5]

The greatest number of graduates from the nation's pharmacy colleges before 1927 were two-year students who received the PhG degree, which at that time satisfied the Ohio Board requirement for licensure. It was not uncommon in many states, however, for two-year graduates to have been granted the PhC degree, the degree that by then was commonly conferred across the country upon graduates from a three-year curriculum. As late as 1916, ONU's College of Pharmacy made it possible for students to take "Special Courses" for degrees beyond that of the PhG degree. The candidate must have earned the PhG degree and completed a prescribed amount of additional work to receive the more intensive PhC degree. To obtain the Pharm D degree, the candidate had to be a graduate of ONU, 21 years of age and a high school graduate, must have had four years' experience in a drugstore, and have completed about twenty weeks of additional course work in formulation and assaying of crude drugs.[4] But that era of rather non-specific educational requirements was about to change—for the better.

A New Era in Pharmacy Education

It will be helpful to highlight some of the important events championed at the national level that are regarded as the genesis of the new era in pharmacy. In 1917, the American Conference of Pharmaceutical Faculties required a four-year high school diploma as a prerequisite for admission to colleges of pharmacy. In 1920, the conference voted that the three-year course should be the minimum required for graduation from pharmacy colleges after July 1, 1925; the two-year curriculum was acceptable up to that time.

Dean Raabe was well aware of these pending changes and mandates, and revised his school's curricula and catalog announcements accordingly.[5] In the university catalog for June, 1925, a full-page "Boxed Announcement" headed up the College of Pharmacy section thusly: "*Important Announcement:* Beginning with the next opening date in September, 1925, the minimum course of study offered in the College of Pharmacy will cover a period of three years. Those students who entered the two-year course prior to this date will be permitted to continue and complete the two-year course and graduate with the degree as indicated. All matriculants in the two-year course must complete such courses of study prior to September, 1927."[6]

Member colleges of the conference, Ohio Northern included, agreed that the four full-year curriculum would be the minimum requirement for graduation in pharmacy beginning in 1932, and that all matriculants in the three-year course, previously offered, must have been completed prior to September, 1932. The National Association of Boards of Pharmacy, sanctioned these upgraded requirements and indicated that a recognized college of pharmacy would be one that offers nothing less than a four-year curriculum after 1932.[7]

The growth of Ohio Northern University's College of Pharmacy is closely interwoven and contemporary with developments championed by the American Association of Colleges of Pharmacy. Throughout its history, the college has been guided by the national organization and its affiliates and has faithfully endeavored to conform to the regulations prescribed for its member colleges. To be convinced that this was the guiding policy of the administration respecting the College of Pharmacy at Ohio Northern, during the years under consideration in this chapter, one needs only to read the explanatory statements found in the front pages of the catalogs that appeared annually except for the war year, 1918. Under the heading "Requirements for Admission," not only were the requirements of the College of Pharmacy clearly stated but those of the Ohio Board of Pharmacy were included as well. The board repeatedly made clear its preliminary educational, and later, its college requirements.

The following is an expression of the concern shown by the College of Pharmacy respecting those who sought admission: "Candidates for admission to the College of Pharmacy must be (1) of good moral character; (2) at least seventeen years of age; (3) graduate of a first-grade high school as defined in Ohio or its equivalent; (4) prepared to present to the University Entrance Examiner an entrance certificate issued by the Ohio Board of Pharmacy; (5) properly certified to the University Entrance Examiner by the authorities under whom the secondary educational qualifications were earned (all preliminary educational qualifications must be done in harmony with the approved plans of the Ohio Department of Public Instruction)."[6]

The discussion continued: "To enter any of the regular courses of study leading to a degree the candidate must (1) get an entrance permit from the University Entrance Examiner; (2) matriculate; (3) prepare a schedule of studies with the aid of an adviser and approval of the Dean; (4) pay tuition and fees as stated elsewhere in this catalog."[6]

Other subjects that were discussed in the catalogs included the laws of Ohio as pertained to pharmacy, the advantages offered at Ohio Northern, suggestion when to enter, and in-depth discussion of the college's laboratories. Much attention was given to the well-equipped laboratories in general biology, chemistry, dispensing, pharmaceutical preparations, microscopy, and physics. Strong training in these disciplines has always been essential for pharmacists' success in practice and still is, although the means for training has changed greatly in today's era of structured internships and clinical experiences. As early as 1915, it was claimed that ONU's College of Pharmacy compared favorably with other pharmacy schools in the country. The laboratories were large and an entire outfit (setup of equipment) including storage closet was assigned to each student.

"The laboratory for practical chemical work is equipped with all the accessories necessary for chemical analysis and synthesis. For advanced courses there is a complete outfit for gold and silver assaying and other metallurgical work. In this laboratory the student is required to perform a satisfactory amount of analytical and synthetical work under the personal attention of the Professor of Chemistry and an able assistant. A Microscopical Laboratory has been installed and equipped with a supply of fine instruments for individual microscopic investigation."[8] The following year another sentence was added: "In the 'specimen room' is an interesting exhibit of all the crude drugs of Materia Medica, a complete line of U.S.P. chemicals, a fine case of salts and alkaloids, and another of biological specimens, such as serums, antitoxins, and the like."[3] It was evident that much emphasis was given to practical training.

n 1917, the courses were listed for the junior (first) year and the senior (second) year. They were then briefly described under the titles of the major areas, such as practical pharmacy, pharmaceutical arithmetic, chemistry, botany, materia medica, human physiology, and microscopy. The descriptions, even though of a general nature, were reasonably clear. The 1917 catalog indicated, in addition to course descriptions, a minimum number of required clock hours for each the junior and senior year. "It will be noticed that while the 1913 Syllabus prescribes a two-year course of fifty weeks and 1,200 hours of instruction, the Ohio Northern offers a two-year course of sixty-four weeks and about 1,500 hours of instruction."[9]

The board of pharmacy's influence on curricular design is noted by reference to a statement in the 1919–20 catalog: "The State Board of Pharmacy announces as follows: 'Two units of credit may be procured by examination in each of the

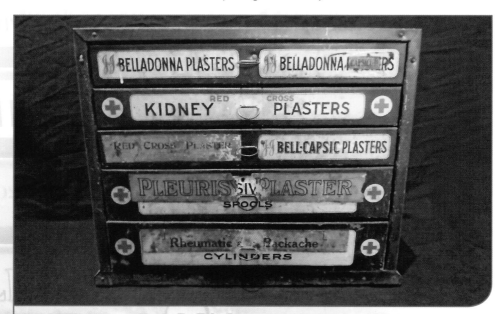

Medical plasters contained drugs mixed with gums and waxes spread upon cloth, leather, muslin or other material for application to the skin. Prepared by druggists in the 19th and early 20th century, they were practically all made by large manufacturers by the 1930s. Belladonna Plaster and Mustard Plaster were two of the most commonly used ones.

following subjects: Latin, German, English, Manual Arts and Home Economics; one unit of credit in each of the following subjects: Algebra, Plane Geometry, General Science, World History and General History; one-half unit of credit in each of the following subjects: Biology, Botany, Physical Geography, General Geography, Physiology, Bird and Animal Study, English History, Advanced American History, Civics, Commercial Geography, Business Correspondence and Bookkeeping."[8] This breadth of course requirements helps explain why university faculty members with titles expressive of expertise in foreign languages, biology, and physics were listed as members of the College of Pharmacy.

By 1919, the catalog included a schedule of the courses required for two years, and listed them quarter by quarter.[8] The 1920 catalog extended the schedule concept to include schedules for the two-year (PhG), three-year (PhC) and four-year (BS) curricula. This schedule plan was followed throughout the 1920s. Course changes were made frequently with the idea of improving the curriculum. Electives were not permitted to be substituted for the major subjects of chemistry, materia medica, or pharmacy. Students were allowed to elect fifteen elective quarter hours in the three-year program and thirty quarter hours in the four-year curriculum.

The separation of lecture and laboratory hours first appeared in 1920. It is to be observed that there was a marked increase in the total hours from 1922 to 1923 and from 1924 to 1925 for all degrees.

The Challenge (!) With Pharmacy Degrees

Among the first to disagree with the system of defining pharmacy degrees was Professor A.B. Prescott of the University of Michigan. Prescott was a physician-chemist in charge of the pharmacy program who believed that the academic study of pharmacy should be moved out of the past and viewed as a full-time endeavor. He refused to require apprenticeship as a requirement for graduation.[7] In 1869, he proposed that the PhC degree would be awarded to his two-year graduating classes at that institution. The older schools were accustomed to the three-year PhC degree and regarded the Michigan PhC degree as an intrusion of the established norm. Nonetheless, this new degree became popular, especially with schools in the Midwest that were established with frequency during the last quarter of the nineteenth century.

At Ohio Northern University, as far as can be determined, of the 603 degrees granted between 1915 and 1929, 510 were PhG, eighty-seven PhC, and six BS degrees. In the earlier years of this period as noted above, the catalog described "Special Courses" whereby students could arrange to work for an advanced degree, especially the PhC and BS degrees.[10] In 1915 the Pharm D degree was described as a special degree, but as emphasized earlier, it was not popular at Ohio Northern.[11] It is also noted that the university catalog for 1920–21 reported that "…a three-year course leading to the degree of Pharmaceutical Chemist and a four-year course leading to the degree of Bachelor of Science in Pharmacy are offered."[3] ONU's programs in pharmacy have been at times unfairly criticized in that students in the early days could "buy any degree" they wanted. Yes, they could. They could obtain a number of different degrees, all of which permitted them to practice pharmacy. Of course, they had to do the work that was required for that particular degree. The schedule showing only the second year for the PhG degree appeared in the 1926–27 catalog, and only the three-year and four-year schedules were shown in the 1927 catalog (Appendix 3).

If the reader is now confused, think how Dean Raabe and the pharmacy faculty, and the university's registrar, must have felt throughout the 1920s and through the late 1930s. One can imagine that with the complexity of scheduling for the various degrees for this era in pharmacy education, it must have been an extremely trying time for the dean and his faculty to assure that every student received what he or she needed and was treated fairly. Truth is, all indications inferred from university and college records of the era showed they all were.

As confusing as this must have been to the pharmacy dean and faculty, one can further surmise that candidates seeking entrance into the program must have had numerous questions. In attempt to help answer why there were so many changes ongoing in the academic world of pharmacy education, the following note was included in the 1926–27 catalog: "This College holds membership in the American Association of Colleges of Pharmacy. The object of this association is to promote the interests of pharmaceutical education. All institutions holding membership in this association must maintain certain minimum requirements for entrance and graduation. Through the influence of this association, uniform and higher standards of education have been adopted from time to time, and the fact that several states by law or Board ruling recognize the standards of the association is evidence of its influence."[12] This catalog copy made it clear that the confusion with pharmacy degrees during this period was due to goings-on at the national, rather than local, level.

An interesting comment appeared in the catalog for 1927–28: "The great demand from the pharmacists for a degree that is distinctly pharmaceutical and not likely to be confused with other degrees led the American Association of Colleges of Pharmacy to adopt the degree of Pharmaceutical Graduate, PhG, as the appropriate degree for the minimum three-year course. In accordance with this action those who satisfactorily complete the three-year course as scheduled below and met all other requirements for graduation will be permitted to choose the PhG degree."[13] It appears that graduates who completed the three-year program listed for the PhC degree could elect to receive the PhG degree instead of the PhC degree, perhaps thinking that the former degree sounded more professional to pharmacy. This catalogue notice was repeated through 1929–30 catalogs. By 1931–32, the statement had been modified to read: "The great demand from the pharmacists for a degree that is distinctly pharmaceutical and not likely to be confused with other degrees led the American Association of Colleges of Pharmacy to adopt the degree of Pharmaceutical Graduate, PhG, as the appropriate degree for the minimum three-year course. Matriculation in the three-year course will be discontinued, July 1, 1932."[14] The following year, this statement was added: "For beginning students registering for the academic year 1932-33 and thereafter, all colleges…shall require for graduation the satisfactory completion of not less than four full college years."[14] Thus, the die was cast at ONU. The question of degrees and length of study had been solidified for the moment. The four-year curriculum would become the law of the land—well, for the moment at least. Incoming freshmen students in 1960 would enter into a five-year program, and those coming in 2000 would enter into a six-year program.

The Good Times End

Aside from the intense turmoil that prevailed throughout the 1920s in deciding the nature of the pharmacy curricula and degrees to award for their completion, the decade, for the most part, championed a period of carefree living. Students studying pharmacy must have been excited to note such great innovations coming on that would reshape their profession and professional standing, and thus their life, well into the future. Their excitement and joy overall that was felt throughout most of the decade was soon to be challenged, however. The many inconveniences and widespread sacrifices of the World War I era were all but forgotten when America's Great Depression of 1929 came on. Its effects would be universal with no one spared the misery and/or despair that soon would engulf the country.

THE DEANS

Rudolph H. Raabe served as dean throughout the period of this chapter. His profile is given in Chapter 4.

SIX
Hard Times Ahead

The Great Depression era meant serious hardship was in store for all Americans and academic institutions in the United States, as well as for millions of individuals around the world. Even today, parents and grandparents often share vivid memories with children and grandchildren of the austere years when this great nation was grinding down to a virtual standstill and the times were truly taxing. As with other professionals and business persons at that time, pharmacists felt the depression's economic sting, but generally did not fare as badly as men and women in many other endeavors.[1] People still became ill and needed medicine. Most drugstores also stocked durable, low-cost items including soap, cosmetics, candy, and tobacco products. No matter how bad things seemed to be getting, the majority of people could still find the cash to purchase these and other convenience items from their local drugstore. Many pharmacists worked for as little as $18.00 per week,[2] but a strong emphasis must be understood when using the term "many" in this context. The fact was that many (or most) of the nation's pharmacists were employed; therefore they were able to feed their families and pay their bills, and did not suffer the insensate boredom from a deepening feeling of lack of purpose in life, a feeling that was commonplace with so many persons of working age across the land.

By the mid-1930s the severity of the Depression had begun to ease a bit and conditions were slowly returning to normal. Recovery came about, in part at least, by reformed banking laws, intense belt-tightening, and Americans' willingness to share whatever they had with one another in many ways.[2]

Ohio Northern University and the Great Depression

The good times of the 1920s had come to an abrupt end. With onset of the 1930s, Ohio Northern University was beginning to face financial failure. With no endowment to speak of through most years of its existence up to that time, the institution, like other private universities, had relied primarily upon income from students for its financial stability. Ohio Northern's debt was overwhelming. Buildings had been erected during the previous decade and facilities enlarged without serious thought or planning as to how the mounting debt would be paid in times of prosperity, let alone be reduced, should financial hard-times prevail. Tuition accounted for nearly eighty percent of income with the balance realized from miscellaneous sources.[3] University enrollment each year declined from a pre-Depression high of 1,056 in 1928–29 to 529 in 1935.[4] With debt totaling more than a quarter-million dollars (a sizeable burden for those days) and growing each day, and with tuition for 1933–34, for example, set at only thirty dollars per term and just barely trickling in,[5] many questions needed immediate answers. Numerous benefactors of the university who had generously supported its programs now found themselves short on cash and thus unable to meet their pledges to the institution. Gifts dwindled to near zero.[6]

A point that came up from time to time for serious discussion was whether the professional programs (engineering, law, and pharmacy) should be eliminated so that the institution's meager resources could be concentrated on strengthening the liberal arts curriculum. The decision each time was to continue the professional programs, decisions that in later years would be shown to have greatly benefitted the university. Indeed, the College of Pharmacy in the early 1930s was more than paying its own way. This was made public when, in 1931, the university was examined by the Commission on Survey of Educational Institutions of the Methodist Episcopal Church. The examiners thoroughly studied all aspects of the university and found that: "The College of Pharmacy is said to be self-supporting. In fact, it is reported that the fees produce more income than the College costs…

An examination of the cost data…indicates that the instructional salary costs in the College of Pharmacy are the lowest found in any division of the University, and the probabilities are that this division pays a net surplus into the University. That the quality of work [within the College of Pharmacy] is high is illustrated by the fact that of the 31 graduates who last year took the Ohio State pharmaceutical examination, 29 passed.…The faculty of the University is favorable to the enforcement of high standards, and the evidence points to good work."

The commission report continued: "At present there are three other accredited schools of pharmacy in Ohio. (Ohio colleges of pharmacy in 1931 were Ohio Northern University, the University of Cincinnati, The Ohio State University, and the University of Toledo.) About 250 pharmacists are needed each year in the state. These facts seem to indicate that there is a place for the College of Pharmacy of Ohio Northern University."[3]

In the midst of its economic woes, there was some good news for all students. The university appeared to be loosening its grip on muffling student behavior,

Pill machine used in the U.S. from early 1800s through 1930s. The druggist prepared a pill mass and rolled it into a small cylinder called a pipe, which was placed on the grooves of the machine (larger piece). Pills were formed by a back and forth motion of the roller (smaller piece with handles). Druggists were thus often referred to as "Pill Rollers."

perhaps thinking that since the times were changing, so must Ohio Northern change, at least on this one issue. Although the 1930s imposed significant financial hardship for the university, it was nevertheless able to brighten its students' lives in this one respect. Its ban on dancing was gradually lifted. Until this time, students had been prohibited from attending dances on or off campus, and violation of this rule was grounds for expulsion from the university. At the beginning of academic year 1929–30, university officials interpreted the ban to apply only to "…dances given in the name of any university organization. That is to say, no attempt will be made to control the activities of students in respect to dancing outside of these regulations."[7] It is interesting to think that the lifting of this ban may have been undertaken solely as a means to reduce student loss and thus preserve tuition income, as a means to help maintain institutional solvency. Informal dances were approved for fraternity and sorority members. Men and women were permitted to dance on Friday and Saturday evenings to music provided by radio or phonograph. Orchestra music was permitted at one formal dance each winter.[8] Even with the few exceptions as noted, at long last the university's ban on dancing at ONU was lifted. Of course, the real dancing, the truly memorable kind, would begin in 1945 when America's sons and daughters began to return from their military service in World War II.

ONU's College of Pharmacy experienced the full consequence of the Great Depression and, as discussed earlier, was not only paying its own bills but was contributing to the total institution's solvency. Money was so scarce during the Depression that many students could not afford to attend college,[2] even at the low tuition rate ONU charged. One federal program, the Civil Works Administration (CWA) was created to provide relief for a large number of students during the winter of 1933–34.[9] It provided financial support through a form of work/study grants. In 1934, for example, roughly ten percent of the student body was eligible to earn between $10.00 and $15.00 weekly by working around the campus.[10] Another program, the Federal Emergency Relief Administration (FERA), provided financial assistance for a few students in 1934-35.[11] These programs helped students supplement their meager incomes and dwindling savings by traditional employment. The sums involved were minuscule by today's standards, but every bit helped at that time.[12]

Pharmacy Through the Depression

The membership of the American Association of Colleges of Pharmacy had voted in 1926 on a date for adoption of a new, revised four-year curriculum. The date agreed to was July 1, 1932. General agreement for the four-year curriculum was evidenced in the association's executive committee response: "You are aware of the action taken by the National Association of Boards of Pharmacy at the last annual meeting to the effect that a recognized college of pharmacy will be one that offers nothing less than a four-year course after 1932."

In 1930, the Committee on Curriculum and Teaching Methods reported that about seventy percent of the country's pharmacy colleges, including Ohio Northern University, offered the bachelor's degree for completion of the four-year course. The committee continued: "We recommend the title, Bachelor of Science in Pharmacy (abbreviated BS in Pharm [BS Pharm]) as most suitable for the degree conferred upon the completion of the four-year course as set forth under the educational policy at the beginning of this report."[13]

With the date settled for initiation of a required four-year curriculum for pharmacists' education (beginning students registering for academic year 1932–33 and thereafter[16]), the next concern was to choose a date beyond which a course of study of less than four years' duration would not be recognized. It was voted upon and accepted that the date of September 1, 1936, shall be the last date that any college may confer a degree for any pharmacy curriculum of less than four years duration. Ohio Northern was on track to meet this requirement.

The format for pharmacy with the 1930 catalog was larger than for previous years although the general discussions and course descriptions were similar. Beginning in 1931 and continuing the following years, increased space was allotted to pharmacy for a general discussion of its curriculum as pertained to both professional and non-professional coursework. The four-year curriculum was outlined along with the three-year curriculum from earlier catalogs, as preparation was underway to convert the pharmacy program entirely to the more lengthy and intense course of study. In later catalogs, the four-year program would be explained and updates made from year to year as seemed necessary.[2] Detail was included relevant to both the required and optional courses, and explanation provided that certain elective courses were acceptable with permission of the dean. Explanations were added in effort to clarify the reasons for including certain courses in the new four-year curriculum. Not only were pharmacy courses explained, but those taken from offerings within the College of Liberal Arts were also considered.

Beginning with the 1930–31 catalog, the statement had been changed. Under the topic of "Curricula" the following statement was included: "The great demand from the pharmacists for a degree that is distinctly pharmaceutical and not likely to be confused with other degrees led the American Association of Colleges of Pharmacy to adopt the degree of Pharmaceutical Graduate, PhG, as the appropriate degree for the minimum three-year course."[14] Outlines of courses for the two degree programs were presented. Instead of the PhC and BS Pharm degrees, the PhG and BS Pharm curricula for the three-year and four-year programs, respectively, were shown. Apparently, the popularity and demand by ONU students for the PhG as their earned college degree in pharmacy, regardless of the time commitment needed to acquire it, exceeded the demand for the newer PhC degree. Course requirements had been tweaked for both degree programs: 3,018 clock-hours in the 1930–31 three-year program versus 2,738 clock-hours in the 1929–30 program, and 4,036 clock-hours in the 1930–31 program versus 3,350 clock-hours in the 1929–30 four-year program. While such prolonged discussion may have seemed like a throwback to the curricular turmoil of the 1920s, it was stated again to assure that every student's needs (as well as their wishes to receive a specified degree) to complete the requirements for graduation were met. The four-year program as the sole offering would be in effect for all students in the not-to-distant future.

The catalog for 1931–32 expanded upon the college's purpose: "This college is a member of the American Association of Colleges of Pharmacy, the object of which is to promote the interests of pharmaceutical education. It aims to prepare men and women to meet not only the legal requirements of the profession but also the increasing public demand for educated and trained pharmacists.

"Through organized courses of study instruction is given in the sciences pertaining to the selection, standardization, preservation, and dispensing of drugs, medicines, and chemicals used in the promotion of personal and public health, and in the service of the pharmacist to the public, to the medical practitioners, and to the profession.

"A knowledge of the business methods involved in the successful distribution of medicinal materials is essential to the successful pursuit of the profession. Through a series of courses in business administration and drug store business methods, the student is given excellent opportunity to elect courses suited to his particular needs."[15]

Included in the catalog of 1931–32 for the first time, under the heading "Description of Courses" was the listing, "Economics and Business Administration." This announcement noted: "Ability to buy, sell, and organize business efficiently is without doubt one of the essentials in the profession of pharmacy. General courses in the principles of accounting, economics, and business organization may be elected by those who wish to acquire a broader knowledge of sound business procedure."[15] Although these disciplines were not part of the required professional curriculum, there was provision for such electives and these courses qualified. Their provision and indeed promotion to students studying pharmacy was no doubt encouraged by the nation's depressed economic climate of the time and the students' belief that a solid understanding of business could help students avoid personal economic failure, as well as aid the nation's ongoing economic struggle.

On the positive side, courses in business and economics would be required for future pharmacy students, and these initial offerings of the 1930s no doubt contributed to the strong appeal that Ohio Northern University had for attracting students in years to come. It was a powerful belief that ONU emphasized the teaching of a practical pharmacy curriculum that positioned pharmacists for successful practice in community pharmacies (i.e., retail settings) and it was this perception that attracted many students into the college in the first place. Its graduates were taught how to be successful over the next thirty to forty years or more, while working in the world in which they believed at the time they would practice their profession. Even today, many of the college's alumni continue to endorse this thought with strong affirmation that the college was on the right track at that time. Until the clinical pharmacy era emerged with the 1970s, which brought sweeping changes in the educational requirements for the profession, this emphasis on business was a strong draw for ONU's program. It was certainly one that many of the heavily research-oriented college programs in the basic pharmaceutical sciences could not match. To Northern's credit, as the new era of clinical practice was coming on strong in the 1970s, ONU's College of Pharmacy would be among the first schools in Ohio to embrace the new direction in practice wholeheartedly and modify its educational approach to meet the many challenges and position its graduates for success well into the future.

One note of interest is the abandonment of the term "materia medica" in 1931–32 as a course title. A requirement for all curricula, dating back to the initiation of the ONU Department of Pharmacy in 1884, materia medica was finally replaced with the more contemporary course, pharmacology.

Student achievement was noted in 1932–33 with the following announcement: "Two kinds of senior honors are recognized and conferred at graduation: honors (with distinction) granted to those who have a quality point average of 2.3 with no grade below D; and honors (with high distinction) granted to those who have a quality point average of 2.6 with no grade below C. These honors in scholarship are recorded on the diplomas, recognition is given at commencement, and the names of the recipients are printed in the catalog. To receive senior honors a student must be in residence at Ohio Northern at least nine quarters."[16] Today, the university recognizes three levels of senior honors: *cum laude*, awarded to students with a cumulative point average of at least 3.5; *magna cum laude*, awarded to students with a cumulative point average of at least 3.7; and *summa cum laude*, awarded to students with an accumulated grade point average of at least 3.9. Students must complete at least thirty hours of graded courses at Ohio Northern to qualify for graduation with distinction. The honor is recorded on students' diplomas.

A glance into the records of pharmacy graduates' scores on their board examinations will serve to convince the reader that the College of Pharmacy was preparing its students well for their life's work. The majority of high honors on the Ohio Board of Pharmacy's licensure examination in the past years had gone to graduates from Ohio Northern. That fact was again evidenced in 1932 when a member of the Ohio Board of Pharmacy reported: "ONU has more students passing our examinations than all the other schools combined."[17]

It is clear that Dean Raabe and his dedicated faculty in the College of Pharmacy were making a sincere effort to educate the future pharmacists of Ohio as best they could, working with extremely limited resources, and that same sincerity of effort remains at the forefront today. The following note from 1929–30 states this very well: "The Student is carefully instructed in the duties of the pharmacist in connection with his services to the public, in the duties of the pharmacist in his relation to the physician, in the duties of the pharmacists to each other, and his duties to the profession at large." It was also stated that the pharmacy program was being improved constantly with the purpose of "…preparing men and women to meet fully not only the legal requirements but also the increasing public demand for education and trained pharmacists."

A New Home for Pharmacy

Lengthened courses of study, thus increasing the number of students in resident study, and the constant demands for improved laboratory facilities, brought the college to the point where an enlarged facility was desperately needed. Pharmacy Hall had been remodeled and enlarged in 1909 when it was moved to its new location and set upon a newly dug partial basement that increased the laboratory space. Other renovations and improvements had been accomplished from time to time as needed. Nevertheless, the college was desperate for more space. By the 1930s, as useful and charming a building as it was in years gone by, Pharmacy Hall had by now become an eyesore and potential firetrap, and was condemned.

Pharmacy's cause was aided greatly when the 1931 commissioners mentioned earlier in this chapter reported to the university trustees that: "The criticism which the survey staff offers of the College of Pharmacy is that the work is done under poor physical conditions. The pharmacy building is one of the old buildings on the campus. It is a dilapidated frame structure which is by no means adapted to education in pharmacy, and this offers a considerable handicap. Better classrooms, laboratories, and offices would add materially to the ease with which the work could be done. This fact is clearly recognized by the faculty in Pharmacy and by the President of the University. Certainly some other arrangement to provide better facilities should be made as soon as funds can be provided."[3] Pharmacy Hall was thus doomed to destruction. Its days were numbered.

It was decided that the College of Pharmacy would move into the much more spacious and constructionally-sound Dukes Memorial where the departments of chemistry and mathematics, and the College of Engineering, were located. That move was undertaken in 1934.

Dukes Memorial was a large, very stately-looking brick structure that screamed with excitement just to look at it. Constructed in 1902–1903, and still in good condition, the new occupant was at last able to spread out. The engineering college moved out. The departments of mathematics and chemistry remained in the lower (basement) floor but this was entirely suitable for pharmacy since mathematics did not require extensive space, and a sizeable portion of the pharmacy curriculum included coursework in chemistry. And as the pharmacy curriculum would later expand and specific courses blending the two disciplines of pharmacy and chemistry, both would benefit by sharing the other's resources.

Dukes Memorial would later undergo several renovations, with the one in 1951–52 the most extensive to that point. An addition to the rear (west side) of Dukes was completed to house an animal quarters and provide updated restrooms. In recent times, it would again be enlarged and remodeled. Special care would be taken to assure that the structural additions blended architecturally with the old. The College of Pharmacy would remain in Dukes until 1966, at which time it moved into its newly constructed facility on the West Campus.

Early in 1937, the once stalwart but now empty Pharmacy Hall was razed. The proud, towering structure that in its early days proudly reflected the bright sun off its angel-white siding but by now gleamed a dull gray hue, had been abandoned three years earlier and was unoccupied since then. A number of options were considered in effort to rescue the facility, but it was too far gone for any amount of repair, and saving it even for a year or two would simply postpone the inevitable. It was estimated at the time of its demolition that approximately two thousand practicing pharmacists had studied in its classrooms and laboratories since its erection and occupancy in 1894.[18]

Also in 1937, an announcement of a new health service appeared in the catalog: "Beginning with the 1937-38 session, the College of Pharmacy of Ohio Northern University will open a prescription dispensary in cooperation with the University Student Health Service. The prescription dispensary will be administered by the registered pharmacists on the staff in the College of Pharmacy. Qualified junior and senior pharmacy students may be assigned to the pharmacist in charge of the dispensary for further instruction in

Dukes Memorial following construction, 1903.

Students at work in Dukes Memorial, circa mid-1930s.

prescription practice."[19] Although the endeavor sounded like a great idea, certainly one that remained in vogue at ONU until recently, whether or not it was successful in its early-onset years is not known. The formal announcement was not continued the following year. However, under the description of inhabitants of Dukes Memorial in 1942, the "Health Service Dispensary" was included.[20]

America's Great Depression was barely over and the atmosphere at Ohio Northern had brightened immensely. As the 1930s were drawing to a close, the institution was gradually recovering from its period of forced austerity and by all means seemed to be on the road to recovery. From a university enrollment low of 529 students in the fall term of 1935, enrollment had improved to 766 by 1939–40. By the end of the decade, progress was even being made toward reducing the university's overall debt. There was high reason for optimism and indeed, conditions were looking up. But all that was before Pearl Harbor grabbed the attention of all Americans. Optimism for Northern's future would again be bashed as the country was pulled into World War II.

Pharmacy Education During World War II

Information concerning enrollment and degrees granted during the Great Depression and World War II years is provided in Appendix 4.[2] The data for enrollment and degrees conferred are correlative. The gradual decrease in enrollment from 1930 through the mid-1930s may be attributed in part to the college's adoption of the four-year curriculum as well as to the economic depression. From about 1935 until the early 1940s, the number of degrees conferred during those years was sparse.

Beginning in the late 1930s, the U.S. government began to fear the actions of Germany, Japan, and Italy. All three countries were expanding their borders through conquest in Europe, Asia, and Africa, respectively. There seemed to be no let-up. The Burke-Wadsworth Bill, known as the Selective Training and Service Act, passed Congress on September 16, 1940, and became law.[21] This ushered in the first peacetime draft in United States history. The registration period for all males between the ages of 21 and 35 began one month later, and on October 29, 1940, Secretary of War Stimson drew the capsule containing the first number of the draft.[22] Between 1940 and 1946 more than ten million men from all parts of the country would be called into service.

With the fall term of 1940, immediately before selective service went into effect, 715 students were in attendance at the university;[23] one hundred of these were enrolled in pharmacy. One year later, the fall enrollment had declined to six hundred,[26] with ninety-six in the pharmacy program. The 1942–43 academic year proved to be a near-disaster for Ohio Northern University with a September, 1942, total enrollment of only 452,[24] with the pharmacy headcount at eighty-six. By spring, only 288 students remained on campus—until a further forty were called up for service. Since three of the four colleges (pharmacy, engineering, and law) were vocational, Ohio Northern's student body consisted of nearly eighty percent men.

Under Selective Service, ONU's student body was rapidly being depleted.[25] Draft boards were calling all who were classified 1-A, and over time, the younger the recruit, the better the individual could meet the challenge for military service.[26] The times indeed were very precarious for the few men remaining on campus. With many being called each day, the others were living on borrowed time as they awaited their call into service. From one day to the next, they did not know how soon they would be leaving. Fraternity men kissed their pin-mates good-by, paid due respect to their professors and fellow students not yet called, and willingly or otherwise accepted the call to serve their country.

As the number of ONU students continued to plummet, the customary enrollment figures were omitted from university publications and newspaper articles. Also absent from the catalogs were the exhaustive lists of faculty members, thus making it difficult then and today to accurately identify the size of the war-time faculty. One estimate holds that during the fall of 1943 only 156 students university-wide, close to the number recorded for Lehr's initial class in 1871, remained.[6]

Once again, the trustees considered whether the professional programs should be terminated and the institution continued solely as a college of liberal arts. It was even discussed that perhaps it was time to close the entire university. The remaining faculty, intensely devoted to the institution, wanted it saved at all cost.[25] This included Dean Raabe and his meager faculty. Along with university administrators, those faculty who were spared from active military duty agreed to deep salary cuts. They taught month after month without vacation time or sabbatical leave. The new university president, Dr. Robert McClure, matched the faculty's sacrifices by accepting no salary during his first year at ONU. It needs to be stressed that there was considerable support from Ada townspeople and businessmen. The Ada Business Association raised over $11,000 to help the institution get through the emergency. The Methodist church added another $10,000 and alumni contributed another $9,933. These gifts demonstrated continued loyalty to Ohio Northern and were sufficient to keep the university open.[6] The university and its College of Pharmacy survived any further thought of abandoning the programs. The College of Pharmacy graduated eighteen, three, five, and five, respectively, in the war years 1943 through 1946.

To meet wartime obligations the university made endless adjustments in its calendar to accommodate the harsh conditions. It lifted restrictions regarding when students could enter the institution. This enabled students to enter most programs of study, pharmacy included, at the beginning of any term, fall, winter, spring, or summer. Course offerings were increased for the summer term, thus making the university a year-round institution. This made it possible for pharmacy students and others to reduce by as much as a year the time necessary to complete their college work by attending consecutive quarters throughout the year. In those instances where the student desired a program that may not lend itself to the new schedule, the university made every effort to meet the needs of the individual. An announcement in the pharmacy section of the 1941–42 catalog read: "Although the curriculum for beginning students is designed for those entering the College of Pharmacy at the opening of the Fall quarter… during the present emergency the student may enter any quarter and complete the course of study by continuing in residence for twelve consecutive quarters. The sequence of courses presented herein should be followed insofar as possible, but every effort will be made to accommodate the needs of the individual student. Students who are entitled to advanced standing may enter at the time approved by the Dean."[27]

Dean Raabe worked hard trying to convince local draft boards to have his students deferred, at least until after they would graduate. The Selective Service Activity and Occupational Bulletin No. 33–6 addressed deferments for students in pharmacy. However, the bulletin served only to advise, not mandate, the actions of local draft boards. The American Pharmaceutical Association's War Emergency Advisory Committee was especially active in attempting to obtain a blanket deferment for students. The committee chairman reported that deferment for pharmacy students based on the same standards as for medical and dental students was impossible for three reasons:

1. "The ratio of pharmacists in the armed forces to the total number of practicing pharmacists was far below that of either physicians or dentists;
2. There were no validated statistics to substantiate that there was an overall shortage of pharmacists or that pharmacists' service then available to the public was inadequate; and,
3. The non-professional appearance of the average drug store and commercial nature of its predominant activities spoke against blanket deferments."[28]

As was the case a generation earlier during World War I, the war department at first chose not to commission pharmacists as officers. It cited the low professional status of pharmacists as its primary reason for this action. The military said that any young man who could read could be trained in ninety days to provide pharmaceutical service.[29] This stance angered leaders of the profession, especially since nurses were routinely commissioned as officers even though they had less education in areas of drug action and therapy than pharmacists.[1] With creation of the Army Pharmacy Corps midway through the war and recognition of pharmacy as a profession by the Public Health Service and Veterans Affairs, this perception began to change for the better.

In 1943, the college received word that the manpower commission had begun to recognize the need for pharmacists in the armed services and authorized local draft boards to defer students in pharmacy for a period not to exceed two years in order to give them time to complete their studies. To collaborate with the government and to encourage young men to train for the profession, accredited colleges of pharmacy were permitted to initiate an accelerated two-year course leading to the regular degree. Each institution was issued a quota based on past enrollment. The quota for Ohio Northern was thirty-nine. Dean Raabe was reported to have been enthusiastic about the plan and asked that the alumni call it to the attention of possible candidates for study.

A Light at the End of the Long Tunnel

There was a bright note for 1944—passage of the Servicemen's Readjustment Act, more commonly known as the G.I. Bill of Rights.[30-32] Although the public's response to this legislation would not be felt until after the war, the austere situation—that is, survival of the College of Pharmacy and Ohio Northern University—was in the process of turning, all for the better. In 1945, faculty and students alike sighed in relief because the war had ended and the institution had withstood the crisis.

THE DEANS

Rudolph H. Raabe served as dean throughout the period of this chapter. His profile is given in Chapter Four.

SEVEN
Out of the Crisis

W orld War II brought with it numerous challenges aside from the conflict itself. During the war years, the nation's colleges and universities, Ohio Northern included, were forced to contend with greatly depleted enrollments, deletions that totally destroyed some programs and greatly weakened others. The loss of students and numerous faculty members who were called into service to fight the battles or work in the war industries affected them all, one way or another. This was an especially difficult time for the private universities including ONU, where the majority of expenses had to be met with student tuition since there was no income from endowments. Northern had only a very meager endowment, if any at all, by that time and this could not be counted on as a major source of revenue.

The College of Pharmacy at Ohio Northern was especially hard pressed during the years 1944, 1945, and 1946. The number of graduates in pharmacy for these years totaled a mere six, five, and five, respectively, each year. It remains a great mystery how the college was able to survive through the era. With tuition at thirty dollars per term, by all standards, survival looked bleak. By 1947, however, the picture looked to be brightening somewhat. The number of graduates had increased to thirteen. From this point onward the student enrollment increased each year to a respectable number. Without a doubt, the college's continued existence can be largely attributed to the loyalty and concern of Dean Rudolph Raabe. It was he who encouraged the meager but highly dedicated faculty to remain on, with he and his fellow faculty surviving at great personal sacrifice.

On June 22, 1944, President Franklin Roosevelt signed into law the Servicemen's Readjustment Act,[1] even though the war would continue for another year. In a move that is all but unheard of in Washington politics today, the bill had passed both chambers of Congress unanimously.[2] This signing addressed higher education, social and economic concerns, veterans' matters and federal legislation in a way never before experienced in the history of the United States.[3] Truthfully, the U.S. government faced the possibility of postwar depression brought on by widespread unemployment. The G.I. Bill helped to keep the anticipated unemployment at bay.

More commonly known as the G.I. Bill of Rights (or, the G.I. Bill), the legislation guaranteed government assistance to World War II veterans when they returned home following military service. The G.I. Bill would provide veterans with low-interest mortgages, unemployment insurance, and of special interest to Ohio Northern and its sister institutions across the nation, financial assistance to attend the college of their choice. All men and women who had served at least ninety days in military service and were not more than 25 years old when they enlisted could receive up to five hundred dollars per school year for tuition, books and supplies, equipment, and a monthly living allowance while pursuing their studies.[4] Although not that large a stipend by today's standards, $500 each year was a true godsend to those receiving it in the mid-to-late 1940s and early 1950s. Millions of veterans would enroll in the nation's universities, including Ohio Northern, with the government subsidizing them.[1] Needless to say, the G.I. Bill helped World War II veterans earn a college diploma when they may not have been able to do so otherwise. It also helped save many institutions of higher education including, Ohio Northern University, at a time when the school's hope for recovery was at an all-time low point. The Veterans Administration was responsible for carrying out the law's key provisions including distribution of aid for education and training.[4]

The war ended in 1945, with Germany surrendering in May and Japan in September. The beginning of what would soon be a flood of returning veterans was underway. Excitement throughout the ONU campus piqued once again. University officials felt sufficiently confident that student numbers would be substantial, so they initiated a survey of the citizens of Ada to determine the extent of accommodations that would be available to house the returning veterans and their families.[5]

Ohio Northern Opens its Doors Wide

As the nation was moving from conflict to peace, the university was making big plans to provide educational and rehabilitation services for those who returned from the armed forces. The institution had been approved by the federal government to provide these services. Some of the programs were designed to continue one or two years and were adaptable to the interests and needs of the veterans. College admission requirements for these veterans were the same as for traditional students, except that the veterans who were first-time college students were required to present a certificate of eligibility from the Veteran's Administration. Returning students could re-enter and pick up from where they left off. Every effort was taken to welcome the veterans and help them feel at home on the ONU campus.[6] An initial group of thirty veterans were enrolled for the Fall term in 1945. By spring 1946, the number had swollen to an estimated 325 veterans. By winter 1946, the university enrollment exceeded nine hundred, and by fall 1948, the class size had expanded to 1,209.[7]

As the larger student body helped resolve the university's financial crisis, it also exacerbated the critical housing shortage in Ada. Reopening of fraternity houses provided limited relief from the overcrowding. Five houses were reopened by February, 1946.[8] Like other educational institutions, Ohio Northern was able to take advantage of the Surplus Property Act of 1944.[9] This legislation allowed the donation of World War II surplus property that was suitable for school, classroom, or other educational use to educational, public, health, local governments, and nonprofit institutions at reduced or no cost. Northern received an odd assortment of trailers and prefabricated dwellings courtesy of the federal government.

By fall, 1946, 114 trailers and five barrack-style dormitories for single men were set in place.[10] These units were grouped in "colonies" around the campus.[11]

Trailers, washing machines, clotheslines, and children quickly became a familiar scene on the campus landscape.[12,13] One colony, informally named *Vetsburg*, consisted of twenty-two trailers situated on the south lawn of Presser Hall. Another colony, termed *Vetsville*, contained twenty-eight units and was located on the athletic grounds near Taft Gymnasium. For married veterans, the low $15.00 monthly rent was a godsend. A former resident, who completed the pharmacy program in three calendar years to graduate in 1950, reminisces about life in one of these colonies: "The trailers had running water but no bathroom, so we had to walk down the boardwalk to take a shower or go to the bathroom (that was always fun on a cold winter night). We heated with a fuel-oil heater and cooked on a two-burner hot plate and used an electric roaster....My transportation was a girls bicycle and since we did not have an electric refrigerator, I would carry a 25-pound block of ice from the ice house (east of the downtown area in the middle of the village) in my bike basket to my icebox in the trailer."[14]

Throughout the next decade, the homely Vetsville and Vetsburg trailers were home to hundreds of students and their families until they were removed from the

Army surplus trailers serve as home to returning soldiers following WWII. Located west of Taft Gymnasium (future site of Heterick Library), 1947.

Trailer colony located near the western edge of the campus, circa 1950.

campus in 1957.[15] A third colony, *Lehr Village*, remained on the site of the present Heterick Memorial library until the summer of 1964.[16]

The post-war student body consisted of a high percentage of veterans who presented a unique challenge to the university. Most were older men, often with a wife and children.

They had adapted to a lifestyle characteristic of the military while in the service and overall, were "more experienced" in the ways of life and in many respects, less flexible than students of typical college age.[17,18] Just months before, many of these veterans were toting rifles and grenades. Now they were carrying textbooks and laboratory supplies. As a group therefore, they were oftentimes impatient with campus traditions (shunning the "Button Frosh" beanie craze completely), the university's restriction on consumption of alcoholic beverages, and mandatory chapel services. Recognizing this exuberant rambunctiousness may have been the reason for including the following notice (printed in a large boldface font so it couldn't be missed) on page one of the university catalog for 1947–48: "Neither the sharp wit nor the trained intellect can save mankind from catastrophe. Only men of good will intelligently directed can provide leadership for the creation of a better world. For this reason the first objective of Ohio Northern University is the development in a broad sense of the enlightened Christian character.

Inside a student trailer home. Note the electric hotplate for cooking dinner, 1947.

"We believe the Christian college is indispensable in the creation of real democracy. With this conviction the University offers its professional training as well as its Liberal Arts curricula under Christian auspices, holding ever in view the purpose that the student be led to approach his life's work and his responsibilities of citizenship with Christian motivation."[19]

The many challenges associated with the large veteran population were lessened as each class graduated and the ratio of veterans versus traditional students decreased with each successive class. As late as fall quarter 1949, the student body still consisted of roughly fifty percent veterans, eighteen down from ninety percent in 1947.[8] By the time the original G.I. Bill ended in July, 1956, 7.8 million of fifteen million World War II veterans had participated in an education or training program nationwide.[3,4]

The Pharmacy College Responds

Along with the special programs designed for veterans, the College of Pharmacy responded to the crisis by scheduling refresher courses in the major areas of the pharmacy curriculum to aid the returning veterans whose studies had been interrupted because of military service or work in the war industries. These refresher courses were often described in the early post-war catalogs. The College of Pharmacy, which had been operating on a year-round plan, had to make numerous adjustments in order to return to its customary schedules of classes. The more pressing task was that of providing for the mass of returning soldiers, some of whom were former students who needed reorientation to the classroom. The college had large enrollments in each of its summer sessions and these aided the veterans so that they could oftentimes complete their course of study in less time than the regular school year required. Today, alumni who took advantage of the summer program in pharmacy often relate that the one single aspect of their college days they recall as being objectionable was the near-stifling heat in Dukes Memorial during the summer, along with the almost overwhelming chemical odors that penetrated every single square inch of the building and prevailed without relief. But as they describe these conditions, a broad smile often overtakes them as they continue their description with comments along the theme that "…those times were among the best of my entire life!"

Along with the many other veterans studying a non-pharmacy curriculum, pharmacy veterans also needed housing for themselves and their families, which was as much a concern to the college as to the university. It must have been disconcerting, albeit an exciting challenge, trying to meet the changing needs of these returning military men who now wanted to finish their college work, find employment in a pharmacy, and get on with their life in all matters. And it must have been even more disturbing to the veterans as they tried to blend in with the traditional college students whose differences in age and interests were oftentimes quite diverse. With former students returning in large numbers to the classroom along with a drove of newcomers, the college was faced with large classes, and with facilities and a faculty size barely able to provide for them. The former soldiers were changed men, industrious and serious about their work. They generally did well with their assignments. Moreover, they appreciated what the institution was attempting to do for them and they were determined to make the best of it.[6]

From its beginning, ONU's College of Pharmacy encouraged women to enroll in its program although historically, the number of women enrolled remained small. During the war years, with many of the men away in the services, Dean Raabe encouraged women all the more to consider pharmacy as their life's work. The college noted that those women who had been trained in pharmacy had established a good reputation for their skill, neatness, and accuracy.[6] For these reasons and others, young women were invited to give serious thought to choosing pharmacy as a career move because the work is pleasant, remuneration satisfactory, and their work years in the practice of the profession could extend well beyond middle life. Even with all this encouragement, especially during the war years, pharmacy would remain a profession dominated by men. However, that would later begin to change. In 1982, the ratio of men to women enrolling in and graduating from pharmacy at Ohio Northern would shift in favor of women and that predominantly female-to-male ratio in enrollment remains through today.

The Pharmacy Curriculum

Throughout the war years the pharmacy program consisted of a four-year curriculum leading to the BS Pharm degree. For the most part, the curriculum remained reasonably stable and generally satisfactory. As has been noted, students enrolled in the pharmacy program at ONU could complete work for their degree in less than the customary four years.

The pharmacy program at Ohio Northern consisted of three major categories of study: pre-professional, professional, and elective courses. The pre-professional (general education—Gen Ed) courses were those required for all freshmen and taken in the College of Liberal Arts. They included subjects of biology, chemistry, English, and mathematics. Organic chemistry and physiology were pre-professional courses also offered in the College of Liberal Arts taken in the second year. Bacteriology, another non-professional course was taught within the College of Pharmacy in the third year. The professional courses comprised most of the curriculum of the second, third, and fourth years, and included study in the areas of pharmacy preparations; pharmaceutical chemistry; pharmacognosy; pharmacology; and pharmacy management, marketing and law. Provision of a few elective courses permitted students some choice in the subjects of most interest to them and could be selected from the technical or cultural areas of study. The catalog for 1953–54 designated the pre-professional courses as the pre-pharmacy curriculum, and constituted the first year's work.[20] Students were enrolled as freshmen in the College of Liberal Arts, not as freshmen in pharmacy.

For many years it had been argued that there was a need for more intensive basic training in all professional areas and many of the nation's leaders in pharmacy felt that the profession had lagged behind its sister health-related professions in this respect. Working with the American Council on Pharmaceutical Education (ACPE), the profession undertook a comprehensive self-study called the Pharmaceutical Survey (1946–49). The ACPE consisted of representatives of the American Association of Colleges of Pharmacy (educators), the American

Pharmaceutical Association (practitioners), and the National Association of Boards of Pharmacy (regulators). It was an independent organization recognized by the U.S. Department of Education as the national group for accrediting professional degree programs in pharmacy.[21] The group continues through today.[a]

The Pharmaceutical Survey was the largest and most broad-ranging evaluation of the profession up to that time.[22,23] Its findings encouraged better training in the basic disciplines deemed necessary for successful pharmacy practice of the future.[24] Also, it was common knowledge that the war department's committee on special training had often questioned the training of pharmacists, noting that in contrast to their level of education during World War I, pharmacists now had a positive effect on the army.[6]

A five-year curriculum and its perceived benefits had been discussed at numerous annual conventions of the American Association of Colleges of Pharmacy, and nearly every other occasion pharmacists met. It was therefore decided in 1954 that, beginning with students entering the study of pharmacy after April 1, 1960, a five-year course of study would be required.[25,26] The survey also concluded that adoption of a standard six-year Doctor of Pharmacy curriculum would assure that the public would view pharmacists as true professionals.[24] But that thought would remain on hold for awhile. It would still be another near-half century before the six-year curriculum would become the standard.

End of an Era

In 1950, Dean Rudolph Raabe, who had served the college forty-five years, thirty-three as its dean, asked to be relieved of his administrative duties so that he could concentrate on his teaching responsibilities. He was appointed dean emeritus and continued to teach full-time within the college for the next five years. Dr. Albert C. Smith, professor of pharmaceutical chemistry since 1944, was appointed acting dean of the college in 1950, and dean in 1951. Dean Smith would hold this position until 1962 when failing health and pressures from his family to "…slow down a bit" brought him to the point where he realized their advice might well be to his advantage.

College Accreditation

The lean years of the 1940s precluded any major renovation of Dukes Memorial or purchase of teaching or laboratory supplies. The college had been operating for many years with antiquated equipment. Supplies were purchased only when absolutely necessary. Faculty size was meager at best, with only four persons listed on the college rolls in 1950–51: two with a doctoral degree (Rudolph Raabe, Pharm D, and Albert Smith, PhD), one with a BS Pharm degree alone (Lois Schultz Baun, BS Pharm) , and Myron Hanna, MD, BS Pharm, who served as the school's medical doctor and taught pharmacology on the side.[27] True, enrollment was up, thanks to the many veterans on campus. But it would take awhile to completely return to normal operation because there was great competition across campus for the funds these veterans brought in.

In 1950, the college was still operating with its "C" accreditation rating from ACPE, the group recognized as the accrediting body for all schools of pharmacy in the United States. ACPE assigned one of three ratings to each college: "A", first-class school; "B", good, but room for improvement; and "C", temporary rating, standards need to be raised.[28] Ohio Northern's College of Pharmacy was one of two colleges of pharmacy in the United States at that time with the provisional rating; furthermore, ONU's "C" rating had been in place since accreditation of pharmacy colleges was first initiated, about fifteen years earlier. Blame for this less-than-stellar rating could not be assigned to either Dean Raabe or Dean Smith. Both men were caught in the middle of what could easily have been full financial failure of the institution. Both men were very successful in maintaining the school's existence. If the money had been available, both would have been able to gain and maintain a top rating much earlier.

An ACPE inspection team visited the campus in September, 1950.[29] Following its extremely thorough two-day inspection, team members made specific recommendations to the university's president, F. Bringle McIntosh, for strengthening the program. Noted were needed curricular changes and updating, equipment supplementation, laboratory facilities updating, expanded library holdings, developing a sound endowment, and increased funding guaranteed for the day-by-day operation of the college.[30] The team indicated it would return to campus the following year to assess the institution's actions taken on its suggestions.

Shortly thereafter, the university trustees approved $25,000 to address the deficiencies, money that it did not have in excess.[31] This allocation solidified the institution's commitment to continue to strengthen the College of Pharmacy. Specific improvements included installation of a modern combination bacteriological-biochemistry laboratory with forty-eight new desk combinations having soapstone countertops and sinks that were acid/alkali-proof. Equipment purchased included five microscopes, a colorimeter used for quantitative and blood analysis, a barrel-type autoclave for steam sterilization and two electric and insulated incubators for bacteriological work. All of this was in place by the beginning of the fall, 1951 term. A new laboratory for pharmacology and physiology was scheduled to be completed by the beginning of the winter quarter.[31,32] A much needed ventilating system was installed in the animal quarters "…to provide better health conditions for animals and students alike."[33]

By fall 1951, work had been started on a 14 x 40-foot brick-faced addition onto the west side of Dukes Memorial.[34] The ground floor contained new and updated restrooms that were long needed to meet state sanitary standards. The second floor housed small animals for use in laboratory work and experimental research in pharmacology, bioassay, and physiology.[35] Above all this was a small attic for equipment storage. As a result of this $15,000 improvement to the building, along with the previously mentioned $25,000 worth of improvements from funds allocated for renovation of other portions of the building and purchase of equipment, the ACPE inspection team was favorably impressed when it returned to Ada in November, 1951. The college received full accreditation to an "A" rating, even with only five faculty members, counting the dean. Years later,

Dean Smith would claim this achievement in accreditation rating as his greatest professional accomplishment during his tenure as dean.

The Ampul

t was during this period that *The Ampul* [Vol 1(1), Spring, 1952] made its debut. It was described by Dean Smith as the college's "first attempt to issue a journal or bulletin that would provide a means to point out the college's accomplishments—first those of the student body, and second, those of the university."[36] The little publication that measured in size scarcely larger than a half sheet of paper, printed in black and white, would be published as the journal of the student branch of the American Pharmaceutical Association at Ohio Northern University. The publication would be issued quarterly or semi-annually. Just twelve pages in size, with one and one-half of these filled with advertising (Lodelyn Drugstore, Mutual of Omaha Insurance), the first *Ampul* was dedicated to Dean Raabe.

The Ampul, Vol 1, Spring, 1952.

The Ampul, modern days, Fall, 2014.

Throughout the years, except for a few issues here and there, *The Ampul* has continued to be published regularly. Now an enlarged-size format with full color layout, the multi-page biannual journal enlightens alumni and others about the wide scope of activity ongoing within the college.

The Real Heroes of the Day

Sharing the story about the college's accreditation is one thing, but there remains another story that needs to be told. Early in October, 1951, word was out regarding the forthcoming accreditation team visit that was only weeks away.[37] Immediately sensing a need for a general spruce-up of the physical plant and recognizing the institution's dearth of funds, a group of pharmacy students decided the time was right for them to lay aside their spatulas and textbooks, replacing them instead with scrub brushes and paint brushes to renovate and redecorate the building. The idea originated within the minds of a few senior students who wished to pay tribute to the college for the education it was providing them. Excitement spread quickly throughout the pharmacy student body. What started as a group project soon ignited a fire under the entire student body to give Dukes Memorial a thorough facelift.[38] Work was coordinated and duties assigned through the local student branch of the American Pharmaceutical Association.[39] Working days and nights for two weeks, often until 1:00 a.m. or later, and afternoons when laboratory or class work did not interfere,[36] student volunteers painted all classroom and laboratory walls white. Laboratory desks in the prescription laboratory received a fresh coat of paint. The students then moved into the hallways and entranceways, painting them a visually pleasing pastel green. Nothing that was paintable was spared.[40]

The students replaced outdated light fixtures in the building with modern fluorescent lights that had been donated by an area pharmacist alumnus and president of the Northwestern Ohio Pharmaceutical Association.[38] They removed outdated equipment from classrooms and laboratories that had not been used for years. They removed old wooden archways at the ends of the hallways, thereby

Pharmacy students in Dukes Memorial, circa mid-1950. Note crowded conditions.

expanding the areas and modernizing the spaces. They had fire extinguishers charged and brought up to code and the fire gong painted bright red. They purchased pencil sharpeners and installed them in each classroom and laboratory. The list of their efforts continued on and on. When the work was nearly completed, the students sanded the wooden floors to remove many years' worth of grime, varnished them, and cleaned the building completely.[41]

With the project completed, the entire pharmacy facility was described as "…a modern home that students would not be ashamed to show to family and friends and that alumni would be proud to return to." The student's work was later described as "…the greatest volunteer project in the history of Ohio Northern"[42] and certainly was at least partially responsible for the accreditation team's favorable impression of the college. In one of those rare moments when Dean Smith was caught without words, he managed to convey his feelings of love and respect for his students when he wrote in *The Ampul*: "May I state as the dean, I have never worked with any group of students that are so cooperative and ambitious as all the ONU students since my coming to this school. The students not only fulfilled all the requirements and obligations for graduation but are always looking for ways and means to make our school a pleasant place in which to pursue an education. These students have the fight and spirit to succeed and to make our College of Pharmacy the best of all."[37]

The college would be re-inspected in May, 1956. That inspection team voted that the college would retain its "A" accreditation rating. Most of the earlier deficiencies had by then been remedied. Faculty size at that point totaled eight persons, with six of them holding the PhD degree, one with the MS degree and one with both the MA and MBA degrees.[43] The two new laboratories were in full operation. Financially, the college seemed to be on solid ground, although it would soon be announced that the ground was not as solid as hoped. Nonetheless, for the moment the "A" rating was retained.[44,45]

The Deans

Two men served the college as its dean throughout the period of this chapter: Rudolph H. Raabe and Albert C. Smith. Dean Raabe's profile is given in Chapter Four.

Albert C. Smith, Dean 1950-1962.

Albert C. Smith

Albert Charles Smith[46] was born in Monroeville, Ohio, on November 10, 1906. The eldest of three brothers, Albert lived with his grandparents on their farm from the age of five until he was fourteen.

Albert was known as a good, but mischievous student—is anyone who knew him personally during his time at ONU surprised to read this? The story is told that he actually began his work in pharmacology early in life, working (playing!) with mice. He would, accidentally of course, turn his captured trophies loose in the schoolroom, then take great delight in the antics of the frightened teachers who would climb onto a desktop and demand that someone catch the scurrying rodents. Albert would play the part of a hero by stepping forth, volunteering to catch the critters. Perhaps the punishment he received for such stunts was even more satisfying to him, for he was required to remain out of school for one, two, or three days according to the severity of the offense, that is, the number of mice released. But this "rewarding punishment" soon had to be abandoned. The school's superintendent reasoned that too many absences would make him ineligible for graduation.[47] Albert did graduate with his class from the Monroeville public school system on May 15, 1924.

He then entered The Ohio State University in the fall of that year to pursue his dream of completing work toward a degree in pharmacy. It has been said that misfortune has a habit of striking at annoying times. For Albert, misfortune occurred during the school's Christmas break that year. He developed scarlet fever, followed a week later with his brother also contracting it. As a result, Albert was quarantined for five weeks, thereby necessitating that he remain out of school until January, 1926. During this illness, Albert lost his brick-red hair, which came in black when it returned.[48] He re-entered OSU and graduated with his BS Pharm degree on June 11, 1929, and easily passed the Ohio pharmacy board licensure examination.

Following graduation, Albert was accepted into the graduate program at Purdue University to work toward his MS degree. At Purdue, he worked under Professor C.O. Lee, who later would join the faculty at Ohio Northern after Albert had become dean. He received his degree in pharmaceutical chemistry in June, 1931.

Albert then returned to Columbus where he worked as a pharmacist. One morning, he received a telegram asking if he had interest in a teaching position at the University of Tennessee College of Pharmacy. His interest was piqued, and he accepted the position in 1932 as assistant professor of materia medica and pharmacognosy.[49] Years later, Albert would tell that on his last night at work in

Columbus, the pharmacy was robbed at gunpoint. He described the assailants' guns as looking like cannons when pointed at him.[50]

Also during 1932, Albert married Edith (Pat) M. Norman of Lafayette, Indiana, on June 16.[46] This union brought forth one daughter, Joy (Mrs. James West), who is an alumnus (BS Pharm '60) of ONU's College of Pharmacy.

Albert remained at the University of Tennessee for two terms, and then returned to Purdue to begin the next era of his life—working toward his PhD degree. While studying at Purdue during the summer of 1936, he was invited to come to the pharmacy college at Ferris State Institute as an instructor, an offer he accepted. While at Ferris, he received scholarship support in 1939 to complete his research project on the assay of aloe for aloin. He succeeded in developing a practical assay in the later part of 1939. In August 1942, Albert Smith received his PhD degree in pharmaceutical chemistry from Purdue University.[51]

In September, 1944, Dr. Smith arrived at Ohio Northern University where he taught a variety of courses—organic chemistry, drug assay, pharmaceutical chemistry, biochemistry and bacteriology. Following Dean Raabe's resignation as the college's chief administrator in 1950, Smith was appointed acting dean, with appointment as dean in November of that year. He held that post until September, 1962, at which time he was granted a sabbatical leave. The following year he returned to his first love at Ohio Northern, teaching pharmaceutical chemistry. He was succeeded as dean by his good friend and former mentor, Dr. C. O. Lee.

During his professional life, Dr. Smith held memberships and was active in a number of various groups and organizations. These included the Kappa Psi Pharmaceutical Fraternity, Phi Rho Alpha honorary pharmacy fraternity, Kappa Alpha Phi fraternity, Sigma Xi Society, the American Pharmaceutical Association, Ohio State Pharmaceutical Association, National Education Association, Northwestern Ohio Pharmaceutical Association, American Association for the Advancement of Science and the American Chemical Society. He was a member of the Ada United Methodist Church and the Ada Kiwanis Club.[52]

Most pharmacists who studied under Dean Smith remember him as one of the most "colorful characters" they ever met, with their descriptions offered out of deep respect and their highest admiration. Dean Smith expected his students to devote themselves completely to their academic pursuit. An alumnus writing in *The Ampul* described it this way: "The first impression of 'Doc' (as he was called by his students) on the first time he has him as an instructor is that Doc thinks you're pretty stupid. The thing that irritates the students is the fact that Smith then goes and proves that fact. After a couple of his tests you are so low in grades that you 'need a ladder to be able to chin yourself on the gutter' (a Dr. Smith quaint saying). Smith gives his tests unannounced and the main topic of student conversation before class each morning is the question, 'Is Doc going to give a test today or not?' Smith has said that someday he is going to write a book containing some of the answers he has received on his tests. An example is the answer one student gave to the question, 'Where are the islets of Langerhans?' The student's answer was, 'Off the coast of Sweden.'"[50]

Doc pretty much summed up his love for his students and his ONU pharmacy school when he said: "I've got the best little school, alumni, and student group of any dean in pharmacy."[50] There can be no doubt in the mind of anyone who knew Doc as to the sincerity of his words. Described as a man of great energy,[47] Doc Smith was a legend in his time, a legend that likely will never be matched.

Dean Smith was active in his church, ushering during its worship services and singing in its choir.[53] He supported all ONU sports and music activities. He served as timekeeper for most ONU home basketball games. He and Mrs. Smith were favored chaperons for many fraternity dances; they loved to dance, and students appreciated their enthusiasm.[48]

Doc passed away peacefully on the morning of August 12, 1972, following prolonged pulmonary and cardiovascular illness. At the time of his death, Doc Smith had served the college for twenty-eight years, twelve as its dean. Eulogizing Doc at his funeral service, his close friend and fellow ONU faculty member, Dr. Marion Tinsler, said: "He [Doc] had, above all, a dream for his students. He knew his students not only by name, but knew the weakness of the weak student and the strength of the strong one. He worked with the individual student because he had a dream for their future."[53]

Mrs. Smith passed away in 2006 at age ninety-six. Albert and Pat Smith rest in the Smith family plot in Riverside Cemetery near Monroeville, Ohio.

The doors to Doc Smith's office and home were open at all times to students, faculty and friends. If the truth were known, many a student would never have graduated from the university were it not made possible by personal loans and gifts they received from Doc, given with love. Following his death, his Kappa Psi brothers placed a bronze wall plaque in the new pharmacy building to honor their departed brother that read: "Appreciated by his students, loved by his brothers, respected by his colleagues and missed by all."

Personal Reflections

Each of us harbors memories of special people who have contributed to who we are at present or to who we will become as we grow older. Oftentimes, these are individuals who influenced us in some way during our years as students, spanning first grade through college. Doc Smith was certainly such an individual who, even though I never had the personal pleasure of having him as an instructor in the formal sense, helped form me into who I am today. But even without his direct instruction, I still count him as one of my greatest mentors.

This admiration began the first day I met him. It was early in the fall of 1958. A pharmacist friend who was a 1953 ONU pharmacy alumnus (and one of the returning solders from World War II) brought me to Ada to "meet the dean" and see if my thoughts of pursuing pharmacy might be right for my life's vocation. From that first moment when Dean Smith came out from behind his desk, grabbing and shaking my hand as though I was his long lost brother, I knew then that pharmacy would be my goal and that Ohio Northern would, hopefully, play a major role in my achievements, assuming that I would be accepted into ONU's program. Doc had a very special way in his talking and actions that made people feel very comfortable and at home. After what seemed, at the time, like a visit with a life-long friend, I returned home with, for the first time in my life, a greater notion of what I wanted to do for the rest of my life. I applied for admission, was accepted, and entered Ohio Northern University as a freshman in September, 1959, to pursue my dream.

Doc remained very cordial to me for the next four years. On a couple occasions when he must have sensed some apprehension or other stress in me, he invited me into his office to study. He would be out of his office for a couple hours or so and told me he needed "…someone to keep his chair warm." There, sitting in his rickety wooden swivel chair with my own notes, at his desk that was cluttered with paper, folders, books and knick-knacks of sorts, was where I would remain until he returned. Indeed, I felt like royalty being able to sit at the dean's desk keeping his chair warm, while trying to study.

It was in September of my senior year, 1962, when Doc called me into his office. He and Pat would be leaving Ada for a few months on sabbatical. "Would you and Phyllis consider moving into our home during the winter term to look after things while we are away?" he asked. Phyllis and I had been married since mid-August and had leased our apartment for the year. Doc sweetened the deal by inviting us to not only enjoy the run of his home, but to eat freely from his pantry and freezer. That was an invitation we couldn't pass up. There was one catch however: Phyllis and I could eat anything from Doc's larder at anytime, except we could only draw from his frozen meat supply once a week. I learned later that Doc wasn't the richest dean around since his salary was "very meager" in contrast to even his own faculty members' salaries, which now that I know what they were, can best be described as pitiful. I have also learned that Doc voluntarily declined salary raises for himself over the years; instead, he asked that these funds be directed to his faculty who he declared needed them worse than he.

Phyllis and I kept our rental apartment during our holiday while living in Doc's home since we would have the spring term to complete after Doc's return to Ada. While at his home we forwarded his mail, took his telephone messages and conducted his household business, and ate freely from his freezer (with meat rationed to once a week, of course). I also listened carefully to his many "off the cuff" comments during his calls home and after he returned to campus, concerning the reasons that prompted his sabbatical. He shared his feelings with me in intimate detail as one friend would speak to another. My admiration for Doc Smith, in view of all of the pressures that were facing him from sources above, continued to increase even more. These pressures prevailing, along with his return to the college not as its chief administrative officer, but as a teacher, might have devastated lesser men, but not Doc. He accepted it all in stride.

After moving into the new building in 1966, Doc's respiratory problems were causing his health to fail big-time. This necessitated the college to provide a special parking spot for him immediately outside the entrance into the pharmacy building so that he could limit his steps. The college placed a bench in the hallway directly inside the building's door for him to rest, allowing him time to catch his breath after trudging up the five steps onto the landing from where he entered the building.

Doc Smith continued to teach and provide for his students until his passing on August 12, 1972. As the Kappa Psi plaque so aptly described Doc: ("Appreciated by his students, loved by his brothers, respected by his colleagues and missed by all.") I am one among many hundreds of ONU pharmacist alumni who appreciated, loved and respected Doc Smith, and even today, nearly forty-five years after his passing, I still miss him.

After Doc's death, Pat asked if I would accept Doc's PhD academic hood. I gladly did and wore it proudly for all graduation ceremonies until my own retirement thirty years later.

My earlier comment about respecting Doc to the point where I consider him to have been a valuable mentor remain true. During my six years as the college's dean, 1993–1999, I was confronted by many of the same routine issues Doc dealt with. From him I learned how to interact with students and alumni and to trust them with my own personal possessions, face budgetary restraints with grace, and deal with higher administrators with forgiveness, as well as tend to the many other issues of the moment. Regularly, I asked myself: "What would Doc have done?" when dealing with similar issues. Then I moved forward. That's hero worship, some might say. But that's all right with me. Like Doc Smith, I could, and still can, handle criticism. After all, we all need heroes to look up to.

EIGHT
A New Beginning

Academic year 1960–61 began on a generally positive note. College enrollment was stable and a full complement of nine faculty members, counting the dean, was in place. Seven of the nine held an earned PhD degree. To returning students entering their sophomore year, the next three years of their four-year program looked bright. Those who had successfully completed all of the requirements for their freshmen year were now full-fledged student members of the College of Pharmacy, having been moved up from their freshman-year pharmacy status in the College of Liberal Arts. These sophomores now felt they were truly *in pharmacy* and overall, life was good. Their next three years would certainly pass swiftly and they would graduate in June, 1963 into a higher calling where they felt they could take on and help solve the healthcare problems of the world.

What a Difference a Year Makes

For freshmen beginning their study of pharmacy in September, 1960, however, it was a somewhat different matter. They were the first class to enroll in the new five-year curriculum that was now required of all who entered the college after April 1, 1960. While the majority of freshmen took it all in stride with some arguing that the five-year requirement would make them better pharmacists (thus, they supported the expanded program), a few were heard to complain that the extra year of study seemed to them to be unnecessary and the university was involved in a ploy to generate an extra year's worth of tuition income. A small number of other negative comments were expressed in a vocabulary tone that even in today's much more liberal society might be shunned from the printed page. No doubt these few students were echoing comments expressed by some ONU seniors a couple years earlier. In a poll taken of the graduating class of 1957,[1] personal feelings that were shared relating to the upcoming five-year program expressed both pro and con opinions. Opinion was strong that the number of qualified students entering the program would decline, meaning there would shortly be a great dearth of pharmacists that would negatively affect healthcare in America. Some students opined that the professional status of pharmacists would not necessarily be elevated with the requirement for an additional year of education. Some felt that earned income for pharmacists with a five-year degree would not be significantly different from salaries pharmacists with a four-year degree earned, so they questioned why the extra year of education, which represented a twenty-five percent increase in "book-learning," was needed. They didn't understand that as early as 1950 a six-year curriculum had been proposed as an entry-level degree into the profession of pharmacy,[2,3] and that many steps had been taken along the way to usher in a new (interim) five-year curriculum to prepare the nation's colleges of pharmacy for a six-year degree program at some point after that.

The suggestion for a national six-year program was made with notation that this would be a goal to be achieved not immediately, but over time.[4] Cited as hindrances to the six-year curriculum were forces such as insufficient numbers of adequately prepared faculty, inadequate facilities, and lack of financial support. Concern was expressed that the community of practitioners and other factions might not support the proposed lengthening of the program. Arguments offered by opponents of an expanded educational program were that the four-year program was sufficient to prepare for the practice of pharmacy and that an anticipated meager financial return from practice did not warrant more than four years of time and expense in educational preparation. Nonetheless, proponents continued to argue that the profession and the public would benefit greatly by the longer period of preparation. They also acknowledged that it may require time for segments of the profession to become convinced of the wisdom of such an enlarged educational experience. The 1950 Pharmaceutical Survey had looked prophetically to an experimentation period whereby both baccalaureate and doctor of pharmacy degree programs would evolve, allowing for comparative evaluation of process and outcomes. It is interesting, historically, to note that the Pharmaceutical Survey had been preceded by a recommendation in 1937 by a joint committee of the National Association of Boards of Pharmacy and the American Association of Colleges of Pharmacy that a five-year or greater curriculum leading to the Doctor of Pharmacy degree should be implemented.[4]

Student negativism heard at ONU from some freshmen in the 1960-61 year toward the new program did tone down in time, with eventual acceptance that the additional year of education had been decided upon at the national, rather than local, level for all colleges of pharmacy, fact that the issue had been studied for many years, and assurance that it would prepare graduates for successful practice many years into the future, and so forth.

And so, the five-year requirement was not a recently hatched idea. Indeed, both sides of the argument had been hotly discussed within pharmacy circles for many years. By 1954 the decision had been made that beginning with students entering the study of pharmacy after April 1, 1960, all would be required to follow a five-year curriculum.[5] At ONU, students would still be transferred from the College of Liberal Arts into the College of Pharmacy after completing one year of pre-pharmacy coursework (forty-five term hours, or thirty semester hours of credit if transferring in from another school). The 1959–60 catalog described the conditions: "Under the four-year plan a total of two hundred and six term hours plus six quarters of physical education are required for graduation. Under the five-year plan a total of two hundred and forty-nine term hours plus six quarters of physical education are required for graduation."[6] This new requirement represented an additional forty-three term (quarter) hours of study. Appendix 5 contrasts the 1960 five-year curriculum with that of the 1959 four-year curriculum. Of note is that the additional forty-three hours were obtained not by addition of experiential work in a professional practice setting; rather, it was, as some students bemoaned, "simply more of the same." At that time, students still obtained their practical experience exclusively in their "after-hours" internships (e.g., working in a pharmacy at times such as Christmas breaks and summers) that were supervised by the State Board of Pharmacy rather than colleges of pharmacy. That, of course, began to change at ONU beginning in the 1970s, as will be discussed in the following chapter.

There were some positive components of the new curriculum. For one, a two-quarter sequence of pharmacy orientation was incorporated into the fall and winter terms of the freshman year. The sequence was "…designed to assist new students in orientating themselves into college courses, to understand the value and use of the library. It also will acquaint the student with the pharmacy curriculum so that he becomes more interested in the profession as well as explains the value of choosing the proper electives so that he will be better prepared to succeed in the area of the profession he plans to follow.

"The course will also help to acquaint the students with the various national associations and try to develop an interest as well as the value of becoming an active member in state and local associations. The student will also be instructed as to the value of continuing his education for advanced degrees and the value of continuing his education at refresher courses. An introduction as to the legal and professional responsibilities will be discussed."[5]

A third term of biochemistry was added to the fourth year. The new curriculum also provided for an additional term of bacteriology.

The other major consideration in contrasting the two curricula was in the individual course loads required in the core curricula for each term. Students enrolled in the four-year program typically took eighteen to twenty credit hours per term. Those in the five-year program had lower course loads of fifteen to seventeen credit hours, with one term requiring only twelve hours of credit in required courses. Writing in *The Ampul*, Dean Smith explained that "…under the five-year plan the student will not be burdened with an excessively heavy schedule but will be on equal footing with his fellow students in a liberal arts program."[7] That benefit might have been an advantage for students at that time, but in years to come the required course loads for pharmacy students would nudge their way back up. By 2002, the pharmacy program would require 324 quarter hours (eighteen hours/term) to complete.[8]

The Night is Darkest Before the Dawn

The college continued operating with its "A" accreditation rating awarded in 1956 by the American Council on Pharmaceutical Education (ACPE) that described the college as being on solid ground. This was a short-lived presumption that would soon be examined again. While the status of the college appeared positive when viewed from the outside, insiders knew better than to rest on their laurels. The accrediting body was now looking very closely at how the college had responded to its repeated suggestions for improvement. Primary issues included provision for adequate finances, a means for proper handling of students transferring from other colleges of pharmacy, reversing the lack of participation by the pharmacy faculty in the academic affairs of the college, increasing the faculty size and expertise, constructing a new pharmacy facility for an anticipated expansion in enrollment, revising the pharmacy curriculum, and developing a vigorous service program (i.e., continuing professional education) for pharmacists in Ohio.[9] Other issues were also at large. By the mid-1960s most of these had been tended to or were in the process of being accomplished.

College Leadership

Dean Smith had been ably leading the college since being appointed interim dean, then dean, in 1950. During those years he served the institution without interruption of his burgeoning teaching load or administrative duties. By August, 1962, his health and other considerations led to a much deserved sabbatical leave. In his place, Dr. C.O. Lee was appointed interim dean until a new dean could be

151

appointed. Once he stepped aside, he would then continue to serve as associate dean until his retirement in September, 1964.[10]

Meanwhile, Dr. Smith would return to Ada to continue with his first love, teaching pharmaceutical chemistry. So, a new dean would be needed. This person would soon be identified as Dr. Robert Fischelis.

In 1963, at the age of 72, Dr. Robert Fischelis[11,12] was asked to accept the deanship of ONU's College of Pharmacy to begin November 1, 1963. At that time, he was also appointed professor of contemporary pharmacy and advisor to President McIntosh on education for the health professions.[13] His appointment consisted of a three-year contract. Dr. Fischelis brought to the ONU campus highly diversified experience as an educator, administrator, author, editor, and government consultant.

He had successfully guided the New Jersey College of Pharmacy through its accreditation difficulties in the early 1920s. It was believed he could help bring ONU's program into full compliance. Writing to college alumni in 1964, he noted that the college had long suffered from under-staffing and lack of financial resources.[14] He also noted that the university was determined to do whatever was needed to ensure that the pharmacy program remained a prominent part of the university. His primary focus would be on revising the curriculum, recruiting qualified faculty, and erecting a new building. The new dean was fully aware that his service to ONU would be temporary until the college became stabilized and responded favorably to ACPE's recommendations that would assure full accreditation. During his years as dean, much would transpire primarily with accreditation issues, and his service to the college and university would be acknowledged again and again.

On September 1, 1965, Dean Fischelis and newly appointed President Samuel Meyer (Dr. McIntosh's successor) co-signed a jointly-written letter addressed to pharmacy alumni describing the college's accreditation situation.[15] The letter stated that "…trouble began six or seven years ago when the need for a new modernly equipped physical plant for the college, greater financial stability, upgrading of faculty and student admission procedures were among the items stressed by the Council [ACPE] from time to time in its recommendations to the University administration during this period, and July 1, 1965, was the date set by the Council as a deadline for complete compliance with continued accreditation requirements." The letter continued: "The Council sent five representatives to the campus last March to examine us. They reported favorably on the quality of our student body, the renovation of our existing facilities and the new building now under construction, the revised curriculum, the additions to our library and teaching equipment, and the generally improved financial conditions of the University. There were also some further recommendations for improvement. However, the list of accredited colleges of pharmacy issued by the Council on July 1, 1965, did not include our college."

So there it was. The axe had finally fallen. The nearly eighty-year-old College of Pharmacy at Ohio Northern had lost its accreditation. The graduating class of 1965 would have been adversely affected since, in order to be eligible for the board licensing examination and enjoy full professional privileges associated with licensing as a pharmacist, including the privilege of reciprocation to other states, candidates must graduate from an accredited college of pharmacy. On June 7, 1965, the Ohio State Board of Pharmacy reiterated its full support of the institution via a resolution (Appendix 6) and granted a waiver for the summer, 1965, class. The board has continued to support the college all the way and that support continues through today.

The university's board of trustees promptly filed a petition with the council and its individual members in response to dropping the college's accreditation. The board requested an extension of time during which the recommended improvements that were already underway, might be completed.[16] The council agreed with the request and set forth specific conditions to be met for restoration of the college to the list of fully accredited schools.

Coincident with all this was that in March, 1964, the university had been routinely visited by representatives of the North Central Association of Colleges and Secondary Schools, an agency that accredits universities, including Ohio Northern University, as a whole. That group voted to continue the accreditation of Ohio Northern University as a baccalaureate degree-granting institution. The group also looked closely at the College of Pharmacy since the college constituted a major part of the university, and commented favorably on the overall progress of the college, thereby affirming its own support of the College of Pharmacy.

The council revisited the college in the spring, 1966. Over the previous year a fine modern building with adequate facilities had been completed and other requirements met. The college was thereby granted a three-year probationary accreditation,[15] the usual action granted to a school of pharmacy emerging from probationary status.

On October 7–8, 1968, a council team revisited the campus to examine the college for possible full accreditation.[17] Team members agreed that the "…Ohio Northern University College of Pharmacy had met or exceeded all the standards set by the Council thus insuring full accreditation." That notice would prompt an affirmative action at council's regularly scheduled meeting on January 13–14, 1969.[18] Since its reinstatement to full accreditation in 1969, the College of Pharmacy has been compliant in all areas and its full accreditation has been maintained.

Every six years (beginning in 2013, the six-year cycle for accreditation was extended to eight years), all colleges of pharmacy in the country, including Ohio Northern University, are required to prepare a self-study of their programs. That self-study report, which can easily contain many hundreds of pages of data and other information relative to the college is then sent to the council in advance of its meeting with college faculty, students, dean, and higher administrative personnel. During its visit on campus that spans three days, council members question these individuals in depth, then decide whether the college has truly lived up to its mission and goals as stated in their college catalogs and other published materials. Colleges are also given any recommendations for modification or improvement of their programs along with suggested deadlines for their completion. These deadlines may be negotiable in cases of special hardship or other anguishing circumstances. Colleges that comply with all recommendations for their improvement are then re-accredited for another period, and the process continues anew.

No doubt about it. Dean Fischelis had confidently and ably led the college through a very difficult period. With the atmosphere brightened considerably, and with Dr. Fischelis understanding that his contract as dean was a temporary one to last until a permanent dean could be found, a search was instituted to find his replacement. That person was identified as Dr. LeRoy D. Beltz.

That first full year of Dr. Beltz's service to Ohio Northern (1966) could certainly be described as a true challenge for the new dean. But it was one Dean Beltz took in stride, accepting each challenge facing him. The college had lost its accreditation the previous June, regaining it on a probationary basis in 1966. Some of the college's critics would have been happy to see it cease operations so that the university could divert its full attention and limited finances into other components of the institution that begged for help. The new dean did not agree. He viewed the college's many problems along the way as opportunities for improvement and accepted the challenges they brought. By now, he also viewed his work for the ONU College of Pharmacy as his own life's intended purpose. He set out immediately to prove the college's value. In doing so, Dean Beltz believed the college's faculty was a great asset to the program and the college itself was a vital resource for the citizens of his newly adopted state. There was no other pharmacy college within the state like Ohio Northern's, whose operation was neither driven by state budgets nor influenced by its politicians, and he let it be known he was determined to preserve the college's rich heritage. The college was housed in a new, fully-modern facility with features that earlier faculty members and deans could only dream of but, during their periods of service to the institution, would never see. Up to that time, the pharmacy program had operated from cramped quarters in Dukes Memorial, existing with equipment that in most cases should have been replaced years to decades earlier.

An important determinant in assuring the college's future, one that cannot be downplayed, was the appointment on September 1, 1965, of a new university president, Dr. Samuel L. Meyer. Dr. Meyer brought to campus a rich background of experience and knowledge. His most recent appointment before coming to ONU had been as academic vice-president at the University of the Pacific, an institution that operated its own very successful pharmacy program. Dr. Meyer, along with ONU's enlightened and far-sighted board of trustees, were completely supportive of the pharmacy program and of Dean Beltz as the college's new chief administrator, and vowed to help the dean return the college to its previous place of prominence and position it for success in the future.

With this support assured, the fact that Dean Beltz was highly successful in his work can not be questioned. Once he engineered the college's full accreditation in 1969, the pharmacy program grew in unprecedented strength. There would never again be further suggestion that accreditation would not be retained. Dean Beltz, along with his determined faculty, dedicated students and faithful alumni, as well as the full support of university administrators and trustees, had turned the tide and the rest is history. College enrollment increased such that by 1974 the graduating class totaled 114 men and women. Dean Beltz was successful in recruiting a full complement of additional faculty members who chose to join ONU's program because of its standing within the state and nation, its commitment to students through great teaching, and the leadership of its dynamic dean. He set the pace for other U.S. colleges of pharmacy in terms of its frontline curricular development that included clinical practice and practical clerkship experiences.

The Robertson-Evans Pharmacy Building upon completion, 1966.

The Robertson-Evans Pharmacy Building

Since 1934, the College of Pharmacy had occupied two floors in Dukes Memorial, which also accommodated the departments of chemistry and mathematics along with the College of Engineering in earlier days. In more recent years, this space-sharing arrangement with pharmacy included only the Department of Chemistry. Although this facility had been suitable in the past, by the 1960s it was obvious that Dukes was no longer adequate to support the demands of a growing and dynamic pharmacy program, and more suitable housing was clearly called for.[19]

The university administration and its board of trustees recognized that separate and modern facilities were mandatory if the College of Pharmacy was to maintain its reputation for quality pharmaceutical education. Additionally, the accrediting agency for the college recommended that such an updated facility be provided. In considering the future of pharmaceutical education at Ohio North-

First floor, south hallway of the Robertson-Evans Building showing the Model Pharmacy, after 1966.

ern and to affirm its continuing support for the pharmacy program, on May 15, 1964, the board of trustees approved a broad package for growth that included construction of a new building for the exclusive use by pharmacy.[20]

During homecoming weekend, October 10 of that year, Dean Fischelis turned over the first ceremonial spadeful of dirt.[21] ONU President McIntosh then announced to the crowd at hand that an anonymous donor had provided a gift of a quarter million dollars toward construction of a science center to be located across the field from Lima Hall on the northern edge of the West Campus. The first unit of the science center was to be the building of what would be the new home for the College of Pharmacy.

Construction began at once. The new building, budgeted to cost $1,450,000 when completed,[22] would contain 47,920 square feet of floor space above a basement, and house classrooms and laboratories fully equipped for the most modern instruction in the pharmaceutical sciences. The building would provide facilities for undergraduate research. Its two stories would contain a large classroom seating 120 students and two smaller lecture halls each providing seating for fifty-five students. Faculty research laboratories would be adequate for the stimulation of advanced study and significant contributions to the advancement of pharmacy and the public's health. Faculty offices would be spacious and comfortable. The fully air-conditioned facility would accommodate a college enrollment projected to expand to three hundred students.[23] The building was completed early in 1966, and the college began to move in on March 28 of that year.[24] An additional $200,000 was budgeted to furnish and equip the facility.

Having a new facility for pharmacy meant there were numerous investment opportunities for individuals and/or corporations to memorialize or honor specific people or enterprises. Dean Beltz suggested the following monetary gifts as a means to do so:

To name a floor (two available)	$750,000
To endow building maintenance	$375,000
To name the pharmacology laboratory	$75,000
To name the microbiology and biochemistry laboratory	$65,000
To name the pharmaceutical chemistry laboratory	$60,000
To name a pharmacy laboratory (two available)	$60,000
To name a manufacturing laboratory	$50,000
To name a student research laboratory	$50,000
To name a classroom (three available)	$25,000
To name a faculty office and personal laboratory (six available)	$15,000

Today, one can note numerous bronze plaques throughout the building that identify the various honorees or enterprises, along with the identity of benefactors who took advantage of these worthwhile investment opportunities.

Over the next four decades the building would be remodeled and re-equipped a number of times to keep up with the changing nature of the profession. In 1995 it would be expanded by a 2,500-square-foot addition (the Pierstorf Annex) given in memory of Dr. Clarence Pierstorf and Dr. Ervin and Mrs. Florence Pierstorf, and in 2006 with addition of the Hakes-Pierstorf Pharmacy Education Center provided

James D. Robertson, PhG., graduated 1898.

by Dr. Vernon and Mrs. Evie Hakes and the Pierstorf family, which provided an additional 17,300 square feet of space. In 2009, the Mathile Center, a three-story addition of more than 95,000 square feet, was added. Built with funds provided by Dr. Clayton and Mary Ann Mathile, the addition added classrooms, laboratory facilities, and other features to accommodate the pharmacy and basic sciences programs.

On homecoming Saturday, October 22, 1966, the new building was officially dedicated with many students, alumni and friends of Ohio Northern University present. Former deans Raabe, Smith, and Fischelis each shared personal remarks. The current dean, LeRoy Beltz, accepted the new structure on behalf of the college's students, alumni, and faculty.[25]

The new facility—the Robertson-Evans Pharmacy Building—was named after two of the college's alumni and generous benefactors, James D. Robertson and Thomas J. Evans. James Robertson was born in 1877 in Holly, Michigan. He received the PhG degree from Ohio Northern in 1898. In April, 1902, he and his brother Dan opened Robertson Brothers Drugstore in Holly, Michigan, a firm that he sold in 1957. At the time of his death on September 18, 1965, Ohio Northern received the bulk of his estate, valued at $451,437.[26,27] Thomas Evans received his PhG degree from Ohio Northern in 1894. He moved to Newark, Ohio, at age 20 and subsequently opened and operated two Evans Drugstores in that city's downtown area. He was also the director of Park National Bank and director of Federal Savings and Loan. At the time of his death on March 3, 1967, Mr. Evans had contributed $350,000 to the university, including more than $100,000 specifically earmarked for construction of the new pharmacy building.[28]

Over the next several decades the West Campus would continue to be developed. Dormitories, fraternity houses, gymnasium, expanded food service, religious center, and a facility to house the College of Engineering would be added. The height of the library would be increased by one floor. Of special interest to the College of Pharmacy would be the Meyer Hall of Science, which would be built next to the pharmacy building. This would become the home for the departments of biology, chemistry, and mathematics, with classrooms and laboratories that all pharmacy students would

Thomas J. Evans, PhG., graduated 1894.

become quite familiar with beginning in their freshmen year.

Program Reorganization

One of Dean Beltz's first orders of business when arriving on campus was to re-organize the college into six departments:[29] pharmacy, pharmaceutical chemistry, pharmacology, pharmacognosy, microbiology, and pharmacy administration. This organization modernized decision making and follow-up, and put the education component of the college directly into the hands of those doing the teaching.

Academic year 1970–71 ushered in another significant change in the organization of the pharmacy college. The new organization permitted incoming freshmen to enroll directly into the College of Pharmacy. Upon successful completion of their P-1 and P-2 years (lower division), they were then eligible to automatically continue in the college's upper division.[30]

The new organization brought both benefits and problems. Benefits to the students were obvious. They would now be advised or counseled by pharmacy faculty members rather than faculty within the liberal arts college. It made sense that pharmacy faculty, most of whom were pharmacists, were better equipped to advise students on professional matters than non-pharmacist faculty members. Students would also benefit by being an "honest-to-goodness" member of their college of choice from the beginning, which was felt to be a psychological advantage to them. Another student benefit was that, in contrast to the three state schools in Ohio whose students competed after their second year with all other applicants within their class for a limited number of seats in the College of Pharmacy, sometimes with perhaps twice the number or more applicants as available positions, the stress to gain admission into pharmacy could be intense. This was not the case with students at Ohio Northern. All students who met the admission standards for entrance into the upper division would automatically be continued on to the next level.

At the same time, this automatic continuation into the third year could be a disadvantage to the professional program. Students who might not be ready to enter upper division coursework because of their less than stellar academic performance in the lower division classes, or to their own uncertainty as to whether the study of pharmacy was absolutely right for them, would still be permitted to continue in the program (assuming they met the minimum standards) perhaps only to fail or drop out later. In other words, completion of the first two years was a logical point at which time a student would assess his or her academic ability and extent of interest in the major for continuing work in the pharmaceutical sciences.

The advantages of the new organization, though, were felt to outnumber the disadvantages. The college was therefore designated as having a "0-5" program, a label that prevailed until the year 2000 when the college would switch to its six-year curriculum. At that time its organization would be described as a "0-6" program, a designation that remains today.

Continued Growth

By 1971, the college had more than doubled in size. During that year, it had grown to the point where it had the largest student body among the four colleges of pharmacy in Ohio. It ranked thirty-fifth in enrollment among the seventy-three accredited pharmacy schools in the nation, ranking sixty-seventh only four years earlier. Half of the entering freshmen had graduated in the upper ten percent of their high school class.[31]

As the era (1960–71) was coming to a close, the college received a federal institutional grant under the Health Professionals Educational Improvement Program in the amount of $216,464.[32,33] Authorized under the Health Manpower Act of 1968, the funds were provided to schools of dentistry, medicine, osteopathy, optometry, pharmacy, podiatry, and veterinary medicine for the purpose of increasing their enrollment and improving the quality of their educational programs. Needless to say, the grant helped greatly to usher in the rapidly advancing clinical era at Ohio Northern University.

The Rudolph H. Raabe College of Pharmacy

The year 1971 marked another significant event in the history of the college. On homecoming Saturday, October 16, 1971, in a service recognizing Dr. Rudolph Raabe's forty-five years of dedicated service to the pharmacy program, the college was officially named the Rudolph H. Raabe College of Pharmacy (see Chapter Four).[34] The service included the unveiling of a life-size bronze bust of Dr. Raabe and announcement of establishment of the Rudolph H. Raabe loan fund. That bust stands today in the main corridor of the pharmacy building.

Dr. Raabe was born in 1881 in Putnam County. He earned three degrees from Ohio Northern, the BS degree in 1903, the PhG degree in 1910, and

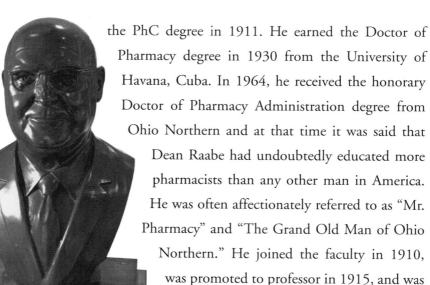
Lifesize bronze bust of Dean Raabe.

the PhC degree in 1911. He earned the Doctor of Pharmacy degree in 1930 from the University of Havana, Cuba. In 1964, he received the honorary Doctor of Pharmacy Administration degree from Ohio Northern and at that time it was said that Dean Raabe had undoubtedly educated more pharmacists than any other man in America. He was often affectionately referred to as "Mr. Pharmacy" and "The Grand Old Man of Ohio Northern." He joined the faculty in 1910, was promoted to professor in 1915, and was named dean in 1917. Dr. Raabe retired from teaching in 1955. He died in 1968 at age 87.

Lemons or Lemonade?

The road leading to the college's current esteemed status included a number of bumps along the way. Even though its enrollment often exceeded student numbers reported for the other colleges of pharmacy in Ohio, available funds to support the program during its first eighty years were usually sparse. Because Ohio Northern University was a church-affiliated institution, the college received no state support. Moreover, throughout those eight decades, tuition remained unbelievably low. The decision to provide quality education at minimum cost was an important issue in Dr. Lehr's passion for all who would come. Along with the low tuition costs must be added the economic crisis associated with America's Great Depression that began in 1929 and continued through most of the 1930s, followed by greatly dwindling numbers of students during World War II. The scarcity of funds often meant delaying purchase of much needed equipment and supplies, and updating accommodations, all of which helped lead to the college's loss of accreditation in the summer of 1965. Although devastating to college personnel at the time, this low-point in its history was, in retrospect, the turning point in its evolution. It was the point at which the juice of sour lemons started tasting more like sweetened lemonade. Realization in the 1960s that the college might be forced to cease operation initiated the momentum that positioned it for unprecedented achievement and growth that continues today. Alumni stepped forward in large numbers to support the college they loved. Industry pumped much needed money into the program. The college faculty, quick to acknowledge what was happening and grasp its potential for turnabout, accepted the challenge with renewed vigor and the college added additional members to its ranks. A new forward-thinking university president, Dr. Samuel Meyer, and a very supportive board of trustees were eager and able to commit whatever resources needed to reverse the trend and move the college into an active, versus restrictive, motion toward its future. A new university library was constructed and its holdings greatly expanded to support the pharmacy program. Most important, students refused to stay away. They could see the potential for the revitalized college that would emerge, and they came in great numbers. With the opening of academic year 2014–15, the College of Pharmacy at Ohio Northern University enrolled a total of 983 students.

Big Changes Ahead

By the mid-1960s, the concept of changing the traditional pharmacy curriculum to one that emphasized the clinical approach to practice was gaining a strong foothold at the national level. In 1967, the U.S. Department of Health, Education, and Welfare established a task force on prescription drugs to study the impact of extending outpatient prescription coverage to Medicare patients. The task force concluded that such coverage was quite feasible. However, the perception of pharmacists as reported by the task force was bleak: "The role of the pharmacist is viewed by many people as simply the transferring of pills from a large bottle to a smaller one—counting tablets, typing labels, and calculating the price. Much of his time is seen as devoted to routine merchandising of cosmetics, shaving supplies, stationery and other commodities that have little or no relationship to healthcare." At the same time, there was also a positive message for pharmacy. The task force commended both community and institutional pharmacists who were already moving into a healthcare role of drug information specialists, including rounding with physicians and overseeing the safe use of medications.[35] The American Association of Colleges of Pharmacy's Committee on Curriculum strongly supported this move and provided a working definition of clinical pharmacy as "…that area within the pharmacy curriculum which deals with patient care with emphasis on drug therapy. Clinical pharmacy seeks to develop a patient-oriented attitude. The acquisition of new knowledge is necessary to the attainment of skills in inter-professional and patient communications."[36]

The College of Pharmacy at ONU had a long history of experiencing what might be called "aha" moments—periods when a certain decision or action was recognized as an invitation to move forward in a specific direction, or remain still and wither away. One such moment was when Dean Beltz recognized that instead of leading the college along its traditional pathway, it would soon need to completely alter its course of instruction if it were to survive. The national trend for change was coming on quickly. That watershed moment for ONU came sometime in early 1970 or 1971 when the dean visualized the changes coming on much more strongly than before and was confident that ONU was ready to join the movement in clinical practice and position the college for service in the new era.

By 1972, the five-year curriculum was well accepted (Appendix 7) and moving forward without apparent problems. The curriculum that began in 1960 (see Appendix 5) showed that numerous changes had been made between 1960 and 1972. The new 1972 curriculum had been adjusted along the way to accommodate new means of thinking in the pharmaceutical sciences. It is tempting to think that the later curriculum was more attuned to preparing ONU's graduates for a type of practice that would soon sweep the country into a clinical frenzy. Although the 1972 curriculum was quite adequate for community pharmacy practice in 1972 and perhaps a few years beyond, it would need a major overhaul soon.

Four men served as dean of the College of Pharmacy during this period: Albert C. Smith, Charles O. Lee, Robert P. Fischelis, and LeRoy D. Beltz. Dean Smith's profile is given in Chapter Seven.

Charles Oren Lee

Charles Oren (or as he was known throughout life, "C.O.") Lee[11] was born near McCune, Kansas, November 25, 1883. He received his early schooling in a one-room county school in McCune and his high school work in the county high school in Cherokee, Kansas.

In 1903, Charles, still a country lad, became apprenticed to James E. Dillard, a druggist in Cherokee, Kansas. Throughout his life he freely admitted that he owed much to Mr. Dillard and his drugstore. There, Charles developed his life-long passion for pharmacy. His earnings also gave him the chance to continue his way through high school and partially through college.

Charles enrolled at Baker University in 1908 then subsequently transferred to the University of Kansas. There, he enrolled in the school of pharmacy in 1911 (already having passed the pharmacy licensing examination earlier that year[37] and received his BS Pharm degree in 1913. Following graduation he taught in the colleges of pharmacy of the Medical College of Virginia (1913–1915) and Purdue University (1915–1920). He spent five consecutive summers (1914–1918) at

Charles O. Lee, Interim Dean 1962–1963.

the University of Chicago majoring in botany and working toward his MS degree, which he received at the end of his fourth summer, 1917. He spent the summer of 1919 at Cornell University studying botany and microchemistry.

He resigned from Purdue in 1920 to head to China, where he served four years (1920–1923) with the Methodist Board of Foreign Missions as chief pharmacist and acting superintendent for the Wuhu General Hospital, Wuhu, China. In 1923 he was transferred to Nanking where he taught chemistry and served as pharmacist at the University of Nanking and the Nanking University Hospital until his return to America in 1925.[37] Charles admitted that the most important events of this excursion to the orient was his marriage to Ester Margaret Hagard in 1924 and his return home the following year with a wife and baby son.

Back home, he continued his graduate studies at the University of Wisconsin until September, 1926, at which time he returned to Purdue. He was granted a leave of absence in 1929 to 1930, during which time he completed work for his PhD degree at Wisconsin.

Throughout his professional career, Dr. Lee remained active in the work of the American Pharmaceutical Association and the American Association of Colleges of Pharmacy, serving on their various committees. He was honored in 1939 by being elected a member of the committee on national formulary and re-elected to that committee on which he served until 1955. He was a member of the Revision Committee of the U.S. Pharmacopeia, 1940–1950.

Dr. Lee was chairman of the Subcommittee on External Preparations of the National Formulary, 1950–1955; and chairman of the Committee of Libraries of the American Association of Colleges of Pharmacy, 1933–1952. He served as second vice-president of the American Pharmaceutical Association (APhA), 1942–1943. His many posts and activities in pharmacy were recognized by his honorary presidency of APhA in 1963–64.[38] He conducted research on the subjects of ointments and ointment bases and the causes of precipitation in fluid extracts, and contributed much to the improvement in formulae and procedures for stabilizing ointments of the U.S. Pharmacopeia. He published more than 160 professional papers on various topics of pharmacy and pharmaceutical education.[39] His textbook, *The Official Preparations of Pharmacy*, was a classic, clearly-written and easy to read and understand handbook that described all the official preparations included in the United States Pharmacopeia and the National Formulary.

Dr. Lee held memberships in the American Pharmaceutical Association, American Association of University Professors, American Association for the Advancement of Science, Society for the Advancement of Education, Indiana Pharmaceutical Association, Indiana Academy of Science, American Institute for the History of Pharmacy, Society of the Sigma Xi and Society of Rho Chi. In addition, for many years he was a member of the Indiana Council of Christian Education and of the N.W. Indiana Conference Board of Education. He was a member of the Ada Masonic Lodge and Ada First United Methodist Church, and served as Sunday school superintendent and teacher in three different churches during his active years.

Dr. Lee was on leave of absence from Purdue University during the school year 1949–50. During this time he served as visiting Professor of Pharmacy at the University of Puerto Rico. He also served as pharmacy consultant for the American-Korean Foundation in 1955.

He taught at Purdue until his retirement in 1954. At that time, Dean Smith invited him to join the faculty at Ohio Northern as Professor of Pharmacy where he taught required courses in pharmaceutical preparations and history of pharmacy and served as interim dean. That invitation reaffirmed Dean Smith's great friendship for Dr. Lee. His move was Purdue's loss and Northern's great gain.

Dr. Charles Oren Lee died in 1980 at age 96 from infirmities of old age.[38] He was living with his daughter in St. Louis at the time of death. Mrs. Lee preceded him in death, on December 12, 1957.

Personal Reflections

There are many reflections of Dr. Lee I could share, but there was one significant event I treasure highly. Few students who had Dr. Lee as a professor in his pharmacy preparations class that was taught during the spring term of the second year, truly understood his method for scoring their completed preparations. I was privileged to work as his laboratory assistant during my third year. Allow me to share a responsibility that has until now remained largely forgotten.

My function was to assess each student's preparations for overall appearance, not assayable content, and assign to it a numerical score. Dr. Lee instructed me as to what to look for—color and clarity of solutions with no precipitates, smooth (non-gritty) ointments without a trace of ointment on the underside of container caps, labels that were attached straight without "dog-eared" corners, as he called them, and were without typos, etc. He then told me to assign a numerical grade, starting with a score of 89 ("B") and move downward. I asked him why no student preparation could be assigned an "A" grade (90 points or higher), to which he shared an extremely valuable lesson with me. He told me that students were at ONU to learn how to become pharmacists of the highest caliber, which included having the skills to prepare perfect pharmaceutical preparations. An "A" grade meant that as a second-year student in "Preps Lab," he or she might start believing there was nothing higher to strive for or to learn to do better. Dr. Lee confided that his own personal motto was to always strive to become better at whatever he did, no matter how old he was growing. He also asked me to not tell any student that it was I who was assigning all those scores of "B" or "C", perhaps some lower. Dr. Lee did examine each preparation after I had seen them. I am also sure he raised (or lowered) some scores before returning the completed preparations or after a student complained to him about their lower-than-expected score. The important thing is that we were learning a very important lesson for life that was not written in the course syllabus: To always strive to do our best, then continue to strive to do even better than before.

Robert P. Fischelis

Robert Philip Fischelis was born in Philadelphia, August 16, 1891.[35] He received his early education in Lutheran schools, graduating from high school in 1908. He accepted employment in a local pharmacy, which led him to enter the

Medico-Chirurgical College, Department of Pharmacy. He graduated in 1911 with the PhG degree and then continued his studies to earn the PhC degree in 1912 and Pharm D degree in 1913. At the same time, he also took chemistry courses at Temple University from where he earned a BS Pharm degree in 1912. Not ready to call it quits academically, Robert received a Master of Pharmacy degree from the Philadelphia College of Pharmacy.[40] Over his lifetime he was awarded honorary degrees from several institutions.

His academic experience included teaching pharmacy students at the Medico-Chirurgical College where he taught courses in pharmacy, pharmacy arithmetic, and organic chemistry. In 1914 he joined the editorial staff of *Druggists Circular*, one of only a few national monthly pharmacy publications. He maintained a part-time lectureship at the Philadelphia College of Pharmacy during 1916. In 1918, he resigned his position with *Druggist Circular* to enlist in the U.S. Army Chemical Warfare Service. From that point onward, he served on a number of influential state and national committees dealing with pharmacy practice. In 1921, he was appointed dean of the New Jersey College of Pharmacy.

Dr. Fischelis served in government posts during World Wars I and II. During World War II he served as Director of the Division of Chemicals, Drugs and Health Supplies for the Office of Civilian Requirements. He was a consultant to the Armed Forces, the United States Public Health Service and other government agencies. In 1946, President Truman appointed him pharmacy advisor to the American delegation of the International Health Conference that formulated the constitution of the World Health Organization for the United Nations.[41] For eighteen years he was chief chemist for the New Jersey Board of Pharmacy, and for eight years he served on that state's board of health.[42]

Dr. Fischelis was co-author of the text *Principles of Pharmacy* and wrote extensively

Robert P. Fischelis, Dean 1963–1966.

for numerous professional and technical journals. He was a skilled communicator and edited the *Journal of the American Pharmaceutical Association* and several other publications. Dr. Fischelis is perhaps best remembered for his fifteen years of leadership of the American Pharmaceutical Association as its secretary and general manager. His tenure as the association's chief executive was marked by his ability to represent the pharmacy organization forcefully in its relations with government agencies and health care organizations.[41]

Throughout a career that spanned seven decades, Dr. Robert Fischelis clearly left a diverse legacy in pharmacy that few others will ever match. Writing in the *Journal of the American Pharmacists Association,* historian Dennis B. Worthen described him thusly: "Robert P. Fischelis clearly was capable of multitasking; no facet of pharmacy escaped his touch. He received the honors of his profession, including honorary degrees from the University of Connecticut, Rutgers, Philadelphia College of Pharmacy, and Ohio Northern. He was the recipient of the highest honors of a number of national pharmacy organizations including the Remington Medal, the Harvey A.K. Whitney Lecture Award of the American Society of Health-Systems Pharmacists, and the Lascoff award given by the American College of Apothecaries. He was named the honorary president of NABP. Throughout his public life, Fischelis returned time and again to the theme of professional standards—whether they be of education, regulation, or practice—and public service. In his 1943 Remington Metal address he noted the need for the profession to be prepared to play a role in the changing environment of health care, adding that the responsibility of pharmacy to serve certainly was as great as that of medicine. He optimistically observed that '…the American public may expect from our profession in the future, as in the days of Remington, responsible, enlightened, and effective service in its behalf.'"[43]

One of his far reaching ideas at ONU was the college's need to provide opportunities for lifelong learning to alumni. He therefore championed the establishment of a separate and fully functioning Pharmacy Continuation Study Center. That building now houses the offices of admissions and financial aid. Dean

Fischelis retired from his post as dean in 1966 after revitalizing the pharmacy program. He maintained a home on the ONU campus and remained active on the national pharmacy scene until his death.

Robert Fischelis married Juanita Deer in 1919. The couple had no children. Robert died on October 14, 1981. At Juanita's request, Dr. Fischelis laid in state within the pharmacy dean's office for a final evening memorial service. He is buried alongside his wife in Ada's Woodlawn Cemetery, adjacent to the gravesite of ONU's founder Henry S. Lehr, and close to Dean Raabe's grave. In 1983, the American Institute for the History of Pharmacy received a bequest of over $1 million from the estate of Robert and Juanita Fischelis with the understanding that the Institute would collect and promote the history and trends in American pharmacy.

Personal Reflections

One of my great disappointments I feel now is that during my early years on the ONU faculty I never got to know Dr. Fischelis better. Although he and Mrs. Fischelis lived in an apartment on the ONU campus that was a short five-minute walk from the pharmacy building, I guess I always thought it was too much of an intrusion on my time to visit with him more than I did. Along with assistant dean Lou Vottero, the three of us agreed to write a series of healthcare-related articles for the *Ada Herald*, Ada's weekly newspaper. I believe it was Dr. Fischelis who first proposed that we prepare the series. The three of us worked together for about a year, but it always amounted to me visiting with him in his apartment for five to ten minutes to solidify our ideas for the moment, then I left. I soon ran out of ideas and dropped away from the project. Dr. Fischelis continued with his submissions for a long while afterward. He never seemed to be short of words or ideas.

One thing I remember about this remarkable man who was then in his mid-80s, was his impeccable appearance. A large man, always fully dressed in a dark-colored business suit and tie, he was an impressive individual. I can now understand how and why he was successful at all he attempted. Yes, I wish I could relive those days of the 1970s. I would have done much more to get to know him better personally as well as professionally.

LeRoy D. Beltz

Born on April 25, 1921, in Pierce, Nebraska, LeRoy Duane Beltz[44] served in the U.S. Navy from 1941 to 1947, including two years in the South Pacific. On June 21, 1944, he married Glenda Marie Reese. The couple reared four children.

Roy earned his BS Pharm degree with distinction from the University of Nebraska in 1951 and PhD degree in pharmaceutical chemistry, along with a minor in biochemistry from the University of Connecticut in 1956. From September, 1952, to January, 1956, he served as instructor in pharmacy at the University of Connecticut while completing his doctorate. He was then appointed assistant professor of pharmacy at the University of Florida from 1956–1958. At that time, Roy Beltz accepted a position at the Ferris Institute where he taught from 1958–1966.[45]

LeRoy D. Beltz, Dean 1966-1986.

In 1966, Dr. Beltz was appointed Dean of ONU's College of Pharmacy, replacing Dr. Fischelis who had served as the college's dean on a temporary basis. At the time of his appointment, Dean Beltz was the third youngest pharmacy dean in the nation.[46,47] He was also a licensed pharmacist in five states.

Dean Beltz was able to accomplish his life's work not only through his determination to elevate the college to superior standing nationally, but also because he was a true friend and confidant to all who knew him. He cared about his students and faculty and expressed genuine concern for each person as an individual. Students and faculty knew they could bring any issue to him and receive a compassionate response. As busy as he was, he was never too rushed to stop and talk with anyone who requested it.[47]

He was a successful administrator because he allowed his faculty full freedom to implement innovative ideas and approaches to teaching, many of which formed the framework that defines the college's mission and goals through today. Through his own dedication and work ethic, he earned the support of the university administration for needed finances and much encouragement for his activities. In essence, he was the archetypical pharmacy dean that the college had attracted since its founding and has continued through today.

Roy Beltz was active in numerous professional societies at the local, state and national levels throughout his career. These included the Ohio State Pharmaceutical Association (now the Ohio Pharmacists Association—OPA), the Ohio Council of Colleges of Pharmacy, the American Pharmaceutical Association, American Institute for the History of Pharmacy, the American Association of Colleges of Pharmacy, and his pharmaceutical fraternity, Kappa Psi. He served on many professional committees and faithfully carried out the work of each group. He was chairman of the board of directors of OPA and later became the association's president. He was also the recipient of numerous awards and citations and was listed in *Who's Who in the Midwest, Who's Who in America, Who's Who in the World,* and *Who's Who in the Association of College Presidents and Deans.*[47]

Dean LeRoy Beltz died quietly of heart failure at his home the morning of January 14, 1986. The cause of his premature death was attributed to a bout of rheumatic fever suffered early in life. At the time of death, Dean Beltz held the distinction of being the third oldest dean in length of service to any college of pharmacy within the nation, having served ONU as dean for twenty years. Roy and Glenda Beltz rest in Ada's Woodlawn Cemetery.

Personal Reflections

Roy Beltz had a keen eye for happenings, many of which were out of the usual. He once went through a period of complaining about the lack of janitorial service in the pharmacy building. His utterances seemed to me to be trivial because I thought the college did have a suitable janitorial service. But for a period of about six months or so, Roy seemed to be focused on one event.

On the floor underneath the clear plastic mat that enabled his secretary's desk chair to roll smoothly over carpet was a small moth. The poor insect, while very visible, was obviously dead. Roy told me and, I am sure, others as well, that the moth had been there for many months. He said that each day he checked to affirm its continued presence. He believed that it would take a janitor only a few seconds to lift the corner of the mat and remove the critter. But it never happened. Day after day the moth remained in the same spot, untouched, and day after day Roy bemoaned the fact that it remained in place. Of course, the same thought could be said for Roy in that it would have taken him only a few seconds to remove the moth *if he had really wanted it removed!* As I think about it now, I have come to the conclusion that it was actually okay with Roy to leave the dead bug where it was. Removing it would nullify his excuse for "checking out" his secretary each day. Yes, she was a fine-looking individual. And Roy Beltz had a keen eye for beauty.

There was a period in the early 1980s when the college attracted a number of Arabic-speaking students. This action may have come about as a result of a trip Roy and Glenda took to Egypt. Roy befriended those students and they, in turn, began teaching him choice words and phrases in their native tongue. I couldn't understand a thing he was saying when he spoke these words in Arabic to me, but I assumed he knew what he was saying. Come to think about it, perhaps I shouldn't assume that. I know for a fact that Glenda didn't always buy into his comments when he spoke to her in what he called Arabic, thinking he was (in her own words), "BS-ing" her. Knowing Roy quite well, I can conclude that Glenda Beltz was a woman of great wisdom as well as an individual who had a keen sense of humor, at least when it came to understanding and accepting her husband.

Roy owned a basset hound that seemed to be almost as large around the middle as Roy. One of my own memories is watching Roy treat that dog as though he was his grandchild. Shortly after dinner during the warm weather months, Roy and his dog would load into the family car and head to the local soft-serve ice cream store. There, he would purchase a single medium-size cone and return to his car, where the treat was quickly devoured—by the dog. Watching the college dean holding that ice cream cone in front of that floppy-eared, short-legged mutt whose belly came close to dragging the ground, while eating the delight held by his master, was more comical than anything else I could imagine. And it was a great pleasure I enjoyed watching many times. Roy and his dog went for ice cream a couple times each week during the summer.

Throughout his service as dean at ONU, Roy Beltz sincerely believed that "… all work and no play can make 'Roy' a dull boy." As a sideline to ease the stress of his busy work schedule, Roy took great delight in penning unforgettable "four-liner limericks" that often began: "There was a young man from Nantucket…" and his "poetry" continued on from that point. Each one who knew him personally might well imagine the contents of his poetic phraseology. While sitting in a meeting or lecture for example, I could imagine Roy's mind going full speed as he recorded the gist of the ongoing activity in such a manner. On many occasions he shared his thoughts after sitting through one of my pharmacology or continuing education lectures. To this day, I never knew there could be so many exciting, although somewhat questionable (seedy!) adventures that a "young man from Nantucket" could get into. Ah, sweet memories indeed.

NINE
Redefining Pharmacy Practice

Pharmaceutical education in the early years of the twentieth century built steadily upon the past and proceeded in an evolutionary manner. By the early 1970s, however, revolutionary, rather than evolutionary, changes in direction and content were underway to set the stage for a vast change in pharmaceutical education that would prepare pharmacists for the twenty-first century and well beyond.[1]

ONU's College of Pharmacy entered a new phase of purpose beginning with the onset of academic year 1972–73. The college had overcome its accreditation problems of the previous decade and the resulting decline in student numbers along with substantial financial woes that came with the much lower student headcount. It had overcome numerous challenges that might have brought down a weaker institution. It now had in place a solid curriculum that had been adjusted a number of times and would continue to be modified over succeeding years. Largely due to the visionary farsightedness of its energetic dean, LeRoy Beltz, academic year 1972–73 was the watershed for ONU that completely re-defined the college's direction. Once underway, Dean Beltz and his successors would not alter their focus for the college's new direction. The college would continue to equip pharmacists very well to provide top-notch professional service as they moved from a product-centric practice to one that was patient-centric, that is, a clinically-oriented practice.

Operating out of a new spacious and well-equipped building with dedicated and enthusiastic faculty, along with strong support from university administrators,

Dean Beltz devoted his full attention toward continuing to bring the college's program into full compliance with the national trend of encouraging and equipping pharmacy professionals to rise above the current standard of practice by providing even greater personalized service to their clientele, and preparing the college to meet that goal straight-on. The era of what was being referred to nationally as "Clinical Pharmacy" was now underway at Ohio Northern. To understand and fully appreciate the direction the college would take requires a brief look at what was going on across the land.

The State of the Profession

As the 1970s were getting underway, it is tempting to say that community pharmacy practice across the nation was still behind in many professional aspects. The restricted nature of professional practice at that time was reflected in the two-decades-old American Pharmaceutical Association's code of ethics, adopted in 1952: "The pharmacist does not discuss the therapeutic effects or composition of a prescription with a patient. When such questions are asked he suggests that the qualified practitioner (i.e., physician or dentist) is the proper person with whom such matters should be discussed." Two decades later, in 1972, pharmacists were still spending the majority of their time, as one observer noted, by "…putting pills from large bottles into little bottles, and pouring liquids from large bottles into smaller ones."[2]

Pharmacy's general adoption of the broad ideals of clinical pharmacy is evident in the revised and updated American Pharmaceutical Association's Code for 1969. Rather than being advised to hide behind the authority of physicians or other prescribers and limit their conversations with patients, practitioners of pharmacy were now told boldly: "A pharmacist should…render to each patient the full measure of his ability as an essential practitioner." Pharmacists who graduated from ONU as late as the early 1970s will remember their instruction in prescription dispensing classes. Specifically, they were taught not to disclose too much information to the patient, which (it was thought) could cause further confusion and even lead to patient non-adherence with medication use. When asked: "What are these 'pills' used for?," pharmacists should rightly respond something to the effect that: "They are used for many things. I don't want to tell you one thing and worry you if you are taking them for a different purpose. You should talk with your doctor about what they are used for."

The term "clinical pharmacy" is difficult to define; it is easier to say what it is not. It is not site-dependent; it is practiced in all pharmacy settings, community, institutional, and academia. Neither is it degree-dependent; it is practiced by pharmacists holding baccalaureate-level (both four-year and five-year) degrees, and some with Pharm D degrees that may have required six, seven, or perhaps even eight years to acquire. A few practitioners who had a three-year college education and perhaps an even fewer number holding only a two-year degree were still practicing in 1972, if only on a part-time basis. Neither is clinical pharmacy exclusionary; it encompasses delivery of the right medicine to the right person at the right time, but only when all of the skills and talents of pharmacists are used to see that the proper outcomes are achieved. Thus, clinical pharmacy is much more than a one-dimensional product distribution function.[2]

Pharmacy education at Ohio Northern University continued to assure graduates in the early seventies that they were well prepared to keep up with the profession as it was being practiced at that time, an admonishment based, perhaps, on graduates' ability to think of the greatest number of excuses to avoid directly answering patients' questions. So, pharmacy graduates were still expected to "count and pour, and lick and stick!" Indeed, ONU's graduates could count and pour, and lick and stick with the best of them. And they were quite able to avoid counseling patients and answering questions relative to their drug needs. This admission is neither intended to belittle the college's educational program of the time nor be disrespectful of ONU's faculty because that was the norm for professional pharmacy education at most of the country's colleges of pharmacy, including Ohio Northern University. It was to prepare pharmacists for practice at the time, with ability to change their focus as needed, as the future might expect them to. There didn't appear to be much momentum to get them thinking seriously about what this practice might be years down the road. Upon graduation, ONU's students were well prepared to enter into practice at that level. Most other pharmacy graduates of sister colleges across the country who had earned their five-year bachelor's degree entered into practice at the same level of proficiency as did ONU's graduates. The five-year curriculum continued to be fine-tuned over time. However, there still remained a vast void in teaching students the finer art of a patient-centric practice.

Throughout the 1960s into the 1970s the phrase "pharmacy is at a crossroads" was heard across the nation.[3] Observers lamented again and again that pharmacists were the most overeducated and underutilized healthcare providers who, unfortunately, did little more than fill prescriptions and pass them on to patients through a clerk or technician without further professional comment.[2] Although this mundane performance provided a valuable service to the citizenry and assured its practitioners a higher-than-average level of living, dissatisfaction was growing among most forward-thinking pharmacists and pharmacy educators concerning the future of the profession. Study after study examined how pharmacists were educated and what they actually did in practice, versus what they should be doing. Almost without exception, the study results urged that pharmacists needed to upgrade their professional image and services to a higher level of patient-oriented practice if they wished to continue to be recognized as healthcare professionals rather than as common merchants. Above all, clinical pharmacy meant that pharmacists needed to view the person across the counter as a patient, rather than a customer. Being at the crossroads was good. The time had come to decide which road to take.

Overall, many of the nation's colleges of pharmacy were slow in moving to a new curriculum in the early 1970s for many reasons. Limited financial resources were a major deterrent. For the most part, pharmacy colleges were adequately, but not generously, funded. Most, especially the private institutions, received relatively few external research dollars, had minimal endowments, and were often housed in aging facilities. Lack of resources to start new programs or greatly expand ongoing ones had a major economic impact on the base institution. Although many established faculty members resisted the curricular changes necessary to accommodate clinical pharmacy and the potential downsizing of traditional courses, others viewed it as a positive move forward. In some situations, this led to confrontation over promotion and tenure decisions between the basic science faculty and the new clinical faculty. Ohio Northern's faculty members were not immune to these considerations.

Federal funding had never before been a significant revenue source for pharmacy, including ONU's college. Thanks in part to some active lobbying of influential officials at the national level, funds to improve pharmacy programs were made available and caught the eye of pharmacy deans across the nation.[4,5] In 1968, Congress turned its attention to promoting increased manpower in the health sciences, which included provision that pharmacy schools could apply for $25,000 grants that were partially conditional, based on an increase in new student enrollments.[6] Although these funding opportunities were important for maintaining the programs of colleges of pharmacy, the impact did not necessarily focus on the shift of curriculum specifically toward the clinical movement.

The task of redefining curricular needs for the 1970s and beyond was aided greatly by passage of the Comprehensive Health Manpower Training Act of 1971.[7] More commonly referred to as capitation funding, federal legislation was passed that provided eligible schools of pharmacy with $800 for each full-time student plus $320 for enrollment of bonus students. To be eligible for these funds, colleges needed to increase their first-year enrollment by at least five percent. After the first year, the schools were required to provide "…increased emphasis on, and training in, clinical pharmacy, drug use and abuse, and, where appropriate, clinical pharmacology." The capitation funds also established special grants for interdisciplinary training in healthcare delivery. The capitation program would be discontinued at the end of fiscal year 1980. By that time, however, virtually every American college of pharmacy had implemented some clinical courses in their curricula.[2]

Those who served on ONU's college faculty during the 1970s and 1980s remember the era with strong emotion. Some will likely harbor negative recollections of the sweeping changes underway, including the downsizing or elimination of previously required courses in the pharmaceutical sciences within their fields of academic specialty. Others likely remember the period as one of great excitement with anticipation that major changes underway at ONU, changes which would measure up to or exceed the national norm for professional practice, would bring the college's graduates in line with expectation that they would practice their profession at a higher level. With all this going on, ONU would soon become a leader in the state with its implementation of professional programs.

Some faculty members may confess that their personal enthusiasm to change would require another decade or longer before they could fully support the new direction. The lack of enthusiasm by some faculty, especially in the earlier periods would come about largely at the urging from prominent trade associations and other groups that opposed such forward thinking and direction, because of what was feared to be a negative force on their own economy. For example, these new-era pharmacists who wished to counsel patients in more detail with each new or refilled prescription would require additional time so that overall practice productivity, it was thought, would be decreased. They might demand increased salaries and benefits because of their expanded abilities. Or, clinically-oriented pharmacists might no longer be willing to perform basic functions such as filling prescriptions, ordering merchandise, and checking in inventory, and so forth.

The Study Commission on Pharmacy

A significant jump-start to update the science-based pharmacy curriculum in the 1970s was publication of the *Report of the Study Commission on Pharmacy.*[8] Completed by Dr. John Millis, former president of Western Reserve University who was particularly knowledgeable in medical and graduate education, the report presented a broad view of a means for pharmacy educators to establish long-range educational policies.[9] The report soon became known as "The Millis Report." Organized in the manner of a citizen's committee that included the views

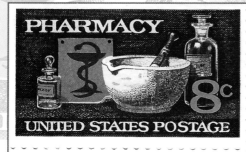

United States postage stamp, issued November 11, 1972, honors the profession of pharmacy. When introduced, the United States Postal Service credited pharmacists as: "The friendly and dedicated men and women" who "stand with the medical profession as partners in health."

of pharmacists from community, institutional and academic practices; physicians and nurses; university educators and administrators; and industry executives, the commission evaluated the profession from an extended societal perspective, rather than from an internal perspective, which is what earlier studies had focused upon. That is, the commission sought to identify what pharmacists should do rather than what pharmacists actually did at present. The overriding mission of the study was to determine specific areas upon which pharmacists should be educated.

It was concluded that, like other members of the health professions, pharmacists were well educated at the level being offered by the nation's colleges of pharmacy. Unfortunately, the majority practiced in isolation from patients. It was determined that if pharmacists were to become truly patient-focused, they would need an appropriate clinically-based education, and importantly, they must assume a proactive role on the healthcare team. Their isolation in education and practice would need to be abandoned. Publication of the commission's report in 1975 brought a mixed response throughout the profession.[10] As expected, some

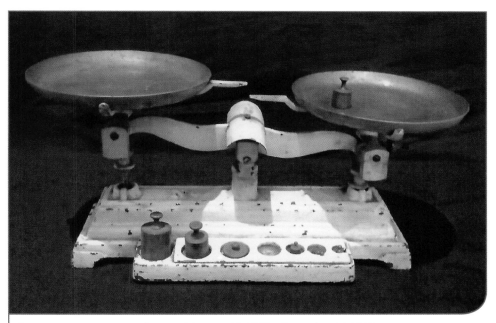

Prescription counter scales used from mid-1850s through mid-1950s.

disagreed with the conclusions citing reasons that reflected largely on a perceived economic disadvantage to certain groups within the profession. Optimists, however, welcomed the report as a guideline to educate professionals who would truly meet a growing societal need.[2]

The spotlight was clearly shining brightly on Northern's decision to work actively toward developing its own clinical program. Pharmacists for the future must be educated alongside other health professionals at the patients' bedside. Their long student hours spent in isolation from patients, working in laboratories while monitoring physiologic responses from rodents, cats, or dogs to administered drugs that, in many cases, were given in doses and/or under conditions that did not accurately reflect human biology, pathology, or therapeutics. This direction in teaching would need to be abandoned in favor of studying drug action in real patients, and responding proactively with other healthcare professionals all to the betterment of the patient. In other words, pharmacy customers must be thought of and treated as patients. The Millis Report further corroborated that ONU's College of Pharmacy by then was indeed on the right track in its decision to prepare its graduates for professional practice at the next higher level. Dean Beltz provided a copy of the Millis Report to each faculty member along with a strong suggestion that it be read and understood.

Back to ONU

Opening day in September, 1972, welcomed four new faculty members into the college. This represented a fifty percent increase in faculty size, one to replace a vacant position, two to expand the basic sciences staff, and one whose primary responsibility was to guide development of Northern's clinical program.

The basic pharmacy science faculty holding MS and/or PhD degrees in the pharmaceutical sciences generally accepted the direction the college was now headed. Today, as one looks back upon those days of the early seventies it is interesting to speculate that some of the science-based faculty at ONU, as was the identical scenario at many other colleges of pharmacy, did not fully understand the importance of this new direction in education ONU's college was headed toward. After all, the guideline for educating pharmacists that was the traditional approach to training had been tested again and again, and seemed, at least on the surface, to be tried and true. There was little reason, in the thinking of these faculty members, to suspect it needed to change. "If it's not broken, why fix it?" or some variation of the theme was heard over and over. As expected, some opponents argued strongly as to why any new coursework needed to be added to the existing curriculum, or why existing courses that were standard fare in the past should now be deleted or greatly revamped. In other words, there was a strong sense to "protect my turf" among a few faculty members that was no doubt synonymous with activity occurring elsewhere across the country.

The college therefore initiated an extensive review of its curriculum to assess what should be retained and what should be replaced, in order to accommodate a strong clinical component into the program.[11] As some wags observed with tongue-in-cheek humor, Ada is indeed located in the middle of cornfields, which in turn, are surrounded by bean fields or wheat fields, with the tallest structure in the village being a grain storage silo. Only a limited number of healthcare facilities were located within a reasonable commuting distance of the campus. There was no medical center close by. It thus appeared that future students would need to spend an extended period off-campus in order to acquire the clinical experience needed to prepare them for an expanded role as clinical pharmacists of the future. Writing in *The Ampul*, Dean Beltz admitted this limitation would pose a difficult, but not insurmountable, problem.[12] But if moving off-campus was what would be required, that is what would be undertaken. Arrangements were established with three off-site clinical facilities to handle the students: Lima Memorial Hospital and St. Rita's Hospital, both in Lima, and Blanchard Valley Hospital in Findlay. On an otherwise clear day, students could make the trip between Ada and either city within twenty or thirty minutes. This was deemed acceptable, especially since students at other universities in large metropolitan areas might require an equal time to drive from their home across town to get to their clinical sites.

By 1974, a beginning course entitled "Introduction to Institutional Pharmacy" had been put in place, supervised by the college, with teaching provided in these hospitals primarily by pharmacists, physicians, nurses, and technicians of one sort or another. The course acquainted students with professional services, concepts, standards of practice, and roles of the pharmacist in contemporary hospitals and related institutions.[13] The course was elective in nature with students commuting to one of the above mentioned sites twice weekly.

Yes, it was a humble beginning, but over time the endeavor would evolve into a full-time, one quarter-long required clerkship (rotation) at the original three sites, or in future years in a growing number of other teaching hospitals within Ohio and outside the state.[13] In addition, structured externships in various healthcare centers were developed.

The push toward greater emphasis on clinical practice was in full motion. Although there had long been proponents for structured clerkships under the supervision of the colleges, no concerted effort to move in this direction evolved until the American Council on Pharmaceutical Education included the requirement for such a program in their accreditation standards to become effective

July 1, 1973.[11] Almost as soon as the suggestion that the structured clerkship might become a requirement for accreditation was voiced, the Council of Ohio Colleges of Pharmacy undertook a study of the issue and organized a committee to make recommendations to the colleges for their consideration. The committee, composed of representatives from the four colleges of pharmacy, the Ohio State Pharmaceutical Association (renamed the Ohio Pharmacists Association on May 5, 1990), the Ohio Society of Hospital Pharmacists, and the Ohio State Board of Pharmacy devised a framework for structured clerkships, which served each of the colleges in development of their program.[11]

Following the guidelines established by the committee, ONU's program evolved into structured clerkships, externships, and other clinically-oriented courses for senior pharmacy students. Eventually it would be necessary for the senior class to be divided into three sections, students in each section being off-campus during two quarters of their senior year, one quarter for their clerkships and one for their externship. The sites were such that each student gained experience in institutional practice, community practice, nursing homes, and so forth, where they worked with preceptors in a one-on-one learning situation. Fifteen quarter-hours of credit were granted upon successful completion of the clinical courses. One might compare this requirement with that of education majors, who must practice-teach one quarter of their senior year in order to qualify for teacher certification. In addition to academic credit earned in the clerkship, however, the student could also receive as much as four hundred hours credit toward the required fifteen hundred hours needed to take the practical examination of the state board. Components of the clerkships in the clinical pharmacy curriculum will be explained in more detail in Chapter Eleven.

During the fall term in 1973, the drug information center opened primarily as an educational program to provide support for college instructors who would be teaching clinical pharmacy in area hospitals. Although the center did not advertise its services, it soon was answering questions from many health professionals across the state. Staffing was with students who were supervised by a faculty member. Student participation was required as part of their educational program. Initially equipped only with a modestly supplied library of reference books, students had access to microfiche copies of 161 current pharmaceutical and medical journals. Today, the center is fully equipped to access by computer the total world's healthcare literature within minutes of receiving a question. The center provides students with the necessary training in data retrieval and drug literature evaluation. It also provides a service at no cost to healthcare professionals and consumers,[14] answering an average of four hundred to five hundred drug information questions each month.[15]

Nineteen seventy-three also witnessed the beginning of extended pharmaceutical services for the University Health Service, getting students prepared for a more one-on-one approach to serving their patients. The Student Health Pharmacy, located within the Robertson-Evans Pharmacy Building, opened to supply prescription drug needs to all full-time university students on campus. Prescriptions issued by the campus physician were honored at the Student Health Pharmacy at no cost to the patient. Mr. James Turner, who along with his pharmacist-wife Mary Ann, co-owners of Gardner's Drugstore in Ada, were employed by the college to supervise the service. Working in the Student Health Pharmacy, senior students were required to receive, fill, then dispense students' prescriptions, and counsel them on their medication. This fulfilled a portion of the requirements of their prescription practice course. Importantly, the experience brought students into a "live" encounter with an honest-to-goodness physician or his office staff along with actual patients. No longer would non-physicians (usually pharmacy faculty members pretending on a phone to be doctors calling in prescriptions for make-believe patients) be the only source of professional contact the student had.

Continuing Professional Pharmacy Education

Every pharmacy practitioner has a responsibility to self and the public he or she serves to maintain proficiency not only in the topics of the pharmacy curriculum, but also in what's going on in the profession at the greater level.[16] It has been estimated that one-half of all scientific education is lost after ten years, with the rate of obsolescence probably increasing every year.

The role that the college assumed in the continuing education of practicing pharmacists had by now been enlarged and formalized. Although the college had provided various programs for many years and attempted to work closely with its graduates, it was now able to point with pride to strong continuing education programming. During the year 1973–74, the college provided at least sixty-four seminars to pharmacists at sixteen different locations throughout the state. The seminars were designed so that locations and meeting times would be convenient to the practicing pharmacists' work schedules.[17]

In succeeding years that number and variety of programming would increase exponentially. With new young faculty members coming on board in the 1970s and beyond, they brought with them many new ideas and teaching experience both about topics practitioners were looking for and means for delivery of that information. Today, continuing professional education programs continue to be an important part of the college's mission and most likely will continue well into the future. At the time of this writing, nearly three dozen programs were available to pharmacists via the Internet.[18]

The Gender Issue

Writing to alumni in 1974, Dean Beltz noted that thirty-six percent of the college enrollment was female and in the following year's class, more than half of all entering students would be female.[17] The year 1982 witnessed the onset of a continuing trend at ONU. That year, there were more women graduates than men (see Appendix 2). What had traditionally been a profession consisting mainly of men throughout the nation, including Ohio, was now becoming more balanced between the genders. The college was honored when one of its graduates, Suzanne Eastman-Wuest, BS Pharm '74, was elected the first female president of the

Ohio Pharmacists Association for 1988. The honor was extended when another graduate, Kathy Karas, BS Pharm '75, was elected the second female president of the Ohio Pharmacists Association for 1998.

The trend at ONU toward admitting more women than men into the college, due largely to the fact that there are fewer males applying than females, continues today and is mirrored at other colleges of pharmacy across the nation. At some point in the near future, women will likely comprise the majority of all practicing pharmacists in America.[19]

Each year the difference in salary between the genders gets smaller.[20] Interestingly, the number of full-time graduate students in U.S. colleges seeking the PhD degree in a pharmacy discipline in 2010–11 was accounted for by 49.7 percent of women. During 2014–15, the number of women on the college faculty at ONU working full time was fourteen, representing nearly fifty percent, of the faculty.[21] This differs from 1960, the first year when beginning students were required to study from a new five-year curriculum. The number of women on ONU's pharmacy faculty at that time numbered only one—Dr. Anna Koffler.

Extending its Direction

The idea had been bantered about for some time that the college should extend its mission of teaching pharmacy to include other allied health services. Two such baccalaureate-degree programs that other colleges of pharmacy had developed and were discussed for ONU were healthcare administration and toxicology. The intended audiences for these programs would be individuals who wished to work in healthcare industries but not as pharmacists. Two faculty members, Ms. Lynn Shoemaker and Dr. Thomas Faulkner, were especially vocal in support of this endeavor and volunteered to develop curricula that would meet the needs of students majoring in either area.

To accommodate these, and perhaps other new areas of study, it was decided that the name of the college should be changed to include its expanded mission. That name change would be noted beginning with the 1979–80 catalog that listed the Rudolph H. Raabe College of Pharmacy and Allied Health Sciences.[22]

Sample curricula were drawn up and the college faculty approved the go-ahead for offering a four-year curriculum described as the Bachelor of Science in Health Care Administration and another for the Bachelor of Science in Toxicology. Descriptions for both programs were included in the 1979–80 catalog. Both programs could exist concurrently along with the present five-year Bachelor of Science in Pharmacy and would utilize current faculty and facilities of both Pharmacy College and College of Arts and Sciences. Neither would require extensive additional resources that would impinge negatively on other ongoing programs in either college.

As it turned out, neither program would appeal to prospective students and after one year, both descriptions were removed from future catalogs. The more inclusive name of the college was continued through most of the following decade until 1988 when it reverted back to its original name, The Rudolph H. Raabe College of Pharmacy.[23]

In Retrospect

One might be tempted to speak critically of the college for bringing only one person onto its faculty in 1972, Dr. Donald Stansloski, to organize such a vast undertaking as development of the college's clinical program. At the same time, it must be understood that Dean Beltz was a strong spokesperson for change and a strong orator to boot. He was able to gain the support of many alumni and other prominent individuals in pharmacy from across the state. Many of them eagerly endorsed the new direction the college was headed and helped in its development and implementation. Dean Beltz was able to convince them to become proactive in its endeavor and help the process along. Thanks to these dedicated alumni and friends of the college and to Dean Beltz specifically, the process advanced smoothly. Many persons volunteered their services by becoming preceptors in the program.

With all these changes underway, the college was very much alive and could boast of its status. The college by then was the largest in the state with an enrollment of 684 students. In 1974, the school had grown in size from sixty-seventh nationally just eight years earlier to eighteenth in the country. Its records showed that more than one-fourth of all registered pharmacists then practicing in Ohio were graduates of ONU. Since 1972, and until recently, the admission process to accept new students into the college has had to be terminated early, thus unfortunately ruling out admission of dozens of extremely well-qualified and highly motivated high school students because of lack of space in the pharmacy program. Interest in ONU was at an all-time high. That interest remains as strong today as before, even with the number of colleges of pharmacy in the state having nearly doubled what it was during the era 1972–1983 (see Appendix 1).

Direction Features

The primary focus of this chapter has been to show how the college reacted to the national trend of converting professional programs of pharmacy into a more clinically-oriented curriculum. The next chapter documents the college's attitude and activity taken toward fulfillment of its decision to adopt the six-year Doctor of Pharmacy degree as its sole curriculum that would permit entry into the profession.

THE DEANS

LeRoy D. Beltz served as dean of the College of Pharmacy throughout this period. His profile is given in the previous chapter.

TEN
The Pace Intensifies

The era encompassing years 1984–1999 continued to be an active one at ONU. The decision had been made earlier to expand the college's focus to implement a new curriculum that embraced a strong clinical component. Massive changes in course content, teaching methods and sites, and in scheduling were underway. Students were now spending more time in off-campus locations with instruction being offered by both pharmacy and allied healthcare practitioners, rather than by traditional campus-based professors, and this off-campus training was increasing even more. The times indeed were changing and the direction the college was headed was changing big time.

During the early years of this era there was still reservation among some faculty members at ONU as to the feasibility of the suggestion that a mandatory six-year program was needed. To understand the college's movement into the six-year curriculum with its awarding only the Doctor of Pharmacy degree, it is first necessary to understand what was underway around the country at that time. The following discussion is but a thumbnail description of events presented to aid our understanding.

The Six-year Curriculum

Pharmacy education leaders had long considered the feasibility of a six-year professional doctorate as the sole degree for entry into the profession. As stated earlier, the 1950 publication, *General Report of the Pharmaceutical Survey, 1946–1949*, made this recommendation.[1] The report stated that the public's perception of pharmacists was less than desired and challenged the profession's leadership to embrace radical changes in the educational requirements that would upgrade this perception. The study report emphasized the inability of the four-year curriculum in vogue at that time to provide both a strong scientific component required by pharmacists, along with a strong general education component associated with a university education. The survey's long-term recommendation was that the profession should eventually move toward a six-year entry-level degree that would enable educational institutions to grant a professional doctorate. This level of education would elevate pharmacists to a higher, more equal basis with physicians. It would certainly improve their esteem from all factions.

Pharmacy educators' reactions to the proposed changes in the pharmaceutical curriculum were mixed, especially in light of an already approved change in the requirement for a baccalaureate degree moving from the then current four-year to a five-year format, a change that had been implemented in the not-too-distant past for all entering classes beginning after April 1, 1960. Some bought into the proposal at once to move forward toward the six-year degree, while others remained opposed to any serious changes that would interfere with maintaining the upcoming five-year program.

The length of time for study and degree debate continued through the 1950s and would continue into the 1980s. By 1977, The American Association of Colleges of Pharmacy's Council of Deans narrowly voted to establish the single degree as a requirement for entry into the profession. The Association's council of faculties, on the other hand, voted overwhelmingly against it.[2] In 1984, a task force established by the American Pharmaceutical Association reported on its exhaustive review of pharmacy education and recommended adoption of the six-year Pharm D degree curriculum as the desired goal for the profession.[3] This recommendation could well be considered the rally cry for moving one way or the other: to move forward to a six-year program or remain complacent with the five-year curriculum. Even with the recommendation, debate continued…on and on and on.

In 1989, the American Association of Colleges of Pharmacy established its Commission to Implement Change in Pharmaceutical Education.[4] Commission members were charged with developing a workable process to ensure that the education of pharmacists would serve societal needs into the twenty-first century. In 1991, the American Pharmaceutical Association, American Society of Hospital Pharmacists, and the National Association of Retail Druggists issued a joint statement in support of the six-year entry-level Doctor of Pharmacy degree. Not unexpectedly, the National Association of Chain Drug Stores led the opposing arguments against the proposal based on its conviction that the move would actually lead to a shortage of graduates because the extra year of education requirement would deter students who wished to pursue the study of pharmacy. This shortage, the group believed, would lead to higher labor costs throughout the industry.[5] The American Association of Colleges of Pharmacy also initially opposed the transition to an all-Pharm D degree program because of its belief that there would continue to be a need for pharmacists educated at the baccalaureate level, as well as at the doctoral level, to meet the full spectrum of societal needs for drug therapy utilization.[2,6] The National Association of Boards of Pharmacy and other professional groups later added their support to the proposal for a six-year entry-level Pharm D degree.[7]

By 1992, the commission concluded that the pharmacy curriculum did indeed require more than five years to adequately prepare practitioners for patient-centric service that the future was sure to require. Not only was it important to expand the curriculum, but also imperative to agree on a single title for the degree, Doctor of Pharmacy. Many of the country's leaders in pharmacy were still bemoaning the fact that the five-year program had not emphasized awarding the doctoral title, or at minimum, a master's degree for completion of the advanced-level BS Pharm curriculum. The report thus proposed that the American Association of Colleges of Pharmacy support the Pharm D degree as the sole entry-level curriculum.[8] The group accepted the proposal.

In 1993, the American Council on Pharmacy Education (its name was changed from the American Council on Pharmaceutical Education in 2003), the national agency for accrediting schools of pharmacy, released its Proposed Revision of Accreditation Standards and Guidelines Leading to the Pharm D Degree. Of note was the requirement of preparing students for contemporary practice as well as for auxiliary roles that may emerge to ensure the rational use of drug therapy in the individualized care of patients.[9] Four years later, the American Council on Pharmaceutical Education announced an implementation date for the six-year all-Pharm D degree program that would begin with entering classes in 2000. Thus, after nearly a half-century of study and intensely emotional debate, the decision that the nation would move forward to advance the profession of pharmacy was affirmed. What had for so long been viewed as a new program that would eventually, but not immediately, be implemented was close at hand.[10] The recommendation of the pharmaceutical survey for a six-year professional doctorate for all graduates of the nation's colleges of pharmacy was finally realized.[11] Five decades of hard work and intense discussion had finally resulted in a positive outcome.

Back to ONU

Overall, Ohio Northern embraced the recommendation for an expanded program. Because of extensive ground work undertaken by Dean Beltz with endorsement by successive deans and the majority of their faculties, the college was well prepared to meet the challenge head-on. But then, tragedy struck a cruel blow.

Early in the morning on January 14, 1986, the college received word that its leader for the past twenty years had died of heart failure at his home earlier that morning. Associate dean Louis Vottero was quickly appointed interim dean and ably led the college through a rough period while faculty and students mourned Dean Beltz' passing.

During Dean Vottero's period of leadership, the college continued to prepare for the big changes that were ahead. But he had no personal desire to remain as dean. After a year and a half, he reminded the higher administration of his wish to step down. A search was immediately organized to locate a permanent dean, a person who had a strong background in and solid knowledge of clinical pharmacy programming. That person identified was associate dean Dr. Stephen Hoag, who was serving as interim dean of the North Dakota University's College of Pharmacy. Dr. Hoag was appointed dean of ONU's College of Pharmacy effective August 1, 1987.[11]

After arriving on campus, Dean Hoag quickly formed a committee to assess where the college was at present and where it intended to go in the future. Part of the committee's duties was to decide whether cities away from Ada, Lima, and Findlay could indeed be used to provide clinical instruction to Northern's students, as Dean Beltz had believed they could. It was Dean Hoag's impression that the number and variety of clinical instruction sites needed to be expanded even farther away from campus to accommodate larger classes anticipated in the future and to continue enhancing the quality of the college's clinical program.[12] This might mean that significant curricular restructuring would need to occur in order to create a fifth-year term in which students could remain away from Ada full time for clinical instruction, similar to their externship quarter, which already kept them away for a term.

The resulting plan was that the college would test the waters and gain valuable experience in administering a doctoral-level degree program by initially offering a six-year entry-level track-in Pharm D program to a small number of students each year as it prepared for the massive change coming later. Under this arrangement all students would have the opportunity during their third or fourth year to compete for acceptance to enter into the Pharm D program. Coursework completed by the students would be basically identical through their first four years of study. Those accepted into the Pharm D program, with the class size initially limited to ten-twelve students per year, would enter a fifth and sixth-year special program that would lead them to the Doctor of Pharmacy degree,[13] while the remaining students would continue to complete the five-year BS Pharm program as usual.

The college's plan, in essence, was to establish an eventual six-year entry-level Pharm D curriculum, rather than offer a two-year post-baccalaureate program as some institutions were planning. The reason for this decision was to preserve the college's history and tradition. Northern had long been known for quality preparation of undergraduate generalist practitioners. Its entry-level Pharm D program would continue with that tradition.

The initial class included nine students.[14] With this class, Ohio Northern thus became the first college of pharmacy in Ohio to offer the advanced degree as an entry-level program.[15] The catalog for 1996–97 described the new degree program thusly: "The Doctor of Pharmacy degree is an advanced professional program that provides a foundation in the basic sciences of pharmacy as well as a comprehensive understanding of health care settings. Specifically, the graduate will have training in clinical skills that will allow entry into advanced practice settings. The program of study leading to the degree of Doctor of Pharmacy requires a minimum of 352 quarter hours of study and is a combination of general education courses, basic sciences, professional pharmacy courses and electives. All of the requirements for general education, basic science, professional pharmacy courses and electives as listed in the Bachelor of Science Requirement section also apply to the Doctor of Pharmacy program. In addition, the Doctor of Pharmacy degree student must complete advanced course work in pharmacy and one year of clerkship experience."[16]

Changing of the Guard

The highlight of Dean Hoag's service to ONU was in directing the work necessary to bring the college to the point where its new programs could be initiated. He followed through on that undertaking quite well. However, wishing to relocate closer to home, Dean Hoag resigned his position in June, 1993, to accept the deanship at Drake University's College of Pharmacy and Health Sciences in Des Moines, Iowa. He was succeeded by associate dean Dr. Thomas A. Gossel, who was appointed interim dean, then dean, of the College of Pharmacy six months later.

It would be Dean Gossel's mission to oversee the actual initiation of the new curriculum as the college began to offer student admission into the programs described previously. As might be expected, assuring that all students received the necessary courses to keep them on schedule would be a herculean task. For example, in Dean Gossel's early years of service, the college had students on five different study tracks. What could have been a formidable task was smoothed out by a very capable faculty. By the mid-1990s, the faculty was excited at what was happening in the college, and members unanimously and collectively stepped up to the plate to help get the new curriculum up and running.

Non-Traditional Pharm D Program

Realizing there were pharmacists in practice who possessed a four-year or five-year BS Pharm degree and now wished to earn their advanced degree without resigning from their jobs, the college responded by offering a non-traditional (also called external-degree) Doctor of Pharmacy degree program. The novel venture, the first to be offered by any Ohio college, was in full swing beginning with the winter term, 1997–98.[17,18] The program enabled pharmacists in current practice to earn their doctoral degree while maintaining a full-time work schedule. They could take up to five years to complete their study. The Pharm D degree would be identical to the one earned in the traditional manner. The primary difference would be in the method the degree was earned.

The non-traditional Pharm D program was designed so that most of the didactic work was completed using the Internet, video-teleconferencing, and other forms of instruction contemporary with non-pharmacy external-degree programs elsewhere in the country. Thus, it was not necessary to return to campus except for an orientation period the first day when beginning the program. Students could still visit with professors in person, but this was not mandated. Pharmacists registered for courses as modules based on pharmacotherapeutic categories (e.g., cardiovascular, renal, infectious diseases, etc.). They typically registered for a single module at a time, paying tuition for only that module. Pharmacists who desired solely to brush up on a specific topic offered without completing all of the requirements for the

First class of non-traditional Pharm D students. Shown are: *Front:* Darla Gaiser '73, Jean Glaser '84, Janice Scheufler '84, Sharon Beebe '65. *Middle:* Jim Graham '76, Kathleen Rand '88, Susan Nold '92, Arthur Kent Kloes '77, Edward Fingers '86. *Back:* Mathew Simari '83, Albert Barber '83 (striped sweater), Michael Fraulini '92, Anthony Patterson ('92 Ferris State Univ.), Richard Woerz '62, Jeff Rubin '81, Chris Patsiovos '91. *Missing:* Kimberly Omler '91.

degree could register for individual modules and receive college credit. They could also earn continuing professional education credit for their work.

Students spanning four decades in age comprised the first class of non-traditional students, and a number of others joined in along the way. The program was continued as long as there were applicants. By 2012, all non-traditional students had completed the work for their Pharm D degree and the program was discontinued.

POP and Modules: A Giant Step Forward

With the college approved by the Ohio Board of Regents to offer the six-year entry-level Pharm D degree, the faculty again initiated a total overhaul of the curriculum. The overhaul had two major objectives.

The first was to spread the experimental work currently required in the upper division throughout the curriculum. The new curriculum introduced a course sequence entitled The Profession of Pharmacy (POP) in which students would begin their experiential work in their first (freshman) year and continue in the sequence each quarter.[19] Again, ONU's College of Pharmacy became the only program in Ohio to place pharmacy students into professional courses beginning with their freshman year.

The second objective was to restructure all professional courses into a modular format. The modular approach is an integrated, multi-disciplinary educational style characteristic of many medical programs. Included within a module would be the components of a topic taken from all applicable disciplines and put together in a way that students would advance within a module from "A to Z"—that is, by studying all relative aspects of the subject. Students would register for one or two modules each term. By concentrating on the broad overview of limited topics at any time, it was felt the students could process the information much better than previously and this would be to their advantage. In time, the modular approach to learning would prove to be superior to traditional course descriptions and scheduling.

With all of this restructuring going on, Ohio Northern thus set the stage in Ohio for its innovative curricular design. First described in the catalog for 1998–99, the college's conversion of its professional coursework into a modular format, and its initiating professional work beginning in the freshman year, were among its significant advancements during this era.[20,21] That approach to education of pharmacy students would be retained into the twenty-first century and presumably, well beyond.

Dual Degree Programs

I t has long been possible for pharmacy students to earn a degree from the College of Liberal Arts—it was renamed the College of Arts and Sciences beginning with the academic year catalog for 1978–79—concurrently with their degree in pharmacy. Noted in the 1972–73 catalog as an arts-pharmacy curriculum the description read: "Superior students may elect to earn the Bachelor of Arts degree in the College of Liberal Arts concurrently with the Bachelor of Science degree in the College of Pharmacy. The student following this option pursues both degrees simultaneously under the supervision of a professional advisor from the College of Pharmacy and an adviser from the department of his chosen major in the College of Liberal Arts…the student receives the appropriate degree in each college upon completion of all graduation requirements."[22] Added to this description in 1979–80 was that a second degree could also be earned from the College of Business Administration.[23]

Beginning with academic year 1991–92, a joint pharmacy-law degree program was announced. The catalog for that year stated: "The joint Pharmacy-Law Degree Program is a seven-year curriculum that provides for substantial educational and research experiences in pharmacy and law. The Bachelor of Science degree in Pharmacy is awarded during the summer of the fifth year; the Juris Doctor, at the end of two additional years of study in the College of Law."[24] This dual-degree program was eventually discontinued with advent of semesters in the pharmacy curriculum. At that time it became impossible to schedule all required courses for both degrees into a seven-year format.

The 2012–13 catalog listed an additional option, a pharmacy/biology dual degrees program, described thusly: "The pharmacy/biology dual degrees program is a six-year curriculum that provides for educational, practice and research experiences in both pharmacy and biology. The Doctor of Pharmacy degree and the biology degree are awarded upon completion of the program of study."[25]

Entry into a joint-degree program in conjunction with another undergraduate college meant that students must carefully plan their course of study early, usually in their freshman year, so that they could be assured admission into appropriate courses in the area of their second major. As with dual-degree programs scheduled within the other colleges, students desiring entry into the pharmacy-law program needed to be formally admitted into the College of Law.

With graduation ceremonies each year, a small number of dedicated students have been able to walk across the stage twice and receive two diplomas. Popular second-degree majors have included music, theater, biology, and chemistry.

Pierstorf Family Pharmacy Museum

It has been said that to truly appreciate the present and future it is first of all imperative to understand the past. With today's emphasis on technological advances in scientific equipment and communication devices, new program development and expanded roles for pharmacists today and beyond, that which is new will be so much better appreciated by knowing what was available, and the general status of the profession in days gone by.

This was the philosophy held by three good friends of the college, Dr. Clarence Pierstorf, and Dr. Ervin and Mrs. Florence Pierstorf. Brothers Clarence and Erv were pharmacists who owned and operated their family pharmacy, the Pierstorf Pharmacy, in Fairview Park, Ohio.

On October 13, 1995, the Robertson-Evans Pharmacy Building was expanded by a 2,500-square-foot addition.[26] That date marked the dedication of the Pierstorf Annex. The addition housed the Pierstorf Family Pharmacy Museum on the entire first floor of the Annex, and a student lounge and state-of-the-art computer laboratory on the second floor. To top it off, the equipment, supplies, counters, and other fixtures from the Pierstorf Pharmacy were also presented to the college.

The Pierstorf Family Pharmacy Museum has become a focal point for the college, and is listed by the Hardin County Historical Society as a recommended attraction. Visitors are invited to tour the facility and take a step back in time as they experience the profession's rich heritage and view the way pharmacy was practiced in the past. The museum is open during the school year throughout the day on Monday through Friday, and Saturday until noon.

Photos of the Pierstorf Family Pharmacy Museum.

The time came during the spring of 1998 when Dean Gossel considered that all the items on his job description had been completed. The new doctoral curriculum was up and running smoothly. Other issues had all been tended to. Most recently, the college had undergone its regularly scheduled accreditation process and again received full accreditation. It was, generally, a period of smooth sailing for the college and its faculty. So he began to give serious attention to returning to the faculty, a lure that was too strong to neglect. The word went out that a replacement dean was needed. The person chosen was a strong clinical pharmacy advocate, Dr. Bobby G. Bryant.

THE DEANS

Five men served as dean of the College of Pharmacy during this period 1984–1999: LeRoy D. Beltz, Louis D. Vottero, Stephen G. Hoag, Thomas A. Gossel, and Bobby G. Bryant. Dean Beltz' profile is given in Chapter Eight.

Louis D. Vottero

Having earned his BS Pharm degree from Duquesne University in 1954, Louis Vottero served in the U.S. military, then pursued the practice of pharmacy in the Cleveland area. In 1963 he completed the MS degree in pharmaceutical chemistry at the Ohio State University. He received a faculty appointment and continued to serve that institution as instructor through 1964.

Lou arrived at Ohio Northern in 1965 and served as assistant professor until 1972 with appointment to associate professor that year. He was appointed professor of pharmacy in 1978, and associate dean of the College of Pharmacy in

1987. His primary areas of teaching expertise included ethics of professional practice and history of pharmacy.[27]

In addition to his teaching and administrative responsibilities at Ohio Northern, Lou Vottero was involved in many professional organizations including the Ohio Pharmacists Association, American Pharmaceutical Association, American Public Health Association, American Association of Colleges of Pharmacy, and the American Institute of the History of Pharmacy. He served the later group as its national treasurer for many years.

Louis D. Vottero, Interim Dean 1987–1992.

Professor Vottero was known statewide for his active involvement in healthcare planning. Areas of service in this arena included the Statewide Health Coordinating Council, with appointment by Governor James Rhodes in 1976 and reappointment in 1979; West-Central Ohio Health Systems Agency, elected to the board of directors in 1977 with re-election in 1979; Cancer Control Consortium of Ohio, becoming a charter member in 1979 with election as secretary of its executive committee in 1980; and a member of the Hardin Memorial Hospital Board, elected in 1982.[27] He was named a fellow of the Institute of Humanities and Medicine in 1988, a group that responds to the need for the humanities in the healthcare professions.[28]

On campus, Lou was faculty advisor for Phi Kappa Theta social fraternity and Phi Delta Chi professional pharmacy fraternity. He was a member of Rho Chi Society and Omicron Delta Kappa.

Named interim dean following the death of Dean Beltz in January, 1986, Lou's service to the institution was exemplary; however, being the permanent dean was not one of Lou's career goals. So in early 1987, he asked to be relieved of his administrative duties. With appointment of Stephen Hoag as dean in August, 1987, Lou continued as associate dean and director of the college's continuing professional education programs until his retirement in 1992. Since that time, Lou has continued to serve his profession through writing and publication. Together with Professor Robert Buerki of the Ohio State University, he coauthored the texts *Ethical Responsibility in Pharmacy Practice* (1994; second edition, 2002), *Ethical Practices in Pharmacy: A Guidebook for Pharmacy Technicians* (1997), and *Foundations of Ethical Pharmacy Practice* (2008). Additionally, he has published other articles on the topic of bioethics in professional journals. In 2006, Lou Vottero was honored by Samford University for his contributions to healthcare ethics.[29] He currently holds the title at ONU of professor of pharmacy emeritus.

Lou Vottero and his wife Barbara are the parents of four sons. The Votteros divide their time between homes in Vero Beach, Florida, and St. Andrews, New Brunswick, Canada.

Personal Reflections

One of my strongest recollections of Lou Vottero was gained during my first year on the faculty. When I interviewed with Dean Beltz and faculty less than a year earlier as a candidate to teach pharmacology, I casually mentioned that in my off-hours I enjoyed reading historical pieces. He in turn, mentioned that the required ONU curriculum at that time included a one-quarter required course on the history of pharmacy. Of course, that was exciting news because I remembered my own student history course taught by Dr. C.O. Lee. Dean Beltz must have remembered my casual comment because the next year he had me teamed with Lou, the course's coordinator.

I recall Lou as being an instructor who was totally passionate about sharing the course material with his students. He presented it in such a way that the subjects seemed alive and quite real. I, on the other hand, always felt I was short-changing the students when it was my turn to lecture because Lou could offer so much more than I ever could.

One other point concerning Lou was, and remains to his credit, his mission to promote professionalism starting with the way pharmacy students looked and dressed. It bothered him greatly to see students (and yes, faculty) with unkempt hair or casual clothing or with other issues showing they did not take their appearance seriously. And in this regard, I can't remember ever seeing Lou at work when he was not wearing a dress shirt and tie. Lou set an excellent example for professionalism and brought a high degree of class to our college.

Stephen G. Hoag

Stephen G. Hoag was born May 13, 1944, in Fargo, North Dakota, and grew up in Duluth, Minnesota.[11] He received his BS Pharm degree from North Dakota State University in 1967. Purdue University awarded him the MS degree in 1971 and PhD degree in 1973, both in clinical pharmacy. Upon graduation, Steve practiced community pharmacy, served as a resident in hospital pharmacy at Indiana University's Medical Center Hospital, and was a clinical pharmacist at a Veteran's Administration hospital.[30]

Dr. Hoag served as assistant professor of pharmacy at the University of Texas at Austin and was director of its community pharmacy externship programs until

1975. That year, he headed north to join the faculty of the North Dakota State University's College of Pharmacy. There, he served as professor and chair of the Department of Pharmacy Practice from 1978 to 1981, and as associate dean and interim dean from 1981 until 1987. He was appointed dean of the Raabe College of Pharmacy at Ohio Northern effective August 1, 1987.[11]

During his tenure at Ohio Northern, Dean Hoag was an avid promoter of clinical pharmacy. It was he who can be credited with much of the groundwork involved in

Stephen G. Hoag, Dean 1987–1993.

preparing ONU's college to convert its five-year BS Pharm degree program to the six-year Pharm D degree program.

Dean Hoag served ONU until 1993 when he resigned to accept the deanship of Drake University's College of Pharmacy and Health Sciences, an appointment he maintained until 2003. He also served Drake University as its interim provost from 1998 to 2000.[31] Steve then returned to the University of Minnesota College of Pharmacy at its Duluth campus in 2003 as professor and head of the Department of Pharmacy Practice and Pharmaceutical Sciences and as senior associate dean. When the college moved into its new quarters in the Life Sciences Building, the student commons area was named the Dr. Stephen G. Hoag Pharmacy Student Commons in his honor.[32]

Areas of teaching responsibility have included pharmacy and healthcare, health quality assurance, and non-prescription medications. His research interests include professional ethics, geriatrics/gerontology and pharmaceutical care, and issues in professional program development.[31] Steve has authored numerous professional articles as a result of his research and served as a reviewer for professional and scientific journals. He has received numerous substantial research grants.[33]

Steve Hoag lists the following as professional memberships: American Society of Health-System Pharmacists, American Association of Colleges of Pharmacy, American Pharmacists Association, Kappa Psi Pharmaceutical Fraternity, and Sigma Xi Scientific Research Society where he served as president of the NDSU chapter 1986–87.[31]

Steve Hoag and his wife Jill are the parents of two sons. The Hoags make their home in the Duluth, Minnesota, area.

Personal Reflections

Steve Hoag was a very positive influence on me. As my immediate predecessor in the dean's office, I was able to move into a position that Steve had under sound control. His discipline for order seemed almost unreal to me as he left nothing undone. Files were in perfect shape. All ongoing college projects were completed. Early in my deanship the college was scheduled for its routine accreditation visit. When the accreditation team arrived for its inspection, it found nothing out of order and the college earned a perfect score. For that I give Steve Hoag full credit. My job as dean from day-one was made so much easier because of Steve's fine attention to detail.

If asked to define Steve's legacy during his term at ONU I would say it was he who pulled the many diverse pieces together that would soon usher in the college's new direction for the future. My responsibility as Steve's successor was to implement what Steve and the faculty had already set up. Without a doubt, Steve Hoag was ONU's "Mr. Clinical Pharmacy/Pharm D Degree" dean.

Thomas A. Gossel

A native of Lancaster, Ohio, Thomas Alvin Gossel was born on October 20, 1941. He attended local grade schools and graduated from Lancaster High School in 1959.

During his junior year in high school at age 15, Tom worked in a neighborhood pharmacy, a building whose square-footage was hardly greater than an average American living room today. His first duty was as stock boy, which was soon moved upward to soda jerk where he began to take serious note of the various aspects of the business and pharmacy profession. The store was owned by the elderly widow of a pharmacist who was most likely a two-year (perhaps one-year!) graduate and had been deceased for as long as anyone could remember. But that didn't stop the widow from continuing to provide pharmacy service to the neighborhood. She filled the one or two prescriptions that were

Thomas A. Gossel, Dean 1993–1999.

brought in each day. Apparently these patients didn't know the widow was not a pharmacist, thus operating outside the boundary of the law. That was as late as 1957.

Several months later, the pharmacy was sold to a small chain of six pharmacies, with two in Lancaster. Soon a new location was selected and a fine new pharmacy built, with closing of the original one. The new pharmacist manager, an ONU alumnus, took Tom under his wing, appointing him clerk, and began teaching him about operating a pharmacy. This was the turning point in Tom's life because he began to seriously think he would be able to succeed in pharmacy as his life's work. When he received his certificate as an apprentice from the Ohio State Board of Pharmacy, Tom had decided for sure that he was on the right career path. By now he was passionate about learning all he could to pursue his work in the profession.

Tom entered ONU in September, 1959, and graduated with his BS Pharm degree in June, 1963. After a short stint working in community pharmacies in Lancaster and surrounding towns, he joined the staff at Risch Pharmacy in Lancaster.

Tom still holds that the next five years in community pharmacy practice were among the most pleasurable times of his life. But he also had a strong yearning to someday return to his adopted hometown of Ada and teach in ONU's pharmacy program. He therefore entered Purdue University in 1968, earning his MS degree in 1970 and PhD degree in 1972, both degrees in pharmacology/toxicology. Several months before completing his work, he received a phone call from Dean LeRoy Beltz asking if he would be interested in applying for a faculty position that would be available beginning with the Fall term of 1972. Tom interviewed and within a couple days was offered the job. The timing of the request to interview and offer of the position seemed more than coincidental to him, so he knew that ONU was where he was meant to be. Over the years that hunch became very clear.

During the next thirty years, Tom taught pharmacology, toxicology, and introduction to disease. He offered elective courses including pharmacy communications and history of pharmacy. He also delivered more than 1,325 lectures and led workshops in professional matters at pharmacy, nursing, and medical meetings and conventions across the nation and in several other countries.

An avid writer, Tom has published more than 730 articles in a variety of professional journals and continues to write. In collaboration with several colleagues, he coauthored six books and three book chapters. His textbook, *Principles of Clinical Toxicology,* 1984; second edition, 1990; third edition, 1994 written with Dr. J. Douglas Bricker, was used at ONU and by pharmacy students across the country and world.

Tom received numerous awards/honors including Most Professional Professor (Ohio Northern University), 1982; Distinguished Service Award (National Association of Boards of Pharmacy), 1988; Professional Service Award (American Pharmaceutical Association/Academy of Student Pharmacists), 1989; Outstanding Alumnus Award (Ohio Northern University), 1989; Most Professional Professor (Ohio Northern University), 1991; Mortar Board Favorite Professor (Ohio Northern University), 1998; and Life Membership for Outstanding Contributions to the Profession (Ohio Pharmacists Association), 2001. He was accepted into the Distinguished Alumni Hall of Fame (Lancaster [Ohio] High School), 1994.

Tom also served as advisor or co-advisor to Phi Delta Chi Fraternity throughout the thirty years of his service to ONU. He served the national fraternity as its vice president.

Starting as an assistant professor, Tom was soon promoted to associate professor, then professor. Along the way he served as chairman of the Department of Pharmacology and Biomedical Sciences, chairman of the Department of Clinical Pharmacy, then assistant dean and associate dean. In 1993, he was named interim dean, then dean of the College of Pharmacy early in 1994. He served until August, 1999, after having asked to be relieved of his administrative responsibilities. He returned to a faculty slot for three years until retirement in June, 2002. He is currently professor emeritus of pharmacology.

Tom and his wife Phyllis (BS Ed '63) continue to call Ada home. Phyllis, their three children and their spouses, and seven grandchildren, remain the joy of his life. He is active in his church (First Presbyterian, Ada) and serves as lay pastor in surrounding area churches.

Bobby G. Bryant

Bobby G. Bryant was appointed the college's twelfth dean beginning July, 1999. He was also named professor of clinical pharmacy, and brought a broad spectrum of interest and capability for continuing to advance ONU's flourishing clinical practice program.

Dean Bryant earned his BS Pharm degree in 1970 and Pharm D degree in 1971 from the University of Tennessee. He then earned his MS degree in clinical research design and statistical analysis from the University of Michigan in 1986, followed by post-graduate work at the University of Michigan, Tufts University, and Harvard University.[34]

Bobby was a member of the faculty at Albany College of Pharmacy in Albany, New York. He served as chairman of the Department of Pharmacy Practice and director of the doctor of pharmacy program before assuming duties as interim president and dean of that institution. He was previously on the faculty of Purdue University's school of pharmacy and pharmacal sciences, where he was director of the externship program and director of the Doctor of Pharmacy program. He served on the staff of the City of Memphis Hospitals, director of pharmaceutical services at North Memphis Community Health Clinic, instructor at the University of Tennessee's College of Nursing in Memphis, and staff pharmacist with Methodist Hospital Pharmacy in Memphis.

Bobby G. Bryant, Dean 1999–2006.

Prior to his appointment at ONU, Bobby served as scholar-in-residence at the American Association of Colleges of Pharmacy in Alexandria, Virginia.[35] While on sabbatical leave, he was a faculty member at the University of Riyadh, Saudi Arabia, and a consultant to the King Faisal Specialists Hospital and Research Centre in Riyadh.

Throughout his professional career, Bobby was an avid member of professional and academic organizations and held leadership roles on many committees. He has written a number of scholarly works, which have been published in professional journals.

Bobby accepted the deanship of the McWhorter School of Pharmacy of Samford University, Birmingham, Alabama, in 2006,[36] where he served until 2008. A southern boy by birth, Bobby and his wife Irene continued to make their home in Birmingham. Bobby died from natural causes at age 66 on November 19, 2014.

Personal Reflections

Bobby Bryant replaced me as dean following my resignation in 1999. I remained a member of the faculty for three additional years until retirement in 2002, and during those three years got to know Bobby quite well. I best remember him as a true gentleman who, to the best of my knowledge, never had a bad word to say to or about anyone. In other words, he reflected the image I have of a true southern gentleman.

A reflection I recall with pleasure relates to one of his hobbies. He was an avid collector of clocks—wall clocks, shelf-clocks, other sit-around clocks, new and old clocks, and any other device designed to keep the time. It seemed there were hundreds of them and I often thought they had some magical ability to reproduce because with each visit into his home I came to believe there were more than the previous visits. Most of his collection was housed in one room of his home and filled every conceivable space on specially built shelves that extended from floor to ceiling. While sitting in his living room "shooting the bull," as is often the custom whenever two or more college profs or deans get together informally, all at once the combined sounds of these clocks announcing the hour in synchrony would be all but deafening.

Bobby once told me that his idea of a real promotion would be to resign as dean and return to full-time teaching clinical pharmacy. He loved working with students.

The millennial year ushered in a new era for the college, one that would witness many significant changes in its overall operation. Beginning with academic year 2000–01, all students entering the college as freshmen would be committed to a six-year period of study. Those who successfully completed all course requirements would graduate in 2006 having earned their Pharm D degree. Returning students in 2000 who had by then completed at least one year of the five-year curriculum would be permitted to continue on their baccalaureate-degree track as long as they graduated not later than 2004. Or they could track into the six-year program and continue on the doctoral path. Five-year students who had a legitimate reason, such as personal illness or death in the family, and therefore could not complete their program by 2004, could petition the Accreditation Council for Pharmacy Education (its name was changed from the American Council on Pharmaceutical Education in 2003) through the dean, for a waiver, which would grant them a special privilege to graduate later than the deadline.

To the surprise of many, the majority of students who entered the pharmacy program as freshmen prior to 2000 elected up front to proceed on the six-year track, so the size of the graduating five-year BS Pharm degree classes through 2004 had quickly dwindled year by year such that fewer and fewer baccalaureate-level students remained in each successive graduation class toward the end. Incoming students prior to 2000 understood the true value of the extra year of study and the doctoral degree they would earn, and elected from the beginning of their freshman year to proceed along the longer clinically-oriented track. That decision would be to their credit and best interest in the long run.

This is mentioned because the mandatory switch to a six-year program at ONU was generally positive overall, likely aided by the fact that graduates would receive a degree that seemed appropriate for their extra time, effort, and tuition dollars. Students entering into the new five-year program back in 1960 would receive the same baccalaureate degree (BS Pharm) as those students before them who had completed the four-year curriculum. For some reason, to them at least, it just didn't seem quite equitable.

Curriculum

The Doctor of Pharmacy curriculum is an advanced professional program designed to provide a foundation in the basic science of pharmacy as well as a comprehensive understanding of healthcare settings. Specifically, the graduate receives training in clinical skills that will permit entry into advanced practice settings. The program of study leading to the Pharm D degree requires a minimum of 216 semester hours of study divided according to the following: general education courses, 30 hours; basic science courses, 44 hours; professional courses, 131 hours; and electives, 11 hours.[1]

Along with traditional classroom and laboratory settings, the college requires a full year of clerkships (rotations) to be taken in the sixth year of the students' program. Clerkships can be scheduled at sites nearby the college or at other locations throughout the United States, for example, from an Indian Reservation in New Mexico to practice sites along the coast of Maine or the wilds of Alaska. Ohio Northern and the U.S. Public Health Service have entered into agreement to make more than 150 additional clerkships available to ONU pharmacy students. Clerkships are also available to ONU students outside the country.

Pharm D clerkships consist of month-long rotations in hospital service areas such as cardiology, intensive care, pediatrics, renal hemodialysis, and surgery to name a few. In addition, clerkships may include rotations in ambulatory and community clinical practice. At these sites students will gain experience in interviewing, compliance monitoring, invalid supplies, OTC counseling, home health care, nursing home services, and community profile review.[2] Students must take nine clerkships in their sixth year.

Residencies

In addition to the six-year curriculum, graduating students may elect to pursue a post-graduate residency. Residencies are scheduled for one or two years. They are paid positions with organizations or groups that commit to teach in-depth topics in specialized areas.[3] Residencies can be described as a bridge between completing the college degree and entering the profession. They are intended to allow residents to specialize in a specific area of practice or patient care, and thus increase options for future practice. Pharmacists who complete a residency say their experience helped them expand their skills of interacting with patients and other healthcare providers. Residents complete a major project, which is usually a research project that spans the length of their residency. A number of residencies are available through the college, from other schools of pharmacy, and professional groups and associations. Twenty-eight percent of the graduating class in 2015 elected to pursue a residency, and that number is expected to increase in successive years.

Changing of the Guard

Dean Bobby Bryant resigned as dean in 2006 to return to his first love—the South—where he assumed the deanship of Samford University's McWhorter School of Pharmacy in Alabama. A wide search was undertaken to find a replacement dean who would lead the ONU College of Pharmacy into the future. After an extensive interview process, the offer was extended to Dr.

Jon E. Sprague. Dr. Sprague had served Ohio Northern earlier, as professor of pharmacology, before accepting the position of professor and chairman of the Department of Biomedical Sciences and Pathobiology at Virginia Polytechnic Institute and State University.

Switch to Semesters

One of the reasons why the North-Western Ohio Normal School was successful in its early days was because of the manner in which courses were scheduled. "Normal" school terms of six weeks' duration were initially offered. The short terms were necessary because President Lehr understood the demographics of his students and responded to their needs. These students were largely from rural areas and most were needed to help back home on the farm or to contribute one way or another to the family's income. Students could pretty much begin and end their study whenever they wished. These six-week terms would soon lead to expanded periods of ten weeks, or the quarter system. Quarters would be transformed into fifteen-week semesters at ONU beginning in 2011.

Ohio Northern's institution-wide faculty initiated discussion in the late 1970s concerning the feasibility of transforming its nearly century-old system of academic quarters into semesters. Interest in such conversion was not strong enough in the undergraduate colleges at that time to formalize the process; the law college, however, did convert its program to semesters. The undergraduate colleges' wish to resume serious discussion on the matter peaked with onset of the new millennium. Discussion resumed and after much consideration, the decision affirmed that beginning with academic year 2011–12, the university's total academic programs and all other operations would convert from quarters to semesters.[4]

The conversion made good sense from an administrative standpoint. University personnel and offices including those of the registrar and controller would need to gear up for term beginnings and endings just two times a year instead of three.

The same considerations would also apply to faculty—only two, instead of three finals and grade reports would be necessary each year. The lengthened study time from ten to fifteen weeks would provide more time for students to absorb and contemplate material, which was believed to be a positive aspect of the semester system.[5] The change would also put ONU on a closer calendar basis with the majority of other academic institutions. This was recognized as a benefit by a sizeable number of students in that their own periods for study and relaxation would correlate more closely with their colleagues at other institutions.

Student concerns relative to the semester proposal were addressed in depth. Concerns were not as strongly negative as believed might have been. What was heard most commonly were concerns based on the unknown, such as having half again as much material to process for final examinations.

Once the eventual conversion was decided upon and student's concerns were addressed, the faculty began one of its most ambitious and comprehensive projects undertaken in recent years—the job of repackaging coursework into new formats, eliminating some topics and courses, and adding others. In Dean Sprague's words: "The conversion from quarters to semesters has given the faculty and students the chance to assess and evaluate our curriculum. This type of assessment really provides us an opportunity to improve the learning opportunities for our students."[6] The conversion was accomplished and, on schedule, students returned to campus in September, 2011, to face their new course formats and semester scheduling (Appendix 8).[4]

One might imagine the intense pressure that Dean Sprague and his faculty must have faced because of the conversion. The college roles included 1,019 students, with 868 of them having P-2 through P-6 status whose quarter-hour credits earned thus far needed to be converted to semester-hour credits. Moreover, the dean and faculty advisors had to assure that no student was left behind in receiving specific topics of any required professional course. Such deficiencies would need to be accounted for with individualized scheduling. All make-ups and deficiencies were, miraculously, accomplished in time and every student was permitted to continue without further problem.

College Faculty and Staff

From an initial faculty size of one individual who taught the pharmacy courses and served as principal (dean) of the Department of Pharmacy at ONU when it was first established, today's faculty size has increased over the years, as have their professional disciplines (Appendix 9, 10 and 11). Additionally, twenty-eight other individuals are listed as shared-faculty meaning they have faculty status within the college and are assigned to off-campus clinical sites. Another eleven persons serve as in-house staff to maintain the active program.[7]

The question may be raised regarding responsibilities of faculty to students and the college. There are three academic models in higher education that can be implemented for evaluating faculty members.[8]

The *scholar-teacher model.* In this model faculty members focus on scholarship over teaching and are expected to generate some portion of their salary from research grants or work in a clinical practice site. This is the model followed in most state-supported, research-intensive, institutions. The model runs the risk of the faculty member's focus being diverted from teaching. His or her contact with students is oftentimes minimized.

The *teacher-only model.* Faculty members focus on their teaching and are rewarded for their efforts. This is the model followed throughout most of the history of ONU's college, primarily because that was the model that President Lehr endorsed, which was the philosophy that attracted many of the faculty members to the college in the early days. Their primary focus emphasized teaching, rather than to spending long periods of time in a laboratory. Moreover, in earlier days the college budget couldn't support research practice and faculty members often taught a large variety of courses so that there was little time left for meaningful research or involvement in an outside clinical activity. To illustrate, when Dr. Albert Smith arrived on the ONU campus in 1944, he was given the following teaching load: organic chemistry, three terms; drug assay, three terms; pharmaceutical chemistry, three terms; biochemistry, three terms; and bacteriology, two terms.[9] Having the responsibility for teaching fourteen different classes each year didn't leave much time for conducting a research program. His full-time teaching load continued through his service years as dean.

In this model, faculty members could run the risk of not staying current within their discipline. Consequently, the faculty member's teaching effectiveness, although good to excellent, could stand the chance of suffering as a result.

The *TEACHER-scholar model*. In Dean Sprague's words: "We are the TEACHER-scholars of pharmacy education."[10] Faculty members are rewarded for excellence in the classroom, while remaining professionally active in scholarship through research and/or maintaining a clinical practice site. This model allows the faculty member to focus on excellence in teaching while remaining current within his or her discipline.

The Raabe College of Pharmacy has adopted the TEACHER-scholar model for evaluating faculty members.[1] While some faculty choose to conduct bench or clinical research, usually involving student participants who have declared interest in pursuing graduate work in one of the pharmaceutical disciplines, others contribute time and talent to serving at an active practice site. Either way, students play important roles in the projects.

As stated earlier, the faculty at Ohio Northern prides itself in maintaining high involvement with its students. While working closely with faculty members, in one year students won the following state and national awards and competition. These included the national regional award for the American Pharmacists Association/Academy of Student Pharmacists' Heartburn Awareness Challenge, American Pharmacists Association/Academy of Student Pharmacists' Project Chance Award, Ohio Pharmacists Association's OTC Challenge, Ohio Pharmacists Association's Pharmacy Olympics, Academy of Managed Care Pharmacy's Elite 9 (National P&T Competition), Red Cross Youth of the Year Award, and the National Community Pharmacists Association's Student Chapter of the Year (national runner-up). College faculty also received national advisor awards from Kappa Epsilon and the National Community Pharmacists Association, and the U.S. Public Health Service for its Excellence in Pharmacy Practice Award during the same time period.

At the conclusion of each term, students are required to evaluate faculty using a five-point Likert scale, with a score of five being the highest. Results are then compiled and analyzed for each academic year. In one recent year, students evaluated individual faculty members, whose scores were then averaged for the entire college. The resulting score was 4.54. The American Association of Colleges of Pharmacy publishes a faculty satisfaction survey based on evaluation scores of the nation's colleges of pharmacy. Compared to a comparison group of nine other colleges of pharmacy, ONU's faculty outperformed all of the other colleges in all 65 assessment measures.

Administrative Structure

The administrative makeup of the college that consisted of six departments and was established by Dean Beltz in 1966 worked well during the period the college was emerging from its accreditation woes. Three of the six were one-person departments that as time went by seemed excessively cumbersome. To respond, in 1973 Dean Beltz restructured the format into just two departments: the Department of Pharmacy and Health Care Administration, and the Department of Pharmacology and Biomedical Sciences. This arrangement worked well for most of the following two decades. By 1992, the clinical program was developing well and numerous practice sites and additional faculty were being added. To help meet the challenge associated with assuring the needs of an actively growing discipline, Dean Hoag split the Department of Pharmacy and Health Care Administration into a third unit, the Department of Clinical Pharmacy. After two years, the dean considered a faculty suggestion that the best administrative move might be to revert back to a two department structure, each having expanded responsibilities. The college, therefore, was again reorganized into the Department of Pharmacy Practice, and the Department of Pharmaceutical and Biomedical Sciences.[12] Within the Department of Pharmacy Practice is the office of experiential education that oversees all student experiential work.

The dean is the chief administrator of the college. To date, all deans throughout the history of the college, have been pharmacists. The dean is aided with two associate deans, an assistant to the dean, and a director of development. The college provides specialized services to students and alumni through the office of pharmacy student services, which oversees college admissions, academic advising, personal counseling, career counseling, and job placement. The office also coordinates professional organization functions and student group activities, and serves as a focus for special project planning and implementation.

Pharmacy Skills Center

One of the trademarks of the College of Pharmacy has been to provide the necessary cutting-edge opportunities for students to apply their coursework in pharmacy practice situations. The evolution of pharmacy practice requires a variety of laboratory and classroom space for optimal learning. At the heart of continuing this tradition of excellence is the college's Pharmacy Skills Center. Today's pharmacist is often the health professional with whom patients remain in closest contact during the critical points in their healthcare process. This was all taken into account during the careful planning of the Pharmacy Skills Center. The center is designed to provide students with practical experiences in many pharmacy-related areas.

The center features six state-of-the-art compound/counseling pods with portable OTC simulation stations and is designed so that instructors can effectively assess students abilities and provide feedback to them quickly. Due to the strategic linkage between pharmacy practice and drug information, the skills center is connected to the Drug Information Center. The center allows the faculty to work closely with students by training them for the real-world practice situations of today and the future. The approximately 2,400 square-foot skills center is located on the first floor of the pharmacy building where the compounding laboratory and some office space were once located.[12]

Hakes-Pierstorf Family Pharmacy Education Center

Over the years there was an ever-present challenge at the Raabe College of Pharmacy to sustain the excellence of an ONU pharmacy education. The college of pharmacy had met its challenge and maintained its enviable position as one of the top-ranked professional programs in the country. As a result, enrollment continued to grow. In the fall of 2014, for example, 983 students were enrolled in the six-year Pharm D program. When the Robertson-Evans Pharmacy Building was first occupied in 1966, approximately 250 pharmacy students were enrolled in a five-year bachelor's program.

One difficult issue for the faculty to overcome has been to provide an ONU pharmacy education in a facility with sufficient space to appropriately accommodate a burgeoning number of academically gifted students. The "Northern Style" of teaching and learning was personal with faculty and students working together in classrooms and laboratories that promoted one-on-one relationships, which had been a focal point of the college since announcement of its founding in 1884.

By the year 2000 the college desperately needed more space and better functioning areas if it were to continue its strong commitment to sustain and protect the heritage of graduating skilled and knowledgeable pharmacists. The faculty believed a top-notch ONU pharmacy education could be provided to the present student size, but the number of students in each class and laboratory would need to be decreased. This would be best achieved by increasing the number of teaching classrooms and student laboratory areas. With the ever-increasing demand for well-prepared pharmacists, and the growing technical needs of higher education, the time had arrived for a physical expansion to the Robertson-Evans Pharmacy Building.

That expansion was first met in October, 1995, with addition of the Pierstorf Annex onto the northeast section of the building, which provided an additional 2,500 square feet of space.[13] The Hakes-Pierstorf Family Pharmacy Education Center (2006), built adjacent to and joining the southeast section

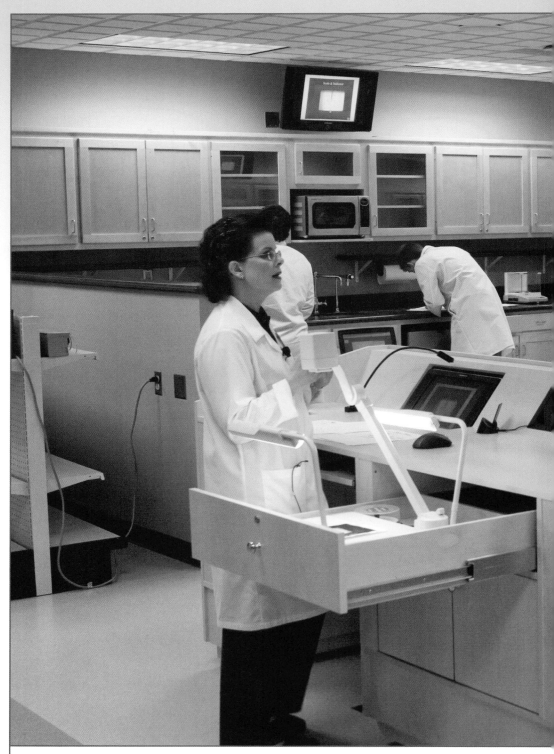

Pharmacy Skills Center.

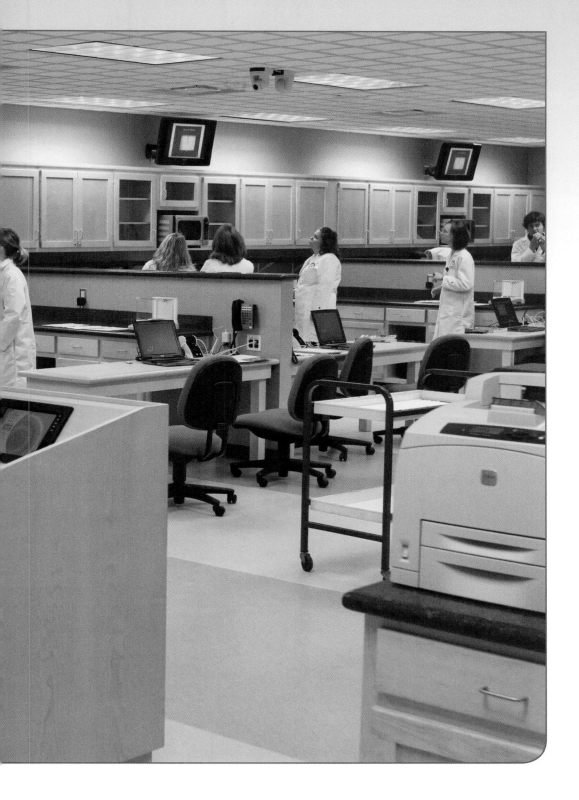

The new additon to the Robertson-Evans Pharmacy Building honors the Hakes (left) and Pierstorf (right) families.

of the building, provided an additional 17,300 square-feet to the existing pharmacy building. These additions provided the space needed for today's ONU pharmacy students to remain among the most sought-after members of their profession.[14,15] ONU graduates consistently have exceptionally high passage rates for the pharmacy licensure examination. For many years, ONU pharmacy graduates have been heavily recruited by employers, with one hundred percent of recruits securing positions.

Included in the two stories of the Hakes-Pierstorf addition were a 250-seat tiered classroom/auditorium (the largest on campus) with projection screens and smart-board technology, and four large flexible classrooms, each seating sixty persons and can be divided into two smaller meeting areas. Also included were restrooms, a lobby, and elevator access. On the second floor were eight faculty offices, eight research laboratories, a vivarium, conference areas and a student lounge. Today, the lounge serves as a focal point for numerous student-oriented events, and/or a place for students to rest a bit.

The college initiated a pilot program in February, 2010, that involved establishing a health and wellness clinic on campus. An interdisciplinary undertaking, termed the ONU HealthWise clinic, faculty and students in the disciplines of pharmacy, nursing, and exercise physiology collaborated to provide healthcare services to ONU faculty, staff, dependants, and retirees at no out-of-pocket expense to them.[16] The program included pharmacist-directed medication therapy management (MTM) and/or disease state management (DSM) along with individualized and group exercise support by ONU exercise physiologists to program enrollees. The program was initiated following enactment of the 2003 Medicare Prescription Drug Improvement and Modernization Act that encouraged the profession of pharmacy to develop non-dispensing clinical services.[17] Such a service for ONU faculty and student enrollees would, hopefully, result in healthier subjects at reduced healthcare costs to third-party providers. For example, a 2010 report showed that medical expenses were reduced by $3.27 for each dollar spent on workplace wellness programs.[18]

Because of the success of the pilot project, the program was expanded to include additional enrollees, and increased health benefits such as nutritional counseling and a pharmacist-directed preventive care clinic.[17,19] ONU HealthWise was also approved for additional funding to maintain it as a permanent program of the university.

In addition to the obvious conclusion that enrollees who participate in the program and adhere to advice given them by HeathWise staff, at least three benefits specific to pharmacy student participants were fulfilled. At the basic core is that students can see for themselves that the profession offers pharmacists opportunities to engage in a wide range of non-dispensing functions that can be performed on either a part-time or full-time basis and can be profitable. Second, the HealthWise project offers real life experience for pharmacy students in interviewing and counseling actual patients, functions that are so important in maintaining a strong clinical image that the college is promoting. Third, it affords pharmacy students valuable experience in working alongside professionals in allied health services. These collaborative engagement opportunities fit in well with the overall mission of the College of Pharmacy.

College Mission

The faculty of the Raabe College of Pharmacy has adopted the following mission. The college is committed to:

- "Preparing students to enter the practice of pharmacy with the knowledge base and skills required to provide pharmacist-delivered patient care and effectively contribute to the profession. Inherent to the fulfillment of this commitment, students will be provided with the ability to develop problem-solving and life-long learning skills which will facilitate their scholarly achievement. As an entry-level program, this commitment also includes assuring the quality of the basic science curriculum and providing a General Education program that facilitates the development of well-rounded individuals with the values necessary to serve society;

- "Contributing to the knowledge base of the practice of pharmacy, pharmacy education, and the scientific disciplines represented by its faculty. Also, the College will encourage, and provide opportunities for student participation in these endeavors; and,

- "Providing information, support and services to students, colleagues, the profession of pharmacy, other health care disciplines, and the university community at large, consistent with the expertise of its faculty. Also, the College will encourage and provide opportunities for students to perform similar services."

Leadership Changes

Dr. Sprague announced his resignation in July, 2013, after having served as dean for seven years. Dr. Tom Kier, associate dean for college operations, was then appointed interim dean. Tom served his appointment very well, but chose not to pursue a long-term deanship. A nationwide search was therefore undertaken to find a successor. Dr. Steven J. Martin was the unanimous candidate of choice and was appointed to begin July 1, 2014.

Shortly after arriving on campus, Dean Martin initiated a comprehensive strategic planning process that involved college faculty, students, and staff, which was designed to set the direction of the college for the next decade. At the time this manuscript was being prepared for printing, the planning process was underway.

Concluding Thoughts

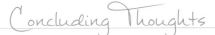

There is pleasure to be gained in casual reading about the history of an institution, but there is an even greater one in understanding the many lessons that can be learned from critically reading the facts. Dr. Anne Lippert, ONU's vice president for academic affairs, provided insightful input to motivate individuals into thinking seriously about Ohio Northern's rich history. In her opening remarks to the faculty in August, 2001, she praised the university and its colleges by quoting a passage from George Schertzer's 1962 *A Brief History of Ohio Northern University*. Schertzer wrote: "To review the history of Ohio Northern University gives cause to wonder why it ever survived as it passed from one major crisis to another. It began and flourished during the years of great need for normal schools, but it continued after the others served their narrow geographical need and died. It survived during depression and war years, when the student body used less than ten percent of the facilities at hand. It survived when there were no funds to pay the administrators and teachers—and they

Present home of the Rudolph H. Raabe College of Pharmacy. Facility includes the Robertson-Evans Pharmacy Building along with the Pierstorf Annex and the Hakes-Pierstorf Family Pharmacy Education Center.

willingly used their private funds or obtained supplemental employment. Ohio Northern has always been a great and respected institution because there has been a solid chain of great teachers employed by dedicated administrators, and all fired up with the mission of extending an education opportunity to those who would otherwise have been denied."[20]

Dr. Lippert continued her praiseworthy acclamations specific to the College of Pharmacy when later she added: "Today the pharmacy college stands out as ONU's college with, perhaps the best regional and even national reputation. The college has a strong and successful continuing education program. A few years ago college faculty members completely redid the curriculum for the doctor of pharmacy degree and established modular courses that help students synthesize knowledge in the fourth and fifth year of didactic courses. An innovative experiential program has been established. Yearly the college successfully brings in the highest number of external grants. Some faculty members are known nationally for their research and student research continues to grow and be strengthened. Graduates hold positions of importance in pharmacy associations and in the pharmacy industry. The college set up the first ONU on-line didactic programs with its non-traditional doctor of pharmacy program. The assessment of student learning is integrated into on-going course evaluations that result in changes to assist student learning. If the ONU Board of Trustees and the president of the university had not chosen to fight to keep the college, none of that would be here today."[21]

Essentially without endowment throughout most of its existence, ONU has had to rely primarily upon student tuition for its financial stability. Certainly, there were many times when a weaker institution might have closed its doors for good. At Ohio Northern, this was especially true for pharmacy and its other professional colleges. On several occasions during the particularly perilous times, the question was raised whether the College of Pharmacy should be closed and its meager resources diverted to the College of Liberal Arts. Understanding the intense passion for the institution by administrators and faculty to continue operation, knowing there would continue to be long periods of austerity, sustained the ONU College of Pharmacy and kept the mother institution moving forward.

Thanks to Dean Raabe and his faculty, especially in the 1930s and '40s, and the following deans and their faculties through the years who were more than willing to personally share the many financial hardships along the way, the college not only survived but grew stronger with each challenge. The key message is not to simply know that the institution survived, but to understand the reasons why Ohio Northern, and its College of Pharmacy, survived. That's where studying history, especially the history of ONU's College of Pharmacy, comes into play. Ohio Northern weathered the storms of its past. There will, no doubt, likely be other, perhaps even greater, periods of turbulence in the future. Let all persons who truly love this college and university rely on the many messages of survival that can be gleaned from its past.

The College of Pharmacy has maintained its original mission established in its founding years. Its emphasis has been, and continues to be, on undergraduate education and that has not changed over the years. Although the College of Pharmacy (and that of law), both offer the doctorate as their sole degree, it should be noted that those degrees are considered first-professional degrees, not graduate-level degrees. In other words, they are degrees that are required to enter into the profession today. While some may wish to think of the Pharm D degree as a graduate degree, it is not. Also, the College of Pharmacy has given no serious consideration to change its focus to offer graduate-level studies. The College of Pharmacy will continue to do what the college does best—to prepare its graduates to enter into the profession of pharmacy, and in offering their services to improve the nation's healthcare and elevate the profession's image even more.

A century ago, people coming into the corner drugstore asked "Doc" for the best "cure" for an ailment. Doc may have completed an apprenticeship with a practicing pharmacist as his sole formal education in pharmacy. Or he may have completed a one-year, or possibly two-year degree in pharmacy. Today, patients continue to put their faith in what Doc, who now holds a six-year doctoral degree, can provide in the way of expanded healthcare services. A century ago, armed with little more than a handful of somewhat effective drugs, Doc could do little more than ease discomfort. Today, Doc controls the distribution of tensof-hundreds of potent and extremely effective medicines, many of which provide absolute cure, rather than simple palliative relief of symptoms of diseases that can kill if not treated.

It has been said many times that the best way to assess an institution's future is by studying its past. During its nearly 130 years, Ohio Northern's College of Pharmacy has graduated more than 9,300 pharmacists,[22] with one in four of all pharmacists in Ohio being Ohio Northern alumni.[23] These men and women have contributed in no small way to improved healthcare delivery throughout Ohio and the nation. This has been possible because of the college's zeal for superb teaching. So long as that commitment remains at highest priority, the college can well expect to serve its constituency for another 130 years and beyond.

The Middle of a Cornfield—So What?

Earlier in this book, it was noted that ONU's College of Pharmacy may best be described as its location being in the "middle of a cornfield." While some might view this description as an attempt at "tongue-in-cheek" humor, the truth of the matter is, indeed, the college is in Ada, and Ada is in rural Hardin County, Ohio. Ada is indeed located in the middle of a cornfield—there is no doubt about that. There is corn growing to the north, east, south and west of the village. During the fall harvest season, especially, there may be nearly as many tractors on Ada's streets pulling wagons filled to overflowing with a bountiful harvest on the way to the village grain storage elevators (the tallest structures in the village, by the way, perhaps in the county) as there are automobiles. The same analogy holds for the number of pickup trucks characteristic of rural settings.

Speaking for many faculty members and staff who have devoted the prime years of their professional lives to teaching or serving ONU's pharmacy students in many ways, we believe that Ada's rural geography offers a strong allurement to student learning. The cornfields are not distracting to the educational process. In fact, Ada remains an effective oasis for Ohio Northern's College of

Pharmacy that encourages nearly uninterrupted study and reflection without the plague of numerous temptations that can readily disrupt study time, the kind of interruptions that many larger towns and cities are noted for. The rural village, with its fresh air and clear skies, bears no impediments to receiving satellite images beamed only seconds earlier from nearly any place on the planet and the college receives them clearly and without interruption. With state-of-the-art satellite and Internet capability, and other technological advancements in communication to assure delivery of any message, the Raabe College of Pharmacy at Ohio Northern University enjoys full access to the world's total academic resources. Tie all this in with a well-educated and industrious faculty that is dedicated to teaching its students can only lead to a superb learning environment. And for those who might remark that pharmacy students in such a setting are deprived of many of the benefits available to students in more metropolitan areas, this is also a false belief.

For example, Hardin County, Ohio, currently ranks fifty-third out of eighty-eight Ohio counties in overall health outcomes and seventy-third for premature death. Compared to Ohio averages, residents of the county have higher incidences of unintentional drug deaths, obesity, and cigarette smoking. They also have lower instances of recommended colonoscopies and mammograms.[24] Much of these poor health outcomes have to do with the county's rural setting, which is also part of the college's makeup and, with it, the special attention given to healthcare needs in a rural community. ONU faculty members have always believed that pharmacists are primary healthcare providers, not simply purveyors of ancillary service in the healthcare process. It is a belief shared by the U.S. Food and Drug Administration, which calls pharmacists "the most accessible healthcare providers."

As a result of the college's strong belief in the value of pharmacists and pharmacy students as providers of quality healthcare services, as well as its geographic positioning, the college is committed to serving the residents of Hardin County any way it can. One means, offered here to illustrate this, is by the college's work through a mobile health clinic to provide healthcare throughout the county. It does this through an innovative project funded by a Health Resources and Services

Administration grant. Totaling $572,973 over three years, the grant was awarded to finance a working model employing a community mobile clinic serviced by a multidisciplinary team consisting of ONU pharmacy faculty and students and interdisciplinary healthcare specialists empowered to deliver educational outreach and healthcare services to residents throughout the county.[25] The mobile clinic thus serves residents in rural Hardin County, as well as being a model for establishing similar clinics to improve healthcare to citizens of the many other rural areas throughout the state. The personal experience gained by participating pharmacy students is very real. And this example is but one of a number that could be discussed here. So to any naysayer who wishes to discredit the value of an education center located in a rural area or to hint that such an institution is by necessity second-rate to those in large metropolitan areas, let it be said that "Corn is good." In Dean Martin's words, "Being in a cornfield is definitely distinctive for us, and it makes our students different by design."

The story is told about a freshman pharmacy student who was looking for entertainment while walking alone on a downtown sidewalk in Ada early one Saturday evening shortly after arriving in town at the beginning of the school year. Approaching an older citizen of the village, the student stopped him and asked: "What can a person do in this tiny town, anyhow? The citizen straightened his posture a bit, looked the young person directly in the eyes, and answered: "Young man, you can start in this tiny town and go anywhere in the world you want to go." That's what the Rudolph H. Raabe College of Pharmacy offers—the opportunity to study hard and earn a prestigious degree that will allow its graduates to go anywhere in the world they want to go.

Throughout this book Ohio Northern University has been linked closely with the village of Ada. In fact, in early editions of the ONU catalog the statement was stated repeatedly that "Ada is a school town." That was, and remains to this day, an important element that has contributed to make the Ohio Northern University College of Pharmacy into the educational powerhouse it is. Readers are encouraged, and indeed urged, to visit the college's website (*www.onu.edu/pharmacy*) for information relative to current pharmacy news and events.

THE DEANS

Four men served as dean of the College of Pharmacy during this period: Bobby G. Bryant, Jon E. Sprague, Thomas L. Kier, and Steven J. Martin. Dean Bryant's profile is given in Chapter Ten.

Jon E. Sprague

A Hoosier by birth, Dr. Jon Eric Sprague was born in Angola, Indiana, April 1, 1965.[26] He earned his BS Pharm degree (with distinction) from Ferris State University in 1989 and PhD degree in pharmacology and toxicology from Purdue University in 1994. He served as a staff pharmacist and assistant manager in several Indiana pharmacies. He maintains an active pharmacy license in Indiana and Ohio.

Jon joined the ONU faculty as assistant professor of pharmacology in September, 1995, and was promoted to associate professor in 1998. In 2004, he left ONU to serve as professor and chairman of the Department of Biomedical Sciences and Pathobiology at Virginia Polytechnic Institute and State University. Two years later, he returned to Ohio Northern with appointment as professor of pharmacology and dean of the Raabe College of Pharmacy.

As an ONU faculty member teaching pharmacology, he was one of the college's top student advocates, one who could advocate effectively without overstepping the boundaries of his position. He was the recipient of numerous student-oriented awards, including (in part) the Panhellenic Council

Jon E. Sprague, Dean 2006–2013.

PREPARING FOR TOMORROW

239

Teachers Recognition; ONU Mortar Board "Favorite" Professor Award; Alpha Xi Delta Professor of the Month; Student-Athlete Advisor Committee Distinguished Professor; VCOM Student Professor Recognition Award; ONU Campus Outstanding Faculty Member (two times); Outstanding Professor Award for P-4 and/or P-5 classes (five times). He also received the ONU Pharmacy Alumni Chair Award. In addition, Dr. Sprague received numerous honors and awards from off-campus state and national sources.

Dr. Sprague is a prolific writer who has published numerous peer-reviewed articles and abstracts describing his research. He has also spoken many times at professional meetings around the state and nation. He holds memberships in the American Association of Colleges of Pharmacy, Society of Neuroscience, Phi Kappa Phi, Mortar Board, Council for Undergraduate Research, and the American Society for Pharmacology and Experimental Therapeutics.

Dean Sprague is married to Aimee Sprague and is the father of a son and daughter. He enjoys spending time with his family, especially pursuing outside activities. He actively makes time in his busy work schedule to relax. Relaxation includes walking the neighborhood and hiking trails with his wife. In his younger years he thought he would like to be a park ranger, especially since his grandfather was one. He also is assistant tennis coach for boys and girls at the local high school. On those rainy days when it is best to remain inside, Dean Sprague enjoys reading books that have a leadership theme. He reads and contemplates a Bible passage each day, rain or shine.

Asked how he got into academia, Dr. Sprague tells about the times while serving as staff pharmacist and a pharmacy intern would ask questions about drugs and therapy. He indicated how much he enjoyed responding to their inquisitiveness. This led to graduate school at Purdue University and a position as graduate teaching assistant, then a tutor in pharmacology and toxicology.

Dean Sprague said that he misses his active student involvement in the classroom and one day he may consider a return to the classroom teaching pharmacology or toxicology, especially topics involving drugs of abuse. He has maintained an active interest in research and also wishes to continue this pursuit.

He indicates the legacy he hopes to leave behind is that in all he did at work or at home, he wants to be remembered as an honest, hard working, loving and caring role model.

That having been said, on July 25, 2013, Dean Sprague notified his faculty that the time had come to step aside. He currently serves as director of the Ohio Attorney General's Center for the Future of the Forensic Sciences at Bowling Green State University.

Personal Reflections

One of my greatest achievements while I was dean was to offer Dr. Sprague a place on our faculty to teach pharmacology. His interview made quite an impression on the faculty, students in attendance, and me, and I knew he would continue to grow professionally as time went on. I was never to be disappointed with this thinking.

Although I had retired from ONU a couple years earlier, I was still disappointed when Jon left the college in 2004 to accept a responsible position in Virginia. But that disappointment would turn favorably when he was tapped two years later to return to ONU as the college's dean. His announcement in July, 2013, that he would be leaving the college was my second disappointment. I wish him well.

Thomas L. Kier

Thomas Lee Kier was born January 24, 1959, in Canton, Ohio, and completed grade school and high school in his hometown. He became interested in pharmacy during his junior and senior years in high school, largely due to a strong influence from his Uncle Lynn Anderson, BS Pharm '50. Lynn was a pharmacist in Canton and an ONU trustee as well. Additionally, his high school biology teacher, Becky Banks, was an ONU alumnus who fanned the fire for Tom to pursue his study in pharmacy at ONU. If that wasn't enough, Joe Banks, BS Educ '40 and BA Phys Ed '45, was ONU's recruiter in Canton. Tom says he was caught in the middle of what seemed to be a marvelous struggle, with his Uncle Lynn touting the strong points of the profession on one hand, and Becky and her father Joe, aiding Lynn in convincing Tom to pursue his dream at Ohio Northern. Tom therefore applied for admission into ONU's College of Pharmacy and was accepted into the entering freshman class in September, 1977. Tom graduated with his BS Pharm degree in May, 1982.

Throughout his career, Tom Kier has enjoyed a rich personal and professional life. While still a student, he took special notice of a classmate named Karen Hillegass who would also graduate in 1982. Karen remained a Hillegass for two years following graduation while she worked on a residency combined with a master's degree at the Ohio State University in Columbus, Ohio. She and Tom were married in 1984. That union brought forth a daughter, Erica, who is a student at Lehigh University.

Following marriage, Tom and Karen moved to Chapel Hill, North Carolina. Tom accepted a position as staff pharmacist for the University of North Carolina, while Karen pursued a specialty residency in drug information. The Kiers then headed north to Pittsburgh, Pennsylvania. There, Tom hired on as staff pharmacist at Divine Providence Hospital, while Karen accepted a position at Allegheny General Hospital.

The lure of returning to Ada burned strongly in both of them and was too great to ignore. The Kiers returned to their alma mater in 1986 with Tom accepting a position as visiting instructor to coordinate the college's externship program. Karen was hired by the college to teach in its expanding clinical pharmacy program at Lima Memorial Hospital in Lima, Ohio. The following year, Tom moved into the college's new office of pharmacy student services where he served

Thomas L. Kier, Interim Dean 2013-2014.

as its assistant director, working with Professor Lou Vottero. Along with his responsibilities for student services, Tom earned the title of assistant to the dean.

Meanwhile, Tom began working on his MA degree in college student personnel, followed by a PhD degree in higher education administration, both in the College of Education at Bowling Green State University. He completed requirements for his PhD degree in 2000. Of note is that he earned both degrees while continuing to work full time at ONU. During his period of academic study, he was promoted first to assistant dean, then associate dean of the Raabe College of Pharmacy, with rank of instructor of pharmacy. Noting the title of his PhD thesis, *"Relationships of Pre-College and Within-College Variables to Test Scores on a Pharmacy Licensure Examination"* illustrates why interim dean Thomas Kier was uniquely qualified to take on the responsibilities of his new position.

Professional memberships include the Northwestern Ohio Pharmaceutical Association, Ohio Pharmacists Association, American Pharmaceutical Association, and the American Association of Colleges of Pharmacy. Tom is a member of Ada's First Presbyterian Church, serving on the church's Session in a number of capacities. He is a member of the Ada chapter of Kiwanis International.

The Kiers make their home in Ada.

Asked what has kept him in Ada for the past nearly three decades, Tom said, without hesitation, that it has been because of ONU's basic philosophy that Dr. Lehr built the institution upon years ago. "I feel like I'm part of a family, the ONU family. Karen and I both feel so fortunate to be able to interact with our students at an institution that truly cares for its clientele."

Tom is a strong proponent of the direction the college and profession are headed. He envisions opportunities continuing to expand within pharmacy and strongly believes Northern's graduates will be well qualified to assume any future role. Tom said that his aspiration as interim dean was always to nurture the passion of students and faculty for the profession.

When not busy at work, Tom is likely to be reading from a variety of books or published articles. "I'm an eclectic reader," he says. "I read anything that's of interest to me at the moment. Sometimes these may be professional or academic books or articles, other times they may be for my spiritual enrichment." Other times, more than likely he'll be found at The Jake (Progressive Field) rooting his favorite team, the Cleveland Indians, on to victory.

Personal Reflections

I was happy to learn that Dr. Tom Kier was selected to serve the college as interim dean following Dean Jon Sprague's service. I felt highly confident that he would continue to represent the college well and very capably lead it into the future. Tom repeatedly stated that he was never a candidate for the deanship and looked forward to the appointment of the new dean.

My earliest solid remembrance of Tom was during academic year 1981–82. He was enrolled in my toxicology class in preparation for his commencement in May, 1982, when he would receive his BS Pharm degree. I also recall him for his service at that time to Ada's First Presbyterian Church, which included a strong youth leadership role and other dedicated service. That work, by the way, continues through today.

Counting his years as a student, Tom and I overlapped twenty-one years in the college, sixteen as colleagues. In all that time, I recall him as a solid role model for other faculty members to emulate. His mood was always jovial and non-criticizing of others. His attention to detail on all projects was commendable. His service and continuing friendship as associate dean during my tenure as dean made my job a lot easier and helped keep me sane during "those times…" and for that I am forever grateful.

Steven J. Martin

A native of Lansing, Michigan, from early age Steve worked in his father's pharmacy, first sweeping the floor, then helping to restock shelves. He eventually rose to the level of clerk. Realizing he enjoyed his work, and watching his father's contentment with his profession and the fact that his father knew every pharmacy patient personally, Steve began to think that pharmacy would be an exciting career path for himself. So he entered Ferris State University where he earned his BS Pharm degree in December, 1983. During his college years, he interned at his father's pharmacy and a local hospital. Following graduation, he established his practice in Lansing in a number of independent and chain pharmacies.

Over the years, Steve investigated a number of professional roles. Wishing to expand his horizons beyond community practice, Steve moved to Dallas, Texas, and worked for Baylor University Medical Center. With his parents facing advancing age and ill health, he returned home to help look after them.

Knowing that advanced education was a necessity for his movement forward professionally, Steve returned to Ferris State University where he earned his Doctor of Pharmacy degree with high distinction in 1992. He also completed post-doctoral fellowship training in critical care and infectious disease pharmacotherapy at the University of Illinois at Chicago.

Steve and his wife, Karen, who is also a pharmacist, decided to investigate working and living opportunities in Toledo in 1997 mainly because it was close to home. They liked what they found and moved there in the summer. Steve accepted a faculty position at the University of Toledo's College of Pharmacy and Pharmaceutical Sciences where he earned the title of professor, and was appointed chairman of the Department of Pharmacy Practice, a post he held since 2004. He was also co-director of UT's infectious disease research laboratory. He served several professional organizations, most consistently the Society of Critical Care Medicine. Steve is a board-certified pharmacotherapy specialist with added qualifications in infectious diseases.

Steven J. Martin, Dean 2014 to present.

He has published numerous book chapters, research papers, and critical reviews on infections and critical illness in a variety of peer-reviewed publications. He recently served as editor of the *Injectable Drug Reference*, published by the Society of Critical Care Medicine.

Steve and Karen Martin have four children. When not working, Steve reports that most of his free time is spent with his family. He runs most mornings and swims daily when weather permits. He confesses to not being good at golf but enjoys the challenges of the game. He also enjoys music and good wine. Along with his family, Steve has traveled to nearly all states, Europe, South America, and throughout the Caribbean. With several members of his church, he traveled on a pilgrimage to the Holy Land in 2013.

Steve is an avid reader, having read nearly daily for most of his life. He regularly enjoys mysteries and other enjoyable books. He also reads to expand his mind. A few favorite books include *David and Goliath* (Gladwell), *Good to Great* (Collins), *The 7 Habits of Highly Effective People* (Covey), *Mere Christianity* (Lewis), *The Divine Comedy* (Dante), *The Old Man and the Sea* (Hemingway), and the *Holy Bible*.

A splendid teacher, scholar, mentor, administrator, and devoted husband and father, Dr. Steve Martin comes to ONU with eighteen years experience in higher education. He recognizes the Raabe College of Pharmacy as one of the country's premier institutions for pharmacist training. He writes that "Our alumni are serving in leadership positions across the profession, and our faculty and staff are well known and well respected in the academy. It is my privilege, and great honor, to serve as the dean during what I expect will be a defining moment for the profession of pharmacy and for our college."

EPILOGUE
Where to Now?

There are many reasons why an individual may wish to write a book. Certainly for this author, one of the things he looked forward to as each chapter neared completion and the next one was developing, was that he would soon be able to express some of his rambling thoughts about pharmacists and the profession he loves most—pharmacy, and the college he most highly reveres—the Rudolph H. Raabe College of Pharmacy.

Pharmacists and Pharmacy Practice

Those who have read the final several chapters of this book may question whether today's community pharmacists are indeed practicing at a higher level and delivering the clinical services described in the text. Admittedly, some are still holding back. But a great many have changed their practice habits, and as new pharmacists are added each year to the pool to inspire those already in practice, the overall climate is changing for the better. For those who have not yet chosen to do so, change is definitely on its way. For example, who would have believed a decade or two ago that pharmacists would ever be encouraged to provide immunizations as part of their professional practice, and even be legally empowered to do so. A friend recently described a visit to his physician's office.[1] Posted in the office for all to see was a sign announcing that the doctor no longer administers flu vaccine immunizations. Instead, patients were encouraged to contact their local pharmacists for this service. Or, who would have imagined that pharmacists might practice in a setting where they had the authority to modify patients' medication directions, dosage, or even the drug of choice to treat specific pathologies. Such settings already exist. Yes, change, exciting change, is on its way and it's all for the better. But remember, real change takes time.

Some pharmacists may continue practicing in settings removed from the public they serve. While waiting at the counter, all a patient may see is the top of the pharmacist's head while he or she fills the prescription a clerk has brought back. Since that same clerk may deliver the finished prescription along with verbal comments for the patient to be sure to read the information sheet stapled to a paper bag that holds the completed prescription, the patient may seldom encounter more than an acknowledgment in the form of a brief nod of the pharmacist's head.

In such settings, the extent of the pharmacist's interaction with patients may be limited because of a lack of sufficient personnel to serve the clientele. Or, the pharmacist's job description all but outright forbids extensive patient interaction. Perhaps the management disapproves of an appropriate one-on-one relationship between pharmacist and patient because of belief that such relationships will get in the way of balancing the pharmacy's budget.

Bear in mind that there is significant change ongoing in this arena. Some

Marker in front of the Robertson-Evans Pharmacy Building presented in memory of Robert B Hakes, BS Pharm, 1955 by his parents Dr. and Mrs. Vern Hakes (PhC, 1933; ScD, 1976). Symbol on top depicts the Rho Chi pharmacy honor society.

pharmacy employers now are placing pharmacists in front of the counter so that patients have easier access to them. Technicians then fill the prescriptions while pharmacists check them for accuracy, then dispense them directly to the patient and engage the patient in meaningful conversation and counseling. This novel arrangement, while still in its formative stage, could very well become the norm for the next generation of pharmacists. Change, real change, while slow to occur, is indeed on its way.

There are many other issues that can impair a strong pharmacist/patient relationship. Perhaps some are characteristic to pharmacists themselves. For example, some pharmacists may prefer to continue their practice in the manner they are most accustomed to, their actions perhaps developed over many years. These pharmacists may not wish to be a part of the change in behavior because of their own introverted personalities or other personal reasons. Others may not wish to change because they feel inadequate to practice at a higher level, perhaps due to their own educational experience from years, including decades before that did not emphasize the new clinical approach to pharmacy practice. Many pharmacists in practice today were taught that counseling patients on their medication should be undertaken, if at all, very cautiously. Counseling was a function best left to physicians. All the continuing professional education in the world, these pharmacists surmise, cannot and will not help them now. It's reminiscent of the old adage "You can lead a horse to water…" routine.

One point that should not be dismissed is that there will always be a need for pharmacists to manage drug product distribution in certain settings where direct contact with patients is not expected and, indeed, is unnecessary much of the time. These may include professional practice in hospitals and certain other institutional settings that exist nearly everywhere in the country.

For non-pharmacist readers of this book who may still belittle today's level of pharmacy practice and believe they see little change from the past, please give the profession time to adapt. The die has been cast and now there is no going back. Pharmacy practice is no longer at the crossroads as described in an earlier chapter. The profession has stepped out onto the path that leads to the future and now cannot, and will not, return to those oft-mentioned pathways that lead to little more than prolonging the status quo.

The College Faculty

In this book, much talk has been given to professional curricula, buildings, equipment, student's antics, and the college's deans, but not much discussion has been extended to the many reputable, honorable, and highly dedicated teachers who, throughout the past 130 years, faithfully and often sacrificially served the College of Pharmacy. The favorable reputation of most colleges and universities around the world can be attributed to the popularity of their great teachers who truly cared about the welfare of their students. Ohio Northern is one of those institutions that has the well-earned reputation of having been blessed with many great teachers. Its College of Pharmacy has had its share of great teachers assigned to the college, along with the added benefit of many equally great ones to teach courses offered outside of the pharmacy college as such that are basic to its students acquiring a well-rounded education in pharmacy. The pharmacy curriculum reaches into many areas of study, and therefore depends largely on a liberal arts faculty for instruction in the basic sciences, chemistry, physics, biology, physiology, and mathematics. A solid pharmacy education also depends on the same faculties for instruction in English, history, physical education, the social sciences, and other areas.

Appendix 9 lists many of the full-time faculty in the College of Pharmacy and includes selected others in the College of Liberal Arts (now, the College of Arts and Sciences) spanning the years 1885 through 1959. Appendix 10 continues the list of faculty beginning with academic year 1960–61, and Appendix 11 lists current faculty for academic year 2015–16. Both Appendix 10 and 11 contain the names of faculty members within the College of Pharmacy and not those in the other colleges. The list of memorable faculty outside the College of Pharmacy itself is extensive and their extraordinary service to pharmacy students is hereby acknowledged.

In reporting the names of teachers from along the way, one runs the risk of omitting someone. My sincere apology is extended if that has happened.

Area Pharmacies

As expected, Ada's pharmacists and pharmacies have had a strong relationship with the college. The first lecturer/dean (principal) of the new ONU pharmacy program was an Ada pharmacist who practiced full time in one of the village's drugstores. Other local pharmacists along the way have sacrificially given of their time and talents to provide teaching skills when needed. The same courtesies were also extended from the pharmacies themselves. The school has long depended upon area pharmacies as sites for extensive externship experience. Moreover, many of the deans and faculty members worked in one or more of Ada's or its surrounding area's pharmacies at night, weekends, and/or holidays to not only serve the public, but also to hone their own professional skills.

To acquire a better understanding of the state of pharmacy practice over the years it might be helpful to read Appendix 12—*History of Drug Stores in Ada*. The Appendix consists of a term paper authored by Mr. Fred Armeni, BS Pharm '77 to fulfill a requirement for his history of pharmacy class. The paper was researched and written in 1976; since that time, significant change has occurred in the Ada pharmacy scene. Both Peper's Drug Store and Gardner's Drug Store have since closed their doors forever. Pharmaceutical service to the village is now provided by a modern pharmacy that is part of a national chain. While not able to purvey the charm reminiscent of Gardner's and Peper's, the newer enterprise does capably serve the needs of citizens of Ada and surrounding communities. For those who miss the organoleptic senses of sight and fragrance of a more traditional corner drugstore suggestive of days gone by, a few still remain but their number is diminishing. An important point to ponder is that it is not the site *per se* that determines the quality of pharmaceutical service, but rather, the quality of the practitioners within the site that determines it.

College alumni and others who have not been on campus for a decade or so are amazed when they view the extent of campus development. What they remember as an open field once inhabited by pheasants, rabbits, and other small game is now a well tailored West Campus with its glistening new buildings, fraternity houses, residence halls, and sports facilities encircling an attractive mall (Appendix 13).

Yes, it's easy to criticize ONU for its seemingly slow development and the manner it responded to many problems encountered along the way. To do that, though, would be akin to comparing its activity in former years based on accomplishments and features of today, sort of like the proverbial comparison of apples to oranges. To consider Ohio Northern University's College of Pharmacy during earlier times, one should do so from the perspective of what was generally available to students and expected in those days, in other words, what the norm was at the time of comparison, rather than comparing the early university with today's standards that include all of our modern technological advancements, and so forth. People at all levels in those earlier days of the university generally looked favorably at the institution and its work.

One can truly appreciate the college all the more by reading about the many hardships encountered in the past and how it overcame them. The title of this work implies that the college's story is "remarkable." So, what's remarkable, anyhow? The fact that the College of Pharmacy is still in existence 130 years after its founding and today is a major player in providing pharmacy education statewide and is nationally known and respected is what is remarkable. To put all this in perspective, ONU's College of Pharmacy currently enrolls the largest number of students of any College of Pharmacy in the state. Approximately one-fourth of all practicing pharmacists in Ohio at present are ONU alumni. All that and much more is what makes for a remarkable story.

The college has grown from an initial ten-week course in pharmacy that was offered by a single pharmacist/teacher who taught the professional courses to its current academic year 2015–16 in-house full-time faculty of thirty-four individuals. Then, there is the nearly equal number of off-campus shared faculty who provide clinical instruction. Along with these are hundreds of preceptors around the region who are committed to offer ONU's students practical education solely because they believe in the institution's mission. In the early days operating funds were so tight that faculty members supplied their personal equipment to teach their courses. Until recently, there was no endowment to speak of and student tuition was so low that the college eventually lost its accreditation partly because it couldn't afford to provide needed equipment and facilities, or pay decent salaries to attract additional faculty needed to accommodate rigid accreditation standards. Ohio Northern University was truly "a poor man's school." Several times the question was poised whether the College of Pharmacy should be disbanded and its meager funds transferred to the College of Liberal Arts, to strengthen it and the institution in general. Each time the answer was a resounding affirmation to keep it open. The college's history is a remarkable story, indeed.

A Final Plea

Writing in the journal *Pharmacy in History*, historian Dr. Robert Buerki addressed an ongoing problem in recording historical events for future generations and offered some excellent advice for those who wish to preserve historical accuracy of any institution or event: "The...challenge facing today's historians is the ephemeral [transitory] nature of our records and communications. We talk over the telephone, e-mail our friends and colleagues, text, and twitter without making a permanent record. These informal communications have replaced the handwritten or typed letters or notes of a simpler age many of us can still remember, sheets or scraps of brittle paper that can make history come alive. Moreover, our electronic records are subject to the relentless pace of software and hardware updates. Think of WordPerfect 5.0 and the five-and-a-quarter-inch floppy disc: who will be able to access these things on whatever outmoded machines still exist ten years from now, let alone fifty years from now? I hope I have convinced you that we can no longer afford to wait twenty-five years to commemorate the introduction of a new class of drugs, fifty years to reflect upon a single piece of federal legislation, or a hundred years to celebrate the founding of a professional association, given the fast-moving pace of American pharmacy today; we must take our doses of history in more manageable bites of five to ten years, a homeopathic approach to history, if you will."[2]

ABOUT THE AUTHOR

THOMAS ALVIN GOSSEL, BS Pharm, MS, PhD, proudly served his pharmacy profession for more than fifty years as a community pharmacist and manager, educator, college administrator, and consultant. He continues that service as an author of educational material.

Tom completed the requirements for licensure as a pharmacist following graduation from Ohio Northern University's College of Pharmacy in 1963. After practicing community pharmacy fulltime for five years in Lancaster, Ohio, he pursued graduate study at Purdue University where he received his MS degree in 1970 and PhD degree in 1972, both degrees earned in Pharmacology/Toxicology. He joined the Ohio Northern University faculty in 1972.

He presently holds the title Professor of Pharmacology, Emeritus at Ohio Northern University's College of Pharmacy, having progressed through the academic ranks beginning as Assistant Professor. Over the years, Tom served the college as Chairman of the Department of Pharmacology and Biomedical Sciences, Chairman of the Department of Clinical Pharmacy, and associate dean. He was appointed acting dean of the ONU College of Pharmacy from 1993–1994, and dean from 1994–1999. Following his deanship, Tom returned to the college faculty for three years before retiring in 2002.

To date, Tom has presented 1,327 seminars, lectures, or workshops to pharmacists, nurses, physicians, dentists, and other health professionals in 47 states, and in Jamaica, Switzerland, and most recently, while cruising the Mediterranean somewhere off the coast of Italy! He maintained a monthly column on OTC drugs in *US Pharmacist* for eighteen years. He has authored or co-authored more than 730 articles for pharmacists that have been published in a variety of professional journals. He has also written three book chapters and six books. His most recent volume, *Principles of Clinical Toxicology*, is a textbook for students of pharmacy and other biomedical sciences. He continues to be a regular contributor to the pharmacy literature.

Tom Gossel was twice the recipient of ONU's Most Professional Professor Award, the Mortar Board Favorite Professor Award, the APhA-ASP Professional Service Award, the ONU Outstanding Alumnus Award, and the National Association of Boards of Pharmacy Distinguished Service Award, among others. He was appointed to the ONU Alumni Endowed Chair in Pharmacy. From the Ohio Pharmacist Association, he received Lifetime Membership for Outstanding Contributions to the Profession and to the Association. Tom was honored by his high school alma mater with induction into the Lancaster (Ohio) High School's Distinguished Alumni Hall of Fame. He became the 30th recipient of this award since its inception. Most recently, he was designated a Distinguished Alumnus by the ONU College of Pharmacy.

Tom is a firm believer in God's omnipotence, omnipresence, and omniscience, and that He is actively working his master plan for his world. Tom devotes considerable time and energy to serving Him. He is an ordained elder in the Ada First Presbyterian Church where he serves on the church Session and is active in its outreach ministries including serving as treasurer of the Ada Food Pantry, one of the church's ministries. Additionally, Tom served the Dola (Ohio) Presbyterian Church as its lay pastor for fourteen and a half years.

Since retirement in 2002, the majority of Tom's days are spent at his desk working on a number of personal and professional projects that include studying and more writing. One of his most enjoyable projects of recent note was to compile an in-depth history of ONU's College of Pharmacy. He is an avid reader who devours historical biographies, and stories and lessons with Christian-based themes. Tom also enjoys powering up all the woodworking tools he purchased over the past half-century, and with them making considerable noise and spewing sawdust galore into the environment!

Tom and his wife Phyllis continue by choice to call Ada their home. Here, they celebrated their golden wedding anniversary and are now enjoying their fifty-third year of marriage. They are greatly blessed with two daughters, a son, and seven grandchildren, all of whom are the delights of their lives.

—TAG, 8/5/15

APPENDIX 1
Ohio Colleges and Programs of Pharmacy*

ADA

Ohio Normal University 1885–1903
    Name changed to Ohio Northern
    University 1903–present

BEREA

Baldwin University 1865–1876 (discontinued)

CEDARVILLE

Cedarville University 2010–present

CINCINNATI

Cincinnati College of Pharmacy 1850–1954
    Merged with the University of Cincinnati
    1954–present
Queen City College of Pharmacy 1912–1920
    Successor to the National
    Normal University
    Merged with the Cincinnati College of
    Pharmacy in 1920

CLEVELAND

Cleveland College of Pharmacy 1882–1917
    Merged with Western Reserve University
    1917–1949 (discontinued)

COLUMBUS

Ohio State University 1882–present
Ohio Medical University 1892–1907
    (discontinued with the merger with
    Starling-Ohio Medical College)

Ohio Institute of Pharmacy 1896–1914
    (discontinued) A correspondence
    program only

FINDLAY

University of Findlay 2006–present

LEBANON

National Normal University 1886–1904
    Classes never held in Lebanon but
    always in Cincinnati

ROOTSTOWN

Northeast Ohio Medical University
    2007–present

SCIO

Scio College 1887–1908
    Merged with the Pittsburgh College of
    Pharmacy 1908–1948
    Merged with the University of
    Pittsburgh 1948–present

TOLEDO

University of Toledo 1904–present

*Dennis B. Worthen, Ph.D.,
Winkle College of Pharmacy,
University of Cincinnati.
Personal communication. August, 2015.*

APPENDIX 2

Diplomas Issued by ONU's Department/College of Pharmacy

Year	Male	Female	Total	Year	Male	Female	Total
1887	6	0	6	1930	51	0	51
1888	2	0	2	1931	52	2	54
1889	6	0	6	1932	36	3	39
1890	11	0	11	1933	21	2	23
1891	31	0	31	1934	33	0	33
1892	46	1	47	1935	16	0	16
1893	67	2	69	1936	15	0	15
1894	78	1	79	1937	9	0	9
1895	55	3	58	1938	15	4	19
1896	68	1	69	1939	15	4	15
1897	62	4	66	1940	22	0	22
1898	80	0	80	1941	22	2	24
1899	76	0	76	1942	24	4	28
1900	75	0	75	1943	17	1	18
1901	91	4	95	1944	4	2	6
1902	84	4	88	1945	3	2	5
1903	73	0	73	1946	5	0	5
1904	70	3	73	1947	12	1	13
1905	90	4	94	1948	24	2	26
1906	26	1	27	1949	51	9	60
1907	15	0	15	1950	71	7	78
1908	14	0	14	1951	61	9	70
1909	16	0	16	1952	57	10	67
1910	33	1	34	1953	78	8	86
1911	30	0	30	1954	67	4	71
1912	27	2	29	1955	65	4	69
1913	21	0	21	1956	44	7	51
1914	33	0	33	1957	62	11	73
1915	32	0	32	1958	60	5	65
1916	33	1	34	1959	63	8	71
1917	57	0	57	1960	68	9	77
1918	15	2	17	1961	78	8	86
1919	9	1	10	1962	61	8	69
1920	21	3	24	1963	69	17	86
1921	25	4	29	1964	22	1	23
1922	25	1	26	1965	37	10	47
1923	39	1	40	1966	28	7	35
1924	53	2	55	1967	34	4	38
1925	55	0	55	1968	10	5	15
1926	72	1	73	1969	30	2	32
1927	46	0	46	1970	30	8	38
1928	38	2	40	1971	44	14	58
1929	59	2	61	1972	48	10	58

Year	Male	Female	Total
1973	60	25	85
1974	75	39	114
1975	107	66	173
1976	73	39	112
1977	86	51	137
1978	80	57	137
1979	62	58	120
1980	81	50	131
1981	69	65	134
1982	78	79	157
1983	48	69	117
1984	48	70	118
1985	35	57	92
1986	39	43	82
1987	42	53	95
1988	40	63	103
1989	52	64	116
1990	47	61	108
1991	33	87	120
1992	45	56	101
1993	40	76	116
1994	59	83	142
1995	56	79	135
1996	68	85	153
1997	55	93	148
1998	55	92	147
1999	56	85	141
2000	31	87	118
2001	59	101	160
2002	42	82	124
2003	57	93	150
2004	31	72	103
2005	39	78	117
2006	39	77	116
2007	53	108	161
2008	76	107	183
2009	66	98	164
2010	59	90	149
2011	64	103	167
2012	62	92	154
2013	64	92	156
2014	70	98	168
2015	48	99	147

* Information in this appendix was obtained from a report by the alumni secretary in 1932, summary reports in the files of the registrar's office, copies of commencement programs and from the alumni office for years 1940 to 1949. Absolute accuracy cannot be assured, especially for the earlier years. Some errors have been discovered in information and corrections made from source documents. Where lists of names were used it was necessary to rely upon the name to identify gender and such classifications may not be absolute. It should also be understood that graduates in the early years included those who completed programs of short duration. Also, numbers in the early years may represent certificates instead of diplomas.

APPENDIX 3
ONU College of Pharmacy Degree Programs, 1926–1927[*]

Degree: Pharmaceutical Graduate

Only the fourth, fifth, and sixth quarters of this course will be offered during the session of 1926–27. Those who matriculated in this course prior to or during the school year of 1924–25 and who will have the first three quarters or its equivalent satisfactorily completed may enter on September 6, 1926, as candidates for graduation in June 1927.

YEAR TWO							
Term One		Term Two		Term Three			
Pharmacognosy	5	Pharmacognosy	5	Materia Medica		2.5	
Chemistry, Organic	5	Chemistry, Organic	5	Toxicology		2.5	
Pharmacy 2 (or)	5	Pharmacy 3	5	Chemistry, Organic or Quant Analysis		5	
Pharmacy N.F.	5	*Total*	15				
Total	15			Pharmacy 4		5	
				Total		15	

At least 1,728 clock-hours are required to complete this course, 648 in lectures and recitations, and 1,080 clock-hours in laboratory.

Degree: Pharmaceutical Chemist

YEAR ONE					
Term One		Term Two		Term Three	
Physiology	5	Materia Medica	1	Pharmaceutical Botany	5
Chemistry	5	Posology	1	Chemistry	5
Pharm. Arithmetic	5	Pharmaceutical Latin	3	Pharmacy 1 or 8	5
Pharm Technique	2	Chemistry	5	*Total*	15
Total	17	Pharmaceutical Botany	5		
		Total	15		

YEAR TWO					
Term One		Term Two		Term Three	
Pharmacognosy	5	Pharmacognosy	5	Materia Medica	2.5
Quant Analysis	5	Quant Analysis	5	Toxicology	2.5
Pharmacy 2 or 8	5	Pharmacy 3 or 9	5	Pharmacy 4	5
Total	15	*Total*	15	Quant Analysis	5
				Total	15

YEAR THREE					
Term One		Term Two		Term Three	
Materia Medica	5	Materia Medica	5	Bacteriology	5
Chemistry, Organic	5	Chemistry, Organic	5	Chemistry, Organic	5
Pharmacy 5	5	Pharmacy 6	5	Pharmacy 7 or Elective	5
Total	15	*Total*	15	*Total*	15

At least 2,738 clock-hours are required to complete this course, 888 clock-hours in lectures and recitations and 1,850 clock-hours in laboratory.

Degree: Bachelor of Science in Pharmacy

YEAR ONE					
Term One		Term Two		Term Three	
Zoology	3	Zoology	3	Zoology	3
Physics	4	Physics	4	Physics	4
Chemistry	4	Chemistry	4	Chemistry	4
German or French	5	German or French	5	German or French	5
Total	16	*Total*	16	*Total*	16

YEAR TWO					
Term One		Term Two		Term Three	
Physiology	5	Materia Medica	1	Pharmaceutical Botany	5
Pharmacy Arithmetic	5	Pharmaceutical Latin	3	Quant Chemistry	5
Quant Chemistry	5	Quant Chemistry	5	Pharmacy 1 or 8	5
Pharm Technique	2	Posology	1	*Total*	15
Total	17	*Total*	10		

YEAR THREE					
Term One		Term Two		Term Three	
Pharmacognosy	5	Pharmacognosy	5	Materia Medica	5
Chemistry, Organic	5	Chemistry, Organic	5	Chemistry, Organic	5
Pharmacy 2 or 9	5	Pharmacy 3	5	Pharmacy 4	5
Total	15	*Total*	15	*Total*	15

YEAR FOUR					
Term One		Term Two		Term Three	
Materia Medica	5	Materia Medica	2.5	Bacteriology	5
Elective Chemistry	5	Elective Chemistry	5	Elective Chemistry	5
Pharmacy 5	5	Pharmacy 6	5	Pharmacy 7	5
Total	15	Toxicology	2.5	*Total*	15
		Total	15		

At least 3,350 clock-hours are required to complete this course, 1,248 clock-hours in lectures and recitations and 2,102 clock-hours in laboratory.

*Core curricula. Additional coursework may be taken.

APPENDIX 4
Degrees Conferred vs. Enrollment, 1930—1945

Year	Total College Enrollment	DEGREE			Total Degrees
		Ph.G.	Ph.C.	B.S.	
1930	184		47	4	51
1931	139	1	48	5	54
1932	111		33	5	38
1933	75		21	2	23
1934	72		26	7	33
1935	58		12	4	16
1936	63			15	15
1937	70			11	11
1938		95		19	19
1939		105		19*	19
1940		100		24#	24
1941		97		24±	24
1942		86		27	27
1943§				18	18
1944§				3	3
1945§				5	5

*Four degrees conferred at end of summer term

#Two degrees conferred at end of summer term

±Five degrees conferred at end of summer term

§Enrollment data not available

Note: The number of degrees granted each year may differ from numbers shown in Appendix 1 due to the timing of their conferring, i.e., academic year versus calendar year.

APPENDIX 5

College of Pharmacy Curricula, 4-year and 5-year Programs
Four-Year Program (1959)*

YEAR ONE					
Term One		Term Two		Term Three	
Physical Education	1	Physical Education	1	Physical Education	1
English	3	English	3	English	3
Social Science	3	Social Science	3	Social Science	3
Mathematics	3	Mathematics	3	Mathematics	3
Biology	4	Biology	4	Biology	4
Chemistry	4	Chemistry	4	Chemistry	5
Total	18	*Total*	18	*Total*	19

YEAR TWO					
Term One		Term Two		Term Three	
Physical Education	1	Physical Education	1	Physical Education	1
Chemistry, Organic	4	Chemistry, Organic	4	Chemistry, Organic	4
Pharmacognosy	4	Pharmacognosy	4	Pharmacognosy	4
Accounting	3	Pharmacy Arithmetic	3	Pharmacy Introduction	4
Physics	4	Physics	4	First Aid	3
Philosophy	3	Philosophy	3	Philosophy	3
Total	19	*Total*	19	*Total*	19

YEAR THREE					
Term One		Term Two		Term Three	
Pharmacy Preparations	4	Pharmacy Preparations	4	Pharmacy History	3
Pharm Chemistry	4	Pharm Chemistry	4	Pharm Chemistry	4
Physiology	4	Physiology	4	Pharm Administration	3
Bacteriology	4	Bacteriology	4	Public Speaking	3
Total	16	*Total*	16	Elective	3
				Total	16

YEAR FOUR					
Term One		Term Two		Term Three	
Prescription Practice	4	Prescription Practice	4	Prescription Practice	4
Pharmacology	5	Pharmacology	5	Pharmacology	5
Pharm Chemistry	5	Pharm Chemistry	5	Pharm Chemistry	5
Pharm Administration	3	Pharm Administration	3	Advanced Survey	3
Elective	2 or 3	Elective	2 or 3	Elective	2 or 3
Total	19 or 20	*Total*	19 or 20	*Total*	19 or 20

*Core curriculum. Additional coursework may be taken; total hours required for graduation are 212.

APPENDIX 5 *continued*

Five-Year Program (1960)*

YEAR ONE						
Term One		Term Two		Term Three	
Physical Education	1	Physical Education	1	Physical Education	1
English	3	English	3	English	3
Mathematics	3	Mathematics	3	Mathematics	3
Chemistry	4	Chemistry	4	Chemistry	5
Social Studies	3	Social Studies	3	Social Studies	3
Pharmacy Orientation	1	Pharmacy Orientation	1	*Total*	15
Total	15	*Total*	15		

YEAR TWO						
Term One		Term Two		Term Three	
Physical Education	1	Physical Education	1	Physical Education	1
Chemistry, Organic	4	Chemistry, Organic	4	Chemistry, Organic	4
Physics	4	Physics	4	Physics	4
Biology	4	Biology	4	Philosophy or Ethics	3
Philosophy	3	Philosophy or Logic	3	*Total*	12
Total	16	*Total*	16		

YEAR THREE						
Term One		Term Two		Term Three	
Pharmacognosy	5	Pharmacognosy	5	Pharmacognosy	5
Pharm Chemistry	4	Pharm Chemistry	4	Pharm Chemistry	4
Accounting	3	Pharmacy Arithmetic	3	Pharmacy Introduction	4
Elective	3 or 4	First Aid	3	Speech	3
Total	15 or 16	*Total*	15	*Total*	16

YEAR FOUR						
Term One		Term Two		Term Three	
Pharm Preparations	4	Pharm Preparations	4	Pharm Preparations	3
Biochemistry	2	Biochemistry	2	Biochemistry	2
Physiology	4	Physiology	4	Physiology	4
Bacteriology	4	Bacteriology	4	Bacteriology	4
Pharm Administration or Elective	2 or 3	Pharm Administration or Elective	2 or 3	Pharm Administration or Elective	3
Total	16 or 17	*Total*	16 or 17	*Total*	16

YEAR FIVE						
Term One		Term Two		Term Three	
Prescription Practice	4	Prescription Practice	4	Prescription Practice	4
Pharmacology	5	Pharmacology	5	Pharmacology	5
Pharm Chemistry	4	Pharm Chemistry	4	Pharm Chemistry	4
Elective	3	Elective	3	Advanced Survey	3
Total	16	*Total*	16	*Total*	16

*Core curriculum. Additional coursework may be taken; total hours required for graduation are 255.

APPENDIX 6
Ohio State Board of Pharmacy Resolution
June 7, 1965

RESOLUTION:

WHEREAS, the Administration and the Board of Trustees of Ohio Northern University have clearly and expressly demonstrated their determination to take any and all steps necessary to bring the Ohio Northern University College of Pharmacy to the status of an outstanding college, and

WHEREAS, the Ohio Northern University College of Pharmacy is presently engaged in a comprehensive program of improvement including finance, facilities and faculty, and

WHEREAS, the Ohio Northern University College of Pharmacy provides a useful and necessary academic service to the pharmacy student candidates, the pharmacists, the profession and the citizens of Ohio, and

WHEREAS, the Ohio Northern University College of Pharmacy program projects a progressive and increasingly important future for the college, and

WHEREAS, the Ohio Northern University has requested the Board of Pharmacy to reconsider the College of Pharmacy for recognition and approval,

THEREFORE BE IT RESOLVED, the Ohio Pharmacy Board reaffirms its previous recognition and approval of the Ohio Northern University College of Pharmacy.

APPENDIX 7

College of Pharmacy Curriculum, 1972

YEAR ONE							
Term One		**Term Two**		**Term Three**	
English 100	3	English 101	3	English 102	3
Mathematics 147	3	Mathematics 148	3	Mathematics 142	3
Chemistry 171	4	Chemistry 172	3	Chemistry 173	5
Biology 100	4	Biology 112	4	Biology 113	4
Pharmacy 101	1*	Pharmacy 102	1*	Pharmacy 103	1*
Physical Educ.	1*	Physical Educ.	1*	Physical Educ.	1*
Total	16	*Total*	15	*Total*	17

YEAR TWO							
Term One		**Term Two**		**Term Three**	
Chemistry 231	4	Chemistry 232	4	Chemistry 233	4
Economics 100	3	Philosophy 100	3	Religion 105	3
Electives	8	Electives	8	Pharmacy 211	4
Total	15	*Total*	15	Electives	4
				Total	15

YEAR THREE							
Term One		**Term Two**		**Term Three**	
Pharmacognosy 321	4	Pharmacy 311	4	Pharmacy 312	4
Physiology 331	4	Physiology 332	4	Physiology 333	4
Biochemistry 341	3	Biochemistry 342	3	Electives	7
Electives	4	Electives	4	*Total*	15
Total	15	*Total*	15		

YEAR FOUR							
Term One		**Term Two**		**Term Three**	
Pharmacy 333	4	Pharmacy 431	4	Pharmacy 421	4
Pharmacology 411	4	Pharmacology 412	4	Pharmacology 413	4
Microbiology 361	4	Microbiology 362	4	Pharmacology 453	3
Electives	4	Electives	3	Pharmacognosy 433	3
Total	16	*Total*	15	Electives	3
				Total	17

YEAR FIVE							
Term One		**Term Two**		**Term Three**	
Pharmacy 501	4	Pharmacy 502	4	Pharmacy 503	4
Pharmacy Adm. 551	4	Public Health 502	3	Pharmacy 540	3
Pharmacology 511	3	Pharmacology 512	3	Pharmacology 513	3
Electives	4	Electives	5	Electives	8
Total	15	*Total*	15	*Total*	18

*Graded Satisfactory or Unsatisfactory (No credit toward honor point average). Total hours for graduation = 234.

APPENDIX 8

Doctor of Pharmacy Curriculum, Semester-based

Fall	CH	Spring	CH
General Chemistry-1	5	General Chemistry-2	5
Introductory Biology	4	Anatomy/Histology	3
Calculus	3	A&H Lab	1
POP-1	1	Biostatistics or Gen Ed	3
Gen Ed	3	POP-2	1
Wellness/Activity	1	Gen Ed or Calculus	3
Open Elective	1	Wellness/Activity	1
		Open Elective	1

Fall	CH	Spring	CH
Organic Chemistry-1	3	Organic Chemistry-2	3
Organic Chemistry Lab-1	1	Organic Chemistry Lab-2	1
Biostatistics or Gen Ed	3	Applied Sci Pharmacy	3
POP-3	2	POP-4	2
Med Microbiology	3	Med Microbiology	3
Gen Ed	3	Gen Ed	3
Gen Ed	3	Gen Ed/Biosci	3

Fall	CH	Spring	CH
Physiology-1	4	Physiology-2	4
Biochemistry-1	3	Biochemistry-2	3
OTC/Home Diagnostics	3	Immunology	3
Extradisciplinary Seminar	3	Pharm Science-Module 1	2
Open Elective(s)	2	Professional Skills-1	3
POP-5	2	Gen Ed	3
Bioscience Lab or Gen Ed	1		

Fall	CH	Spring	CH
Pharm Science Module-2	7	Biomed Sciences Module-2	6
Biomed Sciences Module-1	5	BSPC Module-1	6
Professional Skills-2	3	BSPC Module-2	6
Open Elective(s)	3		

Fall	CH	Spring	CH
BSPC Module-3	3.5	Pharm Administration	6
BSPC Module-4	3.5	Capstone	6
BSPC Module-5	3.5	Special Populations	3
BSPC Module-6	3.5	Open Elective(s)	3

Fall	CH	Spring	CH
Advanced Practice Rotation	4	Advanced Practice Rotation	4
Advanced Practice Rotation	4	Advanced Practice Rotation	4
Advanced Practice Rotation	4	Advanced Practice Rotation	4
Advanced Practice Rotation	4	Advanced Practice Rotation	4
Advanced Practice Rotation	4	Advanced Practice Rotation	4

CH: Credit hours; POP: Profession of Pharmacy; BSPC: Biomedical Science/Pharmaceutical Care

APPENDIX 9
Faculty (full time) at ONU's College of Pharmacy, 1885–1959

1885–1914*	Alspach, Clinton	Curator Chemical Lab	1891
	Ames, CS (MD)	Homeopathic Remedies	1894–1903
	Asbury, Will	Curator Chemical Lab	1900
	Ashbrook, C	Pharmacy	1885–1886
	Beer, Jesse	Asst Inst Physics & Chemistry	1906–1914
	Bell, EL	Physics, Elem Chemistry	1901
	Berger, FL	Asst Inst Physics & Chemistry	1907–1914
	Brubaker PR	Curator Chemical Lab	1894
	Campbell, LW (MD)	Therapeutics & Toxicology	1893–1900
	Collins, FB	Curator Chemical Lab	1893
	Ewing, MJ	Natural Science	1885–1887
	Fess, SD	Botany	1898
	Geiger, IW	Asst Inst Physics & Chemistry	1902
	Gregg, JB	Physics & Chemistry	1893–1907
	Hall, EB	Physics & Chemistry	1891
	Higley, LA	Curator Chemical Lab	1894–1895
	Hook, Thomas	Asst Inst Physics & Chemistry	1905
	Huber, HE	Microscopy, Botany & Physiology	1912–1914
	Jett, FH	Curator Chemical Lab	1898
	Kreglow GC	Microscopy, Botany, Chemistry	1905–1911
	McGirr, Wm	Curator Chemical Lab	1896
	Melhorn NR	Physics & Chemistry	1892
	Mohler, DC	Materia Medica & Toxicology	1904–1914
	Morrison, CO	Sciences	1890
	Park, JG	Botany & Zoology	1885–1897
		Pharmacy, Advanced Chemistry	1896–1903
	Powell, EA	Physics and Algebra	1891
	Raabe, RH	Practical Pharmacy Laboratory	1910–1914
	Ross, RH	Asst Inst Physics & Chemistry	1903
	Scott, CM	Curator Chemical Lab	1897
	Sleesman, L	Director of Laboratories	1905–1914
	Tussing, PI	Physics & Chemistry	1895–1900
	Wier, WO	Curator Chemical Lab	1892

	Young, BS	Adv Chemistry, Materia Medica	1889–1903
1915–1929	Auten, Mary	Biology	1927–1929
	Berger, Frank L	Physics	1915–1929
	Close, Marshall	Pharmacy	1928–1929
	Dobbins, Raymond	Botany	1926–1929
	Hamsher, Harry L	Pharmacognosy	1920–1929
	Harrod, Jesse R	Chemistry	1922–1929
	Huber, Harvey E.	Microscopy, Physiology & Biology	1915–1929
	Mohler, DC	Pharmacy, Materia Medica, Tox	1915–1917
	Raabe, RH	Pharmacy	1915–1929
	Sleesman, Lenix C	Chemistry	1915–1929
1930–1945	Berger, Frank L	Physics	1930–1945
	Close, Marshall	Pharmacy	1930–1936
	Dobbins, Raymond	Biology	1930–1945
	Gibson, Robert C	Chemistry	1931–1935
	Hanna, Myron (MD)	Health Service, Pharmacology	1932–1937
	Harrod, Jesse R	Chemistry	1930–1941
	Hocking, George M	Materia Medica	1938–1940
	Huber, Harvey E	Biology	1930–1945
	Kramer, John (MD)	Physician, Health Service	1940–1941
	Lamb, Clyde A	Health & Physical Education	1930–1945
	McFadden, GH	Pharmaceutical Chemistry	1939–1942
	Miller, Lewis E	Chemistry	1936–1942
	Neuroth, Milton L	Pharmacy	1935–1940
	Raabe, RH	Pharmacy	1930–1945
	Smith, AC	Pharmaceutical Chemistry	1944–1045
1946–1959	Accountis, Mary	Pharmacy	1946–1948
	Araujo, Oscar	Pharmacy	1967–1959
	Baun, Lois	Pharmacy	1949–1950
	Beck, Earl	Bacteriology	1954
	Benton, Lewis S	Pharmacy Administration	1957–1959
	Clark, Fred R	Pharmacognosy	1950–1953
	Dobbins, RA	Biology, Crude Drugs	1946–1948
	Ferguson, Hugh	Pharmacology	1958–1959
	Fryer, Mellville	Pharmacognosy	1949
	Goorley, John	Pharmaceutical Chemistry	1955–1957
	Hanna, Myron (MD)	Health Services, Pharmacy	1946–1950
	Hillman, James	Pharmacology	1951–1953

Jongeward, Mattys	Pharmacy	1950–1957
Koffler, Anna	Pharmacognosy	1953–1959
Lee, CO	Professor	1954–1959
Lepovetsky, Barney	Bacteriology	1955–1959
Levy, Bernard	Pharmacology	1954–1955
Mull, Burt D	Pharmacy	1953–1954
Nelson, Harold	Pharmacy Administration	1953
Raabe, RH	Pharmacy	1946–1955
Ritz, Harriette	Business Administration	1953–1957
Schlosser, Theodore	Biochemistry	1950
Smith, AC	Pharmaceutical Chemistry	1944–1959
Tolstead, Wm L	Biology & Pharmacognosy	1949–1950
Weinstein, Benj	Pharmacognosy	1958–1959
Yoder, David	Pharmaceutical Chemistry	1957–1959

*Dates obtained from annual catalogs; thus, absolute date cannot be assured in some cases. Also, the person may have been gone for a year or more between dates shown. So use the information here to confirm era rather than absolute dates.

Much of the information shown in this Appendix was obtained from data collected by Dr. CO Lee.

APPENDIX 10

Faculty (full-time) of ONU's College of Pharmacy, 1960—2012

Faculty Name	Discipline*	Era**
Allison, J	Pharmacy	1998–present
Araujo, O	Pharmacy	1960–1963
Awad, A	Pharmacognosy	1968–1996
Beltz, L	Pharmaceutical Chemistry	1966–1986
Benton, L	Pharmacy Administration	1960–1964
Benya, T	Pharmacy	1975–1976
Bhattacharya, A	Pharmacology	1971–2001
Bianchi, P	Pharmacognosy	1962–1964
Boner, P	Toxicology	2005–2007
Bricker, D	Pharmacology/Toxicology	1981–1986
Bright, D	Ph Practice	2009–present
Broedel-Zaugg, K	Pharmacy	1998–2012
Bryant, B	Pharmacy	2001–2007
Buyukyaylaci, S	Pharmaceutics	1982–1986
Chereson, R	Pharmacy	1977–1981
Christoff, J	Pharmaceutical Chemistry	1999–present
Crossgrove, J	Toxicology	2007–2010
Cutler, S	Medicinal Chemistry	1991–1993
De, S	Pharmaceutics	2004–2006
DiPietro, N	Ph Practice	2007–present
Earle, S	Ph Practice	1988–1994
Edlin, A	Pharmacology	1970–1972
Faulkner, T	Pharmacology	1985–2007
Ferguson, H	Pharmacology	1960–1962
Finley-Sobotka, K	Ph Practice	2010–present
Fischelis, R	Pharmacy	1964–1966
Fitzgerald, B	Pharmaceutics	1970–1980
Fordham, C	Pharmacology	2007–2008
Fung, E	Pharmacology	1980–1984
Gentry, A	Ph Practice	2009–2012
Goldberg, I	Ph Practice	1987–1993
Gorby, M	Pharmacology	1960–1964
Gossel, T	Pharmacology/Toxicology	1972–2002
Grabowski, B	Pharmaceutical Chemistry	1962–1964
Green, V	Pharmacology	1962–1963

Gundlach, C	Pharmacy	1990–1991
Henderson, M	Pharmacy	1981–1998
Hewitt, W	Pharmacology	1962–1964
Hoag, S	Pharmacy	1988–1993
Holtz-Savino, L	Pharmacy	1987–2008
Hrometz, S	Pharmacology	2000–2014
Hussain, A	Pharmacy	1992–1999
Jacyno, J	Biochemistry	1992–1999
Jarrahian, A	Pharmacology	2008–2014
Jones, R	Ph Practice	1986–2008
Kahaleh, A	Ph Practice	2004–2007
Kier, K	Pharmacy	1987–present
Kier, T	Pharmacy	1987–present
Kinder, D	Pharmaceutical Chemistry	1993–present
Kisor, D	Pharmacy	1998–2014
Kline, J	Ph Practice	2006–present
Knecht, K	Toxicology	2001–2004
Koffler, A	Pharmacognosy	1960–1964
Kuykendall, J	Pharmacology	2004–2006
Lee, CO	Pharmacy	1960–1970
Lepovetsky, B	Bacteriology	1960–1964
Mahalik, M	Pharmacology	1992–1994
Mahfouz, T	Pharmaceutical Chemistry	2006–present
Mallin, M	Microbiology	1965–1993
McCurdy, R	Pharmacy	1996–present
McGee, D	Pharmacology	1979–1980
Malone, P	Pharmacy	1980–1982
Mamidi, S	Ph Practice	2009–2010
Martin, W	Ph Practice	2007–present
Matouk, F	Pharmacy	1983–1985
Milks, M	Pharmacology	1985–2013
Moffitt, R	Pharmacology	1967–1970
Murthy, S	Pharmaceutics	2005–2007
Musser, M	Pharmacy	2010–present
Myers, D	Pharmacy	2000–present
Newcomb, J	Pharmacy	1962–1964
Olah, M	Pharmacology	2008–present
Padron, V	Pharmacy	1977–1982
Parteleno, P	Pharmacy	1999–present
Previte, P	Pharmacy Administration	1969–2007
Rao, S	Pharmaceutics	2001–2004

Reilly, K	Ph Practice	2009–present
Reiselman, J	Pharmacy	1974–2014
Roecker, A	Pharmacy	2003–present
Rojeab, Y	Pharmaceutics	2007–present
Rorabaugh, B	Pharmacology	2005–present
Roth, H	Pharmacy	1965–1967
Rush, D	Pharmacy	1971–1972
Severs, W	Pharmacology	1966–1967
Sheets, M	Pharmacy Administration	1966–1967
Sheumaker, J	Pharmacy	1972–2002
Shields, K	Pharmacy	2004–present
Shoemaker, L	Pharmacy	1971–2002
Smith, AC	Pharmaceutical Chemistry	1960–1972
Smith, E	Pharmacy	1999–2003
Smith, L	Biochemistry	1977–2006
Sobotka, J	Pharmacy	2010–present
Sprague, J	Pharmacology	1995–2013
Stanovich, J	Pharmacy	1976–2007
Stansloski, D	Pharmaceutical Chemistry	1972–1995
Stewart, T	Pharmaceutical Chemistry	1971–1992
Stockert, A	Biochemistry	2005–present
Stuart, D	Pharmaceutical Chemistry	1964–1988
Suffness, M	Biochemistry	1972–1975
Sullivan, D	Pharmacy	1997–2013
Sweeney, M	Pharmacy	2003–2006
Talbot, J	Pharmacology	2006–2013
Theodore, J	Pharmacy	1966–1998
Turner, J	Ph Practice	1977–2002
Vandor, S	Biochemistry	1975–1977
Vottero, L	Pharmacy	1967–1992
Weinstein, B	Pharmacognosy	1960–1962
Willmore, C	Pharmacology	2006–2007
Woodward, W	Pharmacy	1964–1967
Yoder, D	Pharmaceutical Chemistry	1960–1962

* Discipline: Pharmacy and Ph Practice titles are interchangeable.

** Dates obtained from annual catalogs and personal memory; thus, absolute dates of service cannot be assured in some cases. Also, the person may have been away for a year or more between dates shown. So, use the information here to confirm era of service, rather than absolute employment dates. For faculty with a 1960 starting date, check Appendix 9 for a more accurate starting date.

APPENDIX 11

Faculty and Staff at ONU's College of Pharmacy, 2015–2016

Adane, Eyob	BS Pharm (2000), MS (2003), PhD (2010); Addis Ababa University, University of Kentucky
Allison, Jeffery	BS Pharm (1971), Pharm D (1995); Ohio Northern University
Bates, Brittany	Pharm D (2006), Residency (2007); Ohio Northern University, Akron General Medical Center
Chrissobolis, Sophocles	BS (1998), BS w/Honors (1999), PhD (2004); The University of Melbourne
Christoff, Jeffrey	BS Pharm (1988), PhD (1993); Duquesne University, The Ohio State University
DiPietro Mager, Natalie	Pharm D (2001), Masters (2006); Ohio Northern University, Indiana University School of Medicine
D'Souza, Manoranjan	MD (2001), PhD (2007); Seth GS Medical School Mumbai, University of Texas at Austin
Dunbar, Chandra*	AS (1995), BS (2004), MS in Information Systems (2008); Ivy Tech State College, Strayer University
Fanous, Amy	Pharm D (2012), Residency (2013); Ohio Northern University
Finley-Sobota, Kristen	Pharm D (2006), Residency (2007); West Virginia University, The Ohio State University
Hethcox, Mary Ellen	BS Pharm (1977), Residency (1978), Pharm D (1984); University of Rhode Island, Medical College of Virginia, Virginia Commonwealth University
Hinson, Jessica	BSBA (2005), Pharm D (2014), Residency (2015); Xavier University, University of Cincinnati, West Virginia University
Kier, Karen	BS Pharm (1982), Masters (1984), PhD (2000), Residencies (1984, 1985); Ohio Northern University, The Ohio State University, University of North Carolina, Grant Medical Center
Kier, Thomas	BS Pharm (1982), MA (1990), PhD (2000); Ohio Northern University, Bowling Green State University
Kinder, David	BS (1975), MS(1990), PhD (2000); Purdue University, Indiana University, University of Illinois
Kline Grundy, Jennifer	Pharm D (2004); Ohio Northern University
Koh, David	BS (1991), BS Pharm (1994), PhD (2001), Postdoc Fellow (2006); Centre College, University of Kentucky, Johns Hopkins School of Medicine
Leonard, Steven	BS Pharm (2003), Pharm D (2004), Residency (2006), Grad Cert Pub. Health (2008), Fellowship (2008); Purdue University, St. Vincent Hospital, Wayne State University

Mahfouz, Tarek	BS Pharm (1998), MS (2000), PhD (2006); Cairo University, West Texas A&M University, University of Houston
Martin, Steven	BS Pharm (1983), Pharm D (1992), Fellowship (1994); Ferris State University, University of Illinois at Chicago
McCurdy, Robert*	BS Pharm (1965), M Ed (1968), Dr. Pharm (1996); Ohio Northern University, University of Hartford
Musser, Michelle	BS (2005), Pharm D (2005), Residency (2010); Ashland University, The Ohio State University, Blanchard Valley Medical Associates
Myers, Deirdre	BS Pharm (1983); Ohio Northern University
Olah, Mark	BS Pharm (1983), PhD (1988), Fellowships (1988, 1992); Philadelphia College of Pharmacy and Science, The Ohio State University, National Institute General Med. Sciences
Parteleno, Pat	BS Pharm (1994), Pharm D (1996); Ohio Northern University
Peters, Lindsey	Pharm D (2013), Residency (2014); University of Cincinnati, Grandview Medical Center
Petersen, Erin	Pharm D (2011), Residency (2012); Ohio Northern University, Blanchard Valley Medical Associates
Reilly Kroustos, Kelly	AAS (2000), BS (2003), Pharm D (2007), Residency (2008); Columbus St. Comm. College, Ohio Dominican University, The Ohio State University
Roecker, Andrew	Pharm D (2000); Ohio Northern University
Rojeab, Yousif	BS Pharm (1999), PhD (2007); Jordan University of Science & Technology, University of Houston
Rorabaugh, Boyd	AAS (1983), BS (1995), MS (1997), PhD (2002); Mt. Vernon Nazarene University, Bowling Green University, Creighton University
Rush, Michael*	Pharm D (2005), Residency (2006); Ohio Northern University, Physicians Incorporated
Shields, Kelly	Pharm D (2001), Residency (2003); Butler University, University of Missouri-Kansas City
Sobotka, Jenelle	BS Pharm (1987), Pharm D (1989); University of Iowa
Stockert, Amy	BS (1999), MS (2002), PhD (2004); Purdue University-Ft. Wayne, The Ohio State University
Stratton, Hayley*	AA (2001), BS (2009); School of Advertising Art, Franklin University
Wills, Scott*	BSBA (1987), MBA (1991); Ohio Northern University, Ashland University

* Denotes Staff

APPENDIX 12

History of Drug Stores in Ada*
Fred R. Armeni, BS Pharm '77

An historical account of Ada's drugstores dates back to 1853, when the village was founded, although at that time Ada was known as Johnstown. In the early 1860s, the post office came to Johnstown and was called the Ada Post Office. The townspeople wanted to change the name of Johnstown to Sweet Liberty, but since the town greatly increased in size after the coming of the post office, and since the "newcomers" were calling their new home Ada (due to the name the post office assigned it), Johnstown became known as Ada.

The history of Ada's drugstores is difficult to follow for two main reasons: 1) some establishments listed as "drug stores" opened and closed their doors almost overnight because some businessmen who were not druggists sold drugs as a source of extra income, and 2) a written history of the first thirty years of Ada is very sparse. In response to these reasons, I decided it would be best to follow the development of drugstores if they were listed in chronological order, grouped in decades. This will be the general format of this paper.

1850–1859—No drugstores are listed for Ada (Johnstown).

1860–1869—N.B. Holder located in Ada in 1862 and opened what was described as the first drugstore of the area. Holder had no formal education, but claimed to have plenty of experience.

1870–1879—In 1870, two more drugstores opened in Ada and have survived until recent times, albeit under different ownerships. Kemp's Drug Store opened on South Main Street and was advertised as a "first-class drug store." Evidently this terminology carried some weight because other stores also used it. Kemp's eventually evolved into Gardner's Drug Store. J.N. Mahan opened his store on North Main Street and also advertised it as a "first-class drug store." Mahan's was destined to become Peper's Drug Store.

In 1871, two other men were listed as druggists: J.W. Umbaugh and C.F. Runkel, but nothing else is to be found about them. They didn't advertise and it appears drugs were only a small part of their business enterprise, whatever that was.

In 1874, the Peoples' Drug and Book Store opened in the Ream and Sons Building. Ada went through several alternating periods of being dry and wet in reference to liquor sales. During this time period it was dry, so the owners of the People's Drug and Book Store took advantage of the situation and were among the early bootleggers of whiskey in Ada. Their legal sales consisted of "drugs, medicines, chemicals, paints, oils, brushes, lamps and figures."

In 1877, M.H. Mac opened a small drug shop on Main Street, south of the railroad. His ad stated that he "… sold no quack doctors' medicines." His patent medicines were of standard quality.

Also in 1877, A.C. McCamman bought a small store from G.S. Thomas, at Thomas' Old Stand on Main Street and sold patent medicines. He also sold school books, stationery, perfumery, notions, and fancy toilet seats. It is stated that he filled physicians' prescriptions and mixed family recipes.

In 1878, A.M. Fasig, a hardware store owner, went into the drug business. His ad read that he "…has a full line of drugs. Please give him a call. The boss place for drugs and medicines. All kinds of pure drugs."

During the 1870s, there were at least nine different establishments selling drugs, but by 1879, the only ones remaining were Kemp's, Mahan's, the Peoples' Drug and Book Store, McCamman's, and Fasig's. This large number of drug entrepreneurs may partially be due to the fact that the decade was one of rapid expansion of Ada, and its people were strong on "cure-all" drugs and self medication.

1880–1889—J.N. Mahan now advertised as the "best place to buy pure drugs and medicines, books, stationery."

Also in 1880, Sharp's Drug Store appeared on Main Street and advertised as a source for wallpaper. I couldn't find anything more about Sharp's except that they only filled one or two prescriptions and their advertisements stopped in 1882.

The strangest part of all this was in 1880, the *Ada Record* (*Ada Herald*) printed a list of primary businesses of the town and no mention was made of a drugstore.

In 1884, the Ohio legislature passed a law to regulate the practice of pharmacy. The law stated that the governor should appoint a five-member Ohio board of pharmacy whose duty it would be to examine every person who desired to carry on or engage in the business of a retail pharmacy.

The University (ONU) at that time was offering a preparatory curriculum in medicine. Most of the subjects in medicine were of equal importance to pharmacy; therefore, about all that was needed to complete a pharmacy curriculum was to appoint a trained pharmacist to teach the theoretical and practical aspects of pharmacy. Charles Ashbrook is listed as the first teacher of pharmacy at ONU in 1885 and 1886. He operated a drugstore at that time in Ada at the location of the present Peper's Drug Store. Courses in materia medica were of about equal importance to both medicine and pharmacy, and were taught by men trained in either profession.

In 1887, Mahan sold his store to Ashbrook, who had been working for Mahan for several years and also teaching pharmacy at ONU. Ashbrook was a graduate of pharmacy and was described in newspaper advertising as "…a careful, steady, upright businessman of sense and judgment."

Another store opened in Ada in 1887 by the McKinley brothers. They were "regular druggists with proper schooling and ran a strictly first-class drug store." Seems we are back to the old terminology of "first-class store" again.

Approaching the end of this decade, in 1889 there were only three drugstores in Ada: Kemp's, Ashbrook's, and McKinley Brothers' store. The new state law regulating pharmacy pretty much put an end to back room sales of drugs by entrepreneurs without any training as to the drugs' safety or effectiveness. By the end of the century, only twelve percent of the druggists in America were thought to have any formal technical training in pharmacy.

1890–1899—In 1891, N.W. Tobias joined Kemp's and later became the owner of Kemp's along with Kemp's son-in-law, Toby Tobias.

In 1894, the Central Drug Store opened on the corner of the Public Square. It was owned by J.F. Matthews who advertised his services as a dispensing druggist. He sold books and stationery, but prescriptions were his specialty. He must have been good at it because about one-half of the prescriptions written in Ada at that time were dispensed from his establishment.

Some prescriptions were written on scrap paper, and others were on regular prescription pads. In earlier days the druggist's name and store advertising were listed on the prescription pads, rather than the physician's name. Some of the early prescriptions were written in Latin, but most were in English, probably due to the fact that most doctors of the era didn't have an extensive education.

In 1895, Matthews left Ada and sold the Central Drug Store to John Young, who kept it until about 1914.

In 1896, Ashbrook's was sold to Samuel Yates, who was assisted by a Mr. Parker. Advertising stated that "Sammy is full of business, has a smile for everyone, and many other qualifications for the place." Yates kept the name of the store as Ashbrook's until 1901 and then changed it to Yates' Drug Store.

In 1899, Lawrence Drug Store opened on South Main Street and was run by Lyman Conner, a graduate of ONU and also a registered pharmacist. He later sold his store and worked for a man named Young, who was a previous owner of Peper's in the early 1900s.

During the 1890s, anyone could work in a drugstore and compound medicines. Ed Park (a future owner of Peper's Drug Store) was 15 years old and made pills, powders, emulsions, suppositories, and all kinds of mixtures. Druggists of this era had crude drugs which they kept in glass-stoppered bottles and ground them to make most of their own tinctures. Many herbs were packaged in one-ounce units and sold for people to make their own teas or infusions.

1900–1919—Wilson's Drug Store opened, operated by Charles R. Wilson. Not much was written about him and his advertisements only lasted about one year.

Some time before 1919, Brig Young (son of John Young, who used to own Central Drug Store) bought Sam Yates' store and also the building (his name is still on it today). He was a graduate of ONU.

In 1919, Nelson Yates bought his father's store from Brig Young. His advertisements listed liniments, toiletries and manicure sets, Pyrex dishes, stationery, books, cameras, face powders, hot water bottles and fountain pens.

Also in 1919, Dave Welsh opened a store on Main Street where the American Legion is located now. He remained there until the early 1950s. Ed Park (future owner of Peper's) worked for him while attending ONU. As a matter of fact, Ed Park lived and slept in Welsh's store. Welsh also sold cameras, wrapping paper, candy, thermos bottles, books, pens, dishes and leather articles.

In 1919 Ed park graduated from ONU, passed the licensure examination and got a job at Yates' store.

Around 1920, Cliff Landau and his father had a bookstore in Ada near ONU. They sold drugs on the side.

1920–1929—In 1920, N.W. Tobias, Kemp's son-in-law, bought Kemp's store. Tobias also was an insurance salesman and some of the products sold in his store, which would soon become a Rexall Store were Casco-The Cold Killer, Hill's Bromo Quinine, Aspirin Cold Tablets, Mentholated White Pine Tar, Vicks VapoRub, soaps, disinfectant for flies and lice, and potato spray.

In 1921, a fire at Yates' Drug Store was due to defective wiring and caused much damage. The fire occurred on July 29th and the store didn't reopen until September 24th.

In 1922, Burke Gardner graduated from ONU, took the state board (incidentally, he received the highest grade that year) and bought Kemp's Drug Store, also called the Pioneer Drug Store, from Tobias. He maintained the name of Kemp's until 1923.

In the early days, Gardner filled very few prescriptions because doctors dispensed their own medicines. However, some doctors told their patients to return the next day for their medicine because they had to compound it and doing so was a long process. The doctors then called Gardner and told him what to make. Gardner would sell the compounded item to the doctor for 50 cents, who would then re-sell it to the patient for $1.50. Gardner's Drug Store also sold patent medicines, cigars, candy, tobacco, canning supplies, and spices. He made his own Rose Cream and cough syrups containing menthol and ammonium chloride.

In 1924, Ed Park bought Yates' store. Park sold it to Huber in 1926, but Park still had a small store in Ada across from Dukes Memorial where some drug products were sold that didn't have to be compounded. Park had a soda fountain in his drugstore but it didn't pay well, so when he sold the store to Huber, he removed the fountain and put it in this building across from Dukes. A couple years later, Park sold this store to Eli Main, but Main got rid of the medicines.

In 1928, the state of Ohio required all candidates for registration as pharmacists to be graduated from a recognized college of pharmacy before admission to its examination, except

Pharmacy display cabinet. Gift from Timothy Lanese, BS Pharm, 1978.

those qualified under laws existing prior to July 1, 1917. Apprentices were to be registered with the state board of pharmacy. Apprenticeship was not a requirement for state registration, except for those with limited college education.

During the early 1900s, some pharmacists had their own specialty items like worm capsules or a special tonic that they made, advertised in newspapers, and sold by mail order. These were hard times for druggists and very few got rich.

Epsom salts was a very popular item and druggists bought it by the barrel and put it up in paper bags for resale. Many other chemicals came the same way and were weighed out as needed. Most stores sold paint, wallpaper, window blinds, window glass and all kinds of insecticides such as paris green, copper sulfate, and arsenate of lead. They also sold livestock remedies to local farmers. Fireworks were a good July profit item.

Many fortunes were made on patent medicines. A good example is Peruna, a product manufactured and sold by Dr. Samuel Hartman in Columbus, and promoted as a treatment for catarrh (today, defined as bronchitis or excess mucus). He made so much money on Peruna that he bought a large livestock farm just south of Columbus on Route 23. Peruna was nothing more than cheap whiskey with a few harmless herbs in it. He bought alcohol for five to ten cents a gallon and sold his Peruna (about thirty-six proof) for $2.00 a quart. Peruna sales were such a large success in small towns like Ada because most were dry, and a person could get quite intoxicated on Peruna, legally.

All in all, druggists of the early days were usually trusted and beloved members of the community. Many people depended on them not only for medical advice, but for other supplies as well.

1930–1939—There were three drugstores left in Ada in the early 1930s: Welsh's, Gardner's, and Huber's.

In 1938, Gardner bought the store next to his and knocked out the wall to enlarge his enterprise. In 1939, Bert Levine bought Huber's store and called it the Ada Drug Store. Levine was Jewish and didn't want to associate his name with the business. He believed in

Burke Gardner, Proprieter, Garden Drugs, Ada, Ohio. Circa mid-1940s.

those days that it implied the customer would always get the short end of the deal from a Jewish store owner.

1940–1949—In 1941, Sieg Peper arrived in town and bought the Ada Drug Store from Bert Levine. After he passed the Indiana State Board exam, he practiced for several years in Wauseon and Valparaiso, Indiana. He purchased Levine's store because Levine got drafted into WW II service and had to sell his business cheap. It remained the Ada Drug Store for about two years. Peper remodeled it and renamed it Peper's Drug Store. People had been calling it Peper's, anyhow.

The late 1940s were important because this is when physicians began to write a lot more prescriptions. A main reason for this increasing number may have been because antibiotics were introduced. But they were very expensive for the day. Physicians didn't want to tie up their money in drug inventory and also, if they charged $2.00 for an office visit, the people frowned on paying another $3.00 to him for the medicine. They felt that $5.00 was a lot of money to give one person. Prior to this, perhaps only two to five prescriptions were filled a week, and this number gradually began to increase.

1950–1959—During this decade, Gardner and Peper bought Welsh out. Welsh was retiring and Peper and Gardner didn't want more competition, so they bought the store and split the drug inventory. According to their purchase contract, however, they had to keep the store open part time, so their wives ran it for about one and a half years selling the remaining merchandise. By the end of the 1950s, Ada had only two drugstores: Peper's and Gardner's.

1960–1969—In 1969, Orville Doc was a pharmacist for Gardner's and was supposed to purchase the store since Gardner was ready to retire. But Doc died unexpectedly, so Jim Turner and his wife Mary Ann (Gardner) Turner purchased the pharmacy. Jim and Mary Ann had both graduated from ONU in 1963. Thus, when Doc died, Gardner gave them first option for the business and they took it.

1970–present*—In 1973, Dave Peper purchased Peper's Drug Store from his father, Sieg, who was ready to retire and had intended to sell his business to an employee, Bill Calvert, a grandson of Dean Raabe. However, a change of events resulted and Calvert didn't purchase the store. Sieg Peper asked his son Dave, a pharmacist working in Cincinnati at the time (and an ONU graduate), if he would be interested. Dave took control of the business. The 1970s also saw the Turner's remodel their pharmacy and also saw Dave Peper move his pharmacy across the street into a larger building.

REFERENCES

History of Hardin County; Ada Record; Ada Herald; University Herald; ONU Bulletins; interview with Burke Gardner, April 17, 1976; letter from Edgar Park, May 5, 1976; interviews with Jim and Mary Ann Turner, April–May, 1976; interview with Dave Peper, May, 1976.

*Submitted May 10, 1976, by Fred Armeni as part of a class project for the history of pharmacy course. Mr. Armeni graduated from ONU in 1977 and has given permission to reprint his paper here. It is contained in its original form without significant editorial comment so that historians in the future who are interested in the history of Ada's drugstores and pharmacists might find it useful as a starting place for their research. Remember, this paper was submitted in 1976.

APPENDIX 13

Campus Map

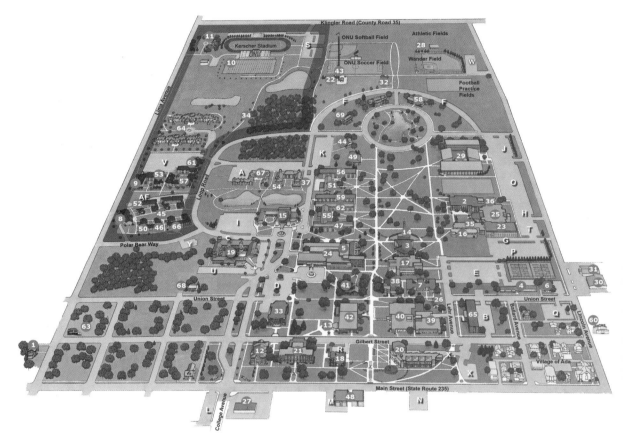

Campus Buildings:

1	Alumni House	24	McIntosh Center
2	Biggs Engineering Building	25	Meyer Hall of Science
3	Burgett Pavilion	26	Multicultural Center-
4	Business Services Building		Lehr Kennedy House
5	Career Services-McIntosh Center	27	Northern on Main
6	Child Development Center	28	Observatory
7	Clark Hall	29	ONU Sports Center/King Horn
8	Commons Building	30	Physical Plant Grounds Dept.
9	Counseling Center	31	Physical Plant Offices
10	Dial-Roberson Stadium	32	Picnic Pavilion (Shelter House)
11	The Dicke House (President's Home)	33	Presser Hall
12	Dukes Memorial	34	Remington Walk
13	Elzay Gallery of Art	35	Robertson-Evans Pharmacy
14	English Chapel		Building
15	Freed Center for the Performing Arts	36	Science Annex
16	Hakes-Pierstorf Family Pharmacy	37	Student Health Center
	Education Center, Alumni & Friends	38	Taft Memorial
	Entrance Plaza, Meijer Terrace	39	Taggart Law Library
17	Heterick Memorial Library	40	Tilton Hall of Law
18	Hill Memorial	41	Weber Hall (Admissions/
19	The Inn at ONU		Financial Aid)
20	James F. Dicke Hall	42	Wilson Art Building
21	Lehr Memorial	43	WONB Radio Transmitter
22	Maintenance Facility		& Tower
23	Mathile Center for the Natural Sciences		

Student Housing:

44	5 University Parkway
45	Affinity Village
46	Alpha Xi Delta
47	Brookhart Hall
48	Courtyard Apartments
49	Delta Sigma Phi
50	Delta Zeta
51	Founders Hall
66	Fiji
52	Kappa Alpha Theta
53	Klondike's Den
54	Lakeview
55	Lima Hall
56	Maglott Hall
57	Northern Commons
58	Northern House
59	Park Hall
60	Phi Delta Chi
69	Phi Mu Delta
61	Polar Place
62	Roberts Hall
63	Sigma Phi Epsilon
64	Stadium View Apartments
65	Stambaugh Hall

Parking Lots:

K	5UP	■
AF	Affinity	■
Y	Bear East	■
O	Biggs	■
E	Clark	■ ■
X	Dicke	■ ■
L	Dukes	■ ■
I	Freed	■ ■
R	Hill	■
J	King Horn	■ ■
A	Lakeview	■
M	Lehr	■
Q	Lincoln	■ ■ ■
N	Main	■ ■
D	McIntosh (Admissions and Financial Aid Parking)	■
T	Meyer East	■
H	Meyer West	■
P	Pharmacy	■ ■
G	Raabe	■
S	Stadium	
B	Stambaugh	■
V	Stadium View	■
U	University Inn	

■	South zone
■	West zone
■	East zone
■	Commuters
■	Faculty and staff
■	Baker Commons

REFERENCES

NOTICE TO READERS:

All reference citations indicated as *accessed online* are now available at the following address: www.onu/edu/academics/heterick_memorial library. Then go to ONU History/ Archives, Genealogical resources, ONU catalogs, or Archive information.

PREFACE

1. Lee CO. To know pharmacy's history is to appreciate it as a profession. *The Ampul*. 1970;21(2):4.
2. Connor JT. To honor the past—look to the future. *Ohio Northern Alumnus*. 1965;26(2):3–4.

CHAPTER ONE, THE EARLY DAYS: PRE-PHARMACY ERA

1. Lehr HS. History of the O.N.U. Serialized memories of Dr. Lehr published in the *University Record* between 1904 and 1909. Available at www.onu.edu/library/onuhistory/histonu/index.htm. Accessed April 24, 2001.
2. Binkley WE. *The History of ONU. A Draft*. Ada, Ohio. Ohio Northern University; 2007:66–67.
3. Miller B. *Small Town Sampler VI*. Ada, Ohio. *Ada Herald*. 1995.
4. Schertzer G. *A Brief History of Ohio Northern University*. Ada, Ohio. Heterick Memorial Library. 1962.
5. Welsh A. *History of the Ada Community*. Ada, Ohio. *Ada Herald*.
6. Welsh A. Ch VI. History of Ada and the University. In Kohler MI. *A twentieth Century History of Hardin County Ohio*. Chicago, Illinois. Lewis Publishing Co. 1910.
7. Kennedy S. *H.S. Lehr and His School*. Ada, Ohio. *Ada Herald*. Ada, Ohio. 1938.
8. Anon. Liberty Township. In *The History of Hardin County Ohio*. Chicago, Illinois. Warner, Beers & Co. 1983.
9. Anon. *An ONU Photo Album*. Accessed online April 23, 2001.
10. Miller B. *Small Town Sampler*. Ada, Ohio. *Ada Herald*. 1985.
11. North-Western Ohio Normal School. Catalog for 1870–71. Accessed online July 1, 2008.
12. Ohio Northern University. Catalog for 1930–31. Accessed online July 3, 2008.

13. Belch GE. Tempered by Crisis. *Ohio Northern Alumnus.* 1971;32(3).

14. Anon. Henry S. Lehr, Founder of Ohio Northern University (taken from the *Kenton News Republican*, November 12, 1898). *A History of the Hardin County Schools.* Ada, Ohio. Brown Publishing Co. 1989.

15. Ohio Northern University. Catalog for 1886–87. Accessed online June 30, 2008.

16. Ohio Northern University. Catalog for 1885–86. Accessed online June 30, 2008.

CHAPTER TWO, THE ONU DEPARTMENT OF PHARMACY: 1885–1904

1. Raabe RH. Progress of the pharmacy college. *Ohio Northern Alumnus.* 1932;5(4):5, 14.

2. Higby GJ. American pharmacy's first great transformation: Practice, 1852–1902. In Higby GJ, Higby G, Stroud E, eds. *American Pharmacy (1852–2002): A Collection of Historical Essays.* Madison, Wisconsin. American Institute of the History of Pharmacy: 2005:1–4.

3. Buerki RA. Pharmaceutical education in nineteenth-century Ohio. *Ohio History.* 1995; Winter-Spring;104:42–84.

4. Laws of Ohio. 1884, vol 81, pg 61, Sec 4405.

5. Buerki RA. The normal school movement in pharmaceutical education. *Pharmacy History.* 2012;54:47–62.

6. Ohio Normal University. Catalog for 1885–86. Accessed online June 30, 2008.

7. Lee CO. Our founder's vision for pharmaceutical education. *Ohio Pharmacist.* 1966;15(1):10–11.

8. Buerki RA. American pharmaceutical education, 1852–1902. *Journal of the American Pharmaceutical Association.* 2000;40(4):458–460.

9. Raabe RH. Pharmacy at Northern—A noble beginning. *Ohio Northern Alumnus.* 1929;2(4):11–13.

10. Ohio Normal University. Catalog for 1882–83. Accessed online January 22, 2009.

11. Anon. An ONU Photo Album. Accessed online April 23, 2001.

12. Lee CO. The Ohio Northern University College of Pharmacy. *The Ampul.* 1971;22(3):3.

13. Raabe RH. A history of O.N.U.—Part I. *The Ampul.* 1956;6(1):8.

14. Belch GE. Tempered by Crisis. *Ohio Northern Alumnus.* 1971;32(3).

15. Ohio Normal University. Catalog for 1888–89. Accessed online June 30, 2008.

16. Ohio Northern University, College of Pharmacy Deans' Profiles (Charles Sherrard). Heterick Memorial Library Archives. June 20, 2008.

17. Ohio Normal University. Catalog for 1886–87. Accessed online June 30, 2008.

18. Kennedy S. *H.S. Lehr and His School.* Ada, Ohio. *Ada Herald.* 1938.

19. Ohio Normal University. Catalog for 1887–88. Accessed online July 1, 2008.

20. Ohio Normal University. Catalog for 1889–90. Accessed online June 30, 2008.

21. Ohio Normal University. Catalog for 1892–93. Accessed online June 30, 2008.

22. Ohio Northern University. Catalog for 1904–05. Accessed online July 1, 2008.

23. Welch A. Ch VI. History of Ada and the University. In Kohler MI. *A Twentieth Century History of Hardin County Ohio*. Chicago, Illinois. Lewis Publishing Co. 1910.

24. Lehr HS. History of the O.N.U. Serialized memoirs of Dr. Lehr published in the *University Record* between 1904 and 1909. Accessed online April 24, 2001.

25. Ohio Normal University. Catalog for 1894–95. Accessed online June 30, 2008.

26. Ohio Normal University. Catalog for 1895–96. Accessed online June 30, 2008.

27. Ohio Normal University. Catalog for 1897–98. Accessed online June 30, 2008.

28. Anon. *Ada Record*. Ada, Ohio. October 15, 1902.

29. Anon. *Ada Record*. Ada, Ohio. January 22, 1902.

30. Anon. *Ada Record*. Ada, Ohio. August 6, 1902.

31. Carter D (ed). Minutes of the Central Ohio Conference of the Methodist Episcopal Church, 48th Session. Held in the First Methodist Church, Findlay, Ohio. September 16–21, 1903. (Cincinnati, Ohio.) Western Methodist Book Concern Press. 1903.

32. Binkley WE. *The History of ONU. A Draft*. Ada, Ohio. Ohio Northern University; 2007:66–67.

33. Anon. Contract: Ohio Northern University and Fort Wayne College of Medicine. Ohio Northern University Archives. April 12, 1904.

34. Logsdon PM. A Pictorial History of Ohio Northern University. Accessed online April 21, 2010.

35. Ohio Northern University. Catalog for 1905–06. Accessed online July 1, 2008.

36. Ankenbruck J. *Twentieth Century History of Fort Wayne, IN*. Fort Wayne, Indiana. 1975:161.

37. Anon. News clip. *Mansfield News*. Mansfield, Ohio. April 16, 1895.

38. Druggists you know: Charles S. Ashbrook. *Northern Ohio Druggist*. Date and volume number unknown.

39. Ohio Northern University, College of Pharmacy Deans' Profiles (Charles Ashbrook). Heterick Memorial Library Archives. Ada, Ohio. June 20, 2008.

40. Anon. Honored son of O.N.U.: Brigham Scott Young. *The Ampul*. 1955;4(3):2.

41. Ohio Northern University. College of Pharmacy Deans' Profiles (Brigham Young). Heterick Memorial Library Archives. Ada, Ohio. June 20, 2008.

42. Letter from C.F. Ashbrook (Dean Charles Ashbrook's son) to Louis Vottero, October 1, 1968.

CHAPTER THREE, A NEW CENTURY: 1905–1916

1. Ohio Northern University. Catalog for 1906–07. Accessed online July 1, 2008.

2. Ohio Northern University. Catalog for 1905–06. Accessed online July 1, 2008.

3. Welsh A. Ch VI. History of Ada and the University. In Kohler MI. *A Twentieth Century History of Hardin County Ohio*. Chicago, Illinois. Lewis Publishing Co. 1910.

4. Ohio Northern University. Catalog for 1904–05. Accessed online July 1, 2008.

5. Benton LC, Lee CO. The early years of the Ohio Northern University College of Pharmacy II. *The Ampul.* 1964;14(3):10.

6. Anon. *Ada Record.* Ada, Ohio. July 19, 1905.

7. Anon. *University Herald*, Ada, Ohio. December 8, 1905.

8. Belch GE. Tempered by Crisis. *Ohio Northern Alumnus.* 1971;32(3).

9. Smith AE. *Souls in Armour and Other Baccalaureate Messages.* New York, New York. GP Putnam Sons. 1930:113.

10. Anon. Doctor Henry Solomon Lehr. *Ohio History.* Date unknown. 32:289

11. Anon. *An ONU Photo Album.* Accessed online April 23, 2001.

12. Anon. *Ada Record.* Ada, Ohio. March 7, 1906.

13. Anon. *Northern Review.* Ada, Ohio. November 14, 1928:1.

14. Cloyd GS. First engineer-pharmic day encounter. *Ohio Northern Alumnus.* 1929;2(4):7–8.

15. Smith AC. The state of the college—1957. *Ohio Northern Alumnus.* 1956–57;17(4):9–10.

16. Miller B. *Small Town Sampler II.* Ada, Ohio. *Ada Herald.* 1987.

17. Anon. Hatchet buried with special ceremonies. *Ohio Northern Alumnus.* 1929;2(4):9.

18. Buerki RA. American pharmaceutical education, 1902–1952. *Journal of the American Pharmaceutical Association.* 2001;41(4):519–521.

19. Ohio Northern University. Catalog for 1913–14. Accessed online July 3, 2008.

20. Ohio Northern University. Catalog for 1907–08. Accessed online July 1, 2008.

21. Ohio Northern University. Catalog for 2014–2015. Heterick Memorial Library. Bound copy.

22. Ohio Northern University. Catalog for 1909–10. Accessed online July 3, 2008.

23. Ohio Northern University. Catalog for 1910–11. Accessed online July 3, 2008.

24. Lee CO. Our founder's vision for pharmaceutical education. *Ohio Pharmacist.* 1966;15(1):10–11.

25. Raabe RH. Pharmacy at Northern—A noble beginning. *Ohio Northern Alumnus.* 1929;2(4):11–13.

26. Anon. *Ada Record.* Ada, Ohio. October 29, 1913.

27. Lehr HS. History of the O.N.U. Serialized memoirs of Dr. Lehr published in the *University Record* between 1904 and 1909. Accessed online April 124, 2001.

28. Ohio Northern University. Summary of diplomas and degrees awarded by year, college, and gender. Accessed online July 2, 2008.

29. Ohio Northern University, College of Pharmacy Deans' Profiles (David C. Mohler). Heterick Memorial Library Archives. Ada, Ohio. June 20, 2008.

CHAPTER FOUR, THE DEAN RAABE STORY: 1917–1950

1. McIntosh FB. To Dean Raabe—A tribute. *Ohio Northern Alumnus.* 1950–51;11(3):9.

2. Anon. Dean Rudolph Henry Raabe. *Ohio Northern Alumnus.* 1929;2(4):10.

3. Fischelis RP. The Dean Raabe story. *Ohio Northern Alumnus.* 1964;25(3):3.

4. Calvert JG. The Ancestors and Descendants of Rudolph Henry Raabe and Mamie Lucille Klinger Raabe. Oakwood, Ohio. Quail Hollow Press. 2008.

5. Anon. Dean Raabe receives degree. *Ohio Northern Alumnus.* 1930;4(2):15.

6. Smailes T. Honored son of O.N.U.: Rudolph H. Raabe. *The Ampul.* 1952;1(1):3.

7. Myers M. Recollection of the man. *Ohio Northern Alumnus.* 1972;33(1):6.

8. Ohio Northern University, College of Pharmacy Deans' Profiles (Rudolph H. Raabe). Heterick Memorial Library Archives. Ada, Ohio. June 20, 2008.

9. ONU to name Pharmacy College in Honor of Dr. Rudolph Raabe. *The Kenton Times,* Kenton, Ohio. September 9, 1971.

10. Lee CO. The Ohio Northern University College of Pharmacy. *The Ampul.* 1971;22(2):3.

CHAPTER FIVE, A PERIOD OF GREAT TRANSITION: 1917–1929

1. Anon. An ONU Photo Album. Accessed online April 23, 2001.

2. Belch GE. Tempered by Crisis. *Ohio Northern Alumnus.* 1971;32(3).

3. Ohio Northern University. Catalog for 1920–21. Accessed online July 3, 2008.

4. Ohio Northern University. Catalog for 1915–16. Accessed online July 3, 2008.

5. Lee CO. The early years of Ohio Northern University, College of Pharmacy III. *The Ampul.* 1964;15(1):3.

6. Ohio Northern University. Catalog for 1925–26. Accessed online July 3, 2008.

7. Sonnedecker G. *Kremers and Urdang's History of Pharmacy,* 4th ed. Madison, Wisconsin. J.B. Lippincott/Sonnedecker (by transfer). 1976.

8. Ohio Northern University. Catalog for 1919–20. Accessed online July 3, 2008.

9. Ohio Northern University. Catalog for 1917–18. Accessed online July 3, 2008.

10. Ohio Northern University. Catalog for 1926–27. Accessed online July 3, 2008.

11. Ohio Northern University. Catalog for 1915–16. Accessed online July 3, 2008.

12. Ohio Northern University. Catalog for 1927–28. Accessed online July 3, 2008.

13. Ohio Northern University. Catalog for 1931–32. Accessed online July 3, 2008.

14. Ohio Northern University. Catalog for 1932–33. Accessed online July 3, 2008.

15. Ohio Northern University. Summary of diplomas and degrees awarded by year, college, and gender. Accessed online July 2, 2008.

CHAPTER SIX, HARD TIMES AHEAD: 1930–1944.

1. Higby GJ. Pharmacy in the American Century. *Apothecary's Cabinet.* 2000; No. 1, Fall.

2. Lee CO. The early years of Ohio Northern University College of Pharmacy IV. *The Ampul.* 1965;15(3):7.

3. Ohio Northern University. Report of a survey of Ohio Northern University Under the Auspices of the Commission on Survey of Educational Institutions of the Methodist Episcopal Church. Chicago, Illinois. 1931.

4. Anon. *Ada Herald*, Ada, Ohio. September 20, 1935.

5. Ohio Northern University. Catalog for 1933–34. Accessed online July 3, 2008.

6. Belch GE. Tempered by Crisis. *Ohio Northern Alumnus*. 1971;32(3).

7. Anon. *Northern Review*. Ada, Ohio. September 25, 1929.

8. Anon. *Ada Herald*. Ada, Ohio. December 18, 1931.

9. Civil Works Administration. Available at http://content.lib/washington.edu/ civilworksweb/index.html. Accessed May 18, 2010.

10. Anon. *Northern Review*, Ada, Ohio. February 28, 1934.

11. Anon. *Ada Herald*. Ada, Ohio. August 31, 1934.

12. Anon. *An ONU Photo Album*. Accessed online April 23, 2001.

13. Anon. *Proceedings of the American Association of Colleges of Pharmacy*. 1930; p 71.

14. Ohio Northern University. Catalog for 1930–31. Accessed online July 3, 2008.

15. Ohio Northern University. Catalog for 1931–32. Accessed online July 3, 2008.

16. Ohio Northern University. Catalog for 1932–33. Accessed online July 3, 2008.

17. Raabe RH. Pharmacy at Northern—A noble beginning. *Ohio Northern Alumnus*. 1929;2(4):11–13.

18. Anon. *Northern Review*. Ada, Ohio. January 13, 1937.

19. Ohio Northern University. Catalog for 1937–38. Heterick Memorial Library. Bound copy.

20. Ohio Northern University. Catalog for 1942–43. Accessed online July 3, 2008.

21. Burke-Wadsworth Act. Available at www.ohiohistorycentral.org/w/Burke-Wadsworth_ Act?rec=1500. Accessed May 15, 2015.

22. Worthen DB. Selective service and the pharmacist: necessary men in WW II. Pharmacy in History. 2001;43:124–133.

23. Anon. *Ada Herald*, Ada, Ohio. September 19, 1941.

24. Anon. *Ada Herald*. Ada, Ohio. September 18, 1942.

25. Binkley WE. *The History of ONU – A Draft*. Ada, Ohio. Ohio Northern University. 1947;126–128.

26. Worthen DB. Robert Philip Fischelis 1891–1981: Pharmacy activist. *Journal of the American Pharmaceutical Association*. 2006;46:294–297.

27. Ohio Northern University. Catalog for 1941–42. Accessed online July 3, 2008.

28. Anon. War Emergency Advisory Committee. *Journal of the American Pharmaceutical Association* (Scientific Edition). 1943;32:435–436.

29. Worthen DB. Pharmacy in World War Two. New York, New York. Pharmaceutical Products Press; 2000:volume unknown:134–135.

30. Anon. Servicemen's Readjustment Act (1944). Available at www.ourdocuments.gov. Accessed May 18, 2010.

31. Anon. Servicemen's Readjustment Act. Available at www.ohiohistorycentral.org/entry. php?rec=1930. Accessed March 25, 2009.

32. Anon. GI Bill of Rights. Available at www.bookrdags.com/research/gi-bill-of-rights-aaw-031. Accessed March 25, 2009.

CHAPTER SEVEN, OUT OF THE CRISIS: 1945–1959

1. Anon. Servicemen's Readjustment Act. Available at www.ohiohistorycentral.org/entry.php?rec=1930. Accessed March 25, 2009.

2. Anon. Servicemen's Readjustment Act (1944). Available at www.ourdocuments.gov. Accessed May 18, 2010.

3. Anon. GI Bill of Rights. Available at www.bookrdags.com/research/gi-bill-of-rights-aaw-031. Accessed March 25, 2009.

4. Anon. Born of controversy: The G.I. Bill of rights. Available at www.gibill.va.gov/GI_Bill_Info/history.htm. Accessed March 25, 2009.

5. Anon. 1944 GI Bill of Rights. Available at www.oise.utoronto.ca/research/edu20/moments/1944gibill.html. Accessed March 25, 2009.

6. Lee CO. Early years of Ohio Northern University College of Pharmacy V. *The Ampul.* 1966;16(3):5.

7. Anon. *Ohio Northern Alumnus.* October. 1948, pg 3.

8. Anon. *An ONU Photo Album.* Accessed online April 23, 2001.

9. Anon. Statement on signing the Surplus Property Act of 1944. Available at www.presidency.ucsb.edu/ws/index.php?pid=16567. Accessed July 3, 2008.

10. Binkley WE. *The History of ONU – A Draft.* Ada, Ohio. Ohio Northern University;1947:126–128.

11. Anon. *Ohio Northern Alumnus.* October, 1946, pg 2.

12. Sponholtz L. The politics of temperance in Ohio, 1880–1912. *Ohio History.* Date unknown;85:4–27.

13. Herrel EM. *The Heritage of a Noble Quest.* Ada, Ohio. Ohio Northern University Press. 1997.

14. Letter written by George J. Bonser to Raymond Schuck. March 9, 2009.

15. Anon. *Northern Review.* Ada, Ohio. November 19, 1957, pg 8

16. Anon. *Ada Herald.* Ada, Ohio. August 7, 1964. pg 1.

17. Belch GE. Tempered by Crisis. *Ohio Northern Alumnus.* 1971;32(3).

18. Anon. *Northern Review.* Ada, Ohio. September, 1949. Pg 1.

19. Ohio Northern University. Catalog for 1947–48. Accessed online July 3, 2008.

20. Ohio Northern University. Catalog for 1953–54. Accessed online July 7, 2008.

21. Wickham FZ. The role of licensing boards and professional organizations. *Ohio Pharmacist.* 2011;60(1):15-20.

22. Sonnedecker G. The American practice of pharmacy, 1902–1952. In Higby GJ, Higby G, Stroud E, eds. *American Pharmacy (1882–2002: A Collection of Historical Essays.* Madison, Wisconsin. American Institute of the History of Pharmacy;2005;volume unknown:5–10.

23. Elliott EC. The General Report of the Pharmaceutical Survey, 1946–1949. Washington DC, American Council on Education. 1950.

24. Higby GJ. Pharmacy in the American Century. *Apothecary's Cabinet.* 2000;No.1, Fall.

25. Lee CO. The Ohio Northern University College of Pharmacy. *The Ampul.* 1971;22(3):3.

26. Smith AC. The Dean's Corner. *The Ampul.* 1959;10(1):2.

27. Ohio Northern University. Catalog for 1950–51. Heterick Memorial Library. Bound copy.

28. Anon. *Northern Review.* Ada, Ohio. May 8, 1956, pg 1.

29. Anon. *Northern Review.* Ada, Ohio. September 12, 1950.

30. Smith AC. The Dean's Corner. *The Ampul.* 1954;3(3):8.

31. Anon. *Ohio Northern Alumnus;* 1951;12(2):3.

32. Anon. $25,000 pharmacy college expansion. *Ohio Northern Alumnus.* 1951–52;12(2):5.

33. Anon. Dukes gets new pharmacology lab. *The Ampul.* 1955;4(2):16.

34. Anon. *Ohio Northern Alumnus.* 1952; volume and pagination unknown.

35. Anon. *Northern Review.* Ada, Ohio. October 23, 1951.

36. Smith AC. The Dean's Corner. *The Ampul.* 1952;1(1):10.

37. Anon. A.Ph.A. news. *The Ampul.* 1952;1(1):2.

38. Smith AC. The Dean's Corner. *The Ampul.* 1952;2(1):10.

39. Anon. College of pharmacy sets pace. *Ohio Northern Alumnus.* 1951–52;12(4):3–4.

40. Smith AC. The state of the college—1957. *Ohio Northern Alumnus.* 1956–57;17:9–10.

41. Scott JW. Achievements of the A.Ph.A. *The Ampul.* 1954;3(3):4.

42. Hotaling GE. Can we count on you? *The Ampul.* 1952;1(1):5.

43. Smith AC. The Dean's Corner. *The Ampul.* 1956;5(2):4.

44. Anon. Pharmacy school gets "A" rating. *The Ampul.* 1956;6(1):3.

45. Anon. O.N.U. retains rating. *The Ampul.* 1958;8(2):13.

46. Ohio Northern University, College of Pharmacy Deans' Profiles (A.C. Smith). Heterick Memorial Library Archives. Ada, Ohio. June 20, 2008.

47. Lee CO. Albert C. Smith testimonial dinner. *The Ampul.* 1962;12(2):2.

48. Personal correspondence from Mrs. Joy West (Dean Smith's daughter). Colorado Springs, Colorado. April 12, 2013.

49. Anon. In memoriam: Dr. Albert C. Smith. *The Ampul.* 1972:24(1):2.

50. Anon. Honored son of O.N.U.: Dean Smith. *The Ampul.* 1957;6(2):2.

51. Smith AC. Personal notes on his thoughts concerning the college and university. Date unknown.

52. Martin S. Uniting for one pharmacy degree. *American Pharmacy.* 1992;32:52–55.

53. Funeral service for Albert C. Smith. Ada, Ohio. August 15, 1972.

CHAPTER EIGHT, A NEW BEGINNING: 1960–1971

1. Fried C. Pharmacy in 1960. *The Ampul*. 1957;6(2):13.

2. Nona DA, Wadelin JW. Pharmaceutical education in the 21st century. *Journal of Pharmacy Practice*. 1990;3:69–79.

3. Elenbaas RM, Worthen DB. Transformation of a profession: an overview of the 20th century. *Pharmacy in History*. 2009;59:151–2182.

4. Elliott EC. The General Report of the Pharmaceutical Survey, 1946–1949. Washington DC. American Council on Education, 1950.

5. Ohio Northern University. Catalog for 1960–61. Accessed online July 7, 2008.

6. Ohio Northern University. Catalog for 1959–60. Accessed online July 7, 2008.

7. Smith AC. The Dean's Corner. *The Ampul*. 1959;10(1):2.

8. Ohio Northern University. Catalog for 2002–03. Bound copy. Heterick Memorial Library.

9. American Council on Pharmacy Education. Examiners Report to the Council of Ohio Northern University College of Pharmacy. March 15, 1963.

10. Worthen DB. Robert Phillip Fischelis 1891–1981: Pharmacy activist. *Journal of the American Pharmaceutical Association*. 2006;46:294–297.

11. Curriculum vitae: C.O. Lee. Heterick Memorial Library Archives. Ohio Northern University. July, 2008.

12. Vottero LD. Fischelis notes. *Pharmacy in History*. 2006;48:171–173.

13. Anon. In memoriam: Dr. Robert P. Fischelis. *Ohio Northern Alumnus*. 1981;42(3):37.

14. Stuart DM. A Pharmacist's Diary. *Ada Herald*. Ada, Ohio. March 14, 1984.

15. Anon. Pharmacy college gets 3-year accreditation. *Ada Herald*. Ada, Ohio. June 10, 1966.

16. Anon. Pharmacy, law deans named. *Ohio Northern Alumnus*. 1987;47(3):14.

17. Anon. ONU pharmacy college gets full accreditation. *Ada Herald*. Ada, Ohio. January 23, 1969.

18. Beltz LD. Dean's Corner. *The Ampul*. 1969;20(1):2.

19. Anon. An ONU Photo Album. Accessed online April 23, 2001.

20. Anon. Trustees approve plans for pharmacy building and science center. *The Ampul*. 1964;14(3):6.

21. Lee CO. The Ohio Northern University College of Pharmacy. *The Ampul*. 1971;22(3):3.

22. Beltz LD. Ohio Northern University College of Pharmacy. *American Journal of Pharmaceutical Education*. 1968;32:26–34.

23. Anon. The university begins a new era. *Ohio Northern Alumnus*. 1964;25(4):3–4.

24. Anon. *Ada Herald*, Ada, Ohio. April 1, 1966.

25. Anon. Pharmacy building dedication held. *The Ampul*. 1966;17(1):7.

26. Miner SA. Portrait of a benefactor: James D. Robertson, PhG '98. *Ohio Northern University Alumnus*. August, 1968.

27. Reed C. Letter to LeRoy Beltz, re: James D. Robertson. September 18, 1965.

28. Anon. ONU buildings. Accessed online July 14, 2008.

29. Sheets MRF. A faculty-member's review of recent changes in the College of Pharmacy. *The Ampul*. 1966;17(1):5.

30. Ohio Northern University. Catalog for 1970–71. Accessed online July 7, 2008.

31. Anon. College of pharmacy grows. *The Ampul*. 1971;22(2):8.

32. Beltz LD. Dean's Corner. *The Ampul*. 1970;21(3):2.

33. Beltz LD. Dean's Corner. *The Ampul*. 1971;22(2):2.

34. ONU to name Pharmacy College in Honor of Dr. Rudolph Raabe. *The Kenton Times*. Kenton, Ohio. September 9, 1971.

35. Ohio Northern University, College of Pharmacy Deans' Profiles (Robert Fischelis). Heterick Memorial Library Archives. Ada, Ohio. June 20, 2008.

36. Anon. $179,000 pledged to O.N.U. *The Ampul*. 1957;6(3):12.

37. Anon. *Ohio Northern Alumnus*. 50(4):2–3.

38. Anon. Charles O. Lee (1883–1980) Historian in pharmacy. *Pharmacy in History*. 1980;22:165.

39. Fischelis RP. Message from the dean. *The Ampul*. 1965;15(2):2.

40. Fischelis R. Report of the dean. College of Pharmacy, Ohio Northern University. Heterick Memorial Library Archives. Ada, Ohio. 1984.

41. Fischelis RP. Message from the dean. *The Ampul*. 1965;15(2):2.

42. Sonnedecker G, Williamson M. The personal papers of Robert P. Fischelis. *Pharmacy in History*. 1993;35:83–85.

43. Worthen Dennis B. Robert Phillip Fischelis 1891–1981: Pharmacy activist. *JAPhA*. 2006;46(2):294–297.

44. Anon. Dr. Beltz appointed pharmacy dean. *The Ampul*. 1966;16(2):3.

45. Ohio Northern University, College of Pharmacy Deans' Profiles (LeRoy Beltz). Heterick Memorial Library Archives. Ada, Ohio. June 20, 2008.

46. Anon. Students, faculty, and friends remember Dean Beltz. *The Ampul*. 1986;Spring:2.

47. Anon. Dr. LeRoy D. Beltz. *Ohio Northern Alumnus*. 1985;46(3):13.

CHAPTER NINE, REDEFINING PHARMACY PRACTICE: 1972–1983

1. Nona DA, Wadelin JW. Pharmaceutical education in the 21st century. *Journal of Pharmacy Practice*. 1990;3:69–79.

2. Elenbass RM, Worthen DB. Transformation of a profession: an overview of the 20th century. *Pharmacy in History*. 2009;59:151–182.

3. Penna RP. Pharmacy: A profession in transition or a transitory profession? *American Journal of Hospital Pharmacy*. 1987;44:2053–2059.

4. Anon. Health Professions Educational Assistance Act of 1963 PL88–129. *United States Statutes at Large*. Washington DC. Government Printing Office. 88th Congress. 1964:77:164–173.

5. Anon. Health Professions Education Assistance Act Amendments of 1965 PL89–290. *United States Statues at Large*. Washington DC. Government Printing Office. 89th Congress. 1966:79:1052–1058.

6. Anon. Health Manpower Act of 1968. *United States Statues at Large*. Washington DC. Government Printing Office. 90th Congress. 1969;82:773–789.

7. Anon. Health Manpower Training Act of 1971. PL92–157. *United States Statues at Large*. Washington DC. Government Printing Office. 92nd Congress. 1972:85:431–464.

8. Nona DA, Wadelin JW. Pharmaceutical education in the 21st century. *Journal of Pharmacy Practice*. 1990;3:69–79.

9. Millis JS. *Pharmacists for the Future*. Ann Arbor, Michigan. Health Administration Press. 1975.

10. Worthen DB, ed. *The Millis Study Commission on Pharmacy: A Road Map to a Profession's Future*. New York, New York. Pharmaceutical Products Press;2006:5.

11. Beltz LD. Dean's Corner. *The Ampul*. 1973–74;25(2):2.

12. Beltz LD. Dean's Corner. *The Ampul*. 1977;29(1):2.

13. Ohio Northern University. Catalog for 1974–75. Accessed online July 7, 2008.

14. Anon. Drug center answers tough questions. *Ohio Northern Alumnus*. 1975;36(4):26.

15. Ohio Northern University. Drug Information Center. Available at www.onu.edu/pharmacy. Accessed April 15, 2013.

16. Buerki RA. Continuing education today in Ohio. *The Ampul*. 1967;17(2):7.

17. Anon. Vital member of the health care team—Pharmacy. *Ohio Northern Alumnus*. 1974;35(2):2–5.

18. Ohio Northern University. Continuing Pharmacy Education. Available at www.onu.edu/pharmacy. Accessed April 15, 2013.

19. Higby GJ. Pharmacy in the American Century. *Apothecary's Cabinet*. 2000;No 1, Fall.

20. Enderle L. Closing the gender gap in pharmacy ownership. Available at www.pharmacytimes.com/news/Closing-the-gender-Gap-in-Pharmacy-Ownershsip. Accessed March 15, 2013.

21. American Association of Colleges of Pharmacy. Academic pharmacy's vital statistics. Available at www.aacp.org/about/pages/vitalstats.aspx. Accessed March 15, 2013.

22. Ohio Northern University. Catalog for 1979–80. Accessed online July 9, 2008.

23. Ohio Northern University. Catalog for 1988–89. Accessed online July 17, 2008.

CHAPTER TEN, THE PACE INTENSIFIES: 1984–1999

1. Elliott EC. The General Report of the Pharmaceutical Survey, 1946–1949. Washington DC. American Council on Education. 1950.

2. Nona DA, Wadelin JW. Pharmaceutical education in the 21st century. *Journal of Pharmacy Practice*. 1990;3:69–79.

3. The Final Report of the Task Force on Pharmacy Education. Washington DC. American Pharmaceutical Association. 1984.

4. Miller WA. Planning for Pharmaceutical Education in the 21st Century. Presented at the 1989 Annual Meeting of the American Association of Colleges of Pharmacy. Portland, Oregon. 1989.

5. Martin S. Uniting for one pharmacy degree. *American Pharmacy*. 1991;32:52–55.

6. Anon. AACP Commission to Implement Change: Entry-Level education in pharmacy: Commitment to change. *American Journal of Pharmacy Education*. 1993;57:366–374.

7. Anon. AACP White Paper. Pharmaceutical education: a commentary from the American College of Clinical pharmacy. *Pharmacotherapy*. 1992;12:419–427.

8. Buttaro M. House of delegates vote: Colleges to move to sole-entry-level Pharm.D. *American Journal of Hospital Pharmacy*. 1992;49:2346–2350.

9. Nona DA. The American Council on Pharmaceutical Education: Annual Report 1997–1999. *American Journal of Pharmacy Education*. 1998;62:34–38.

10. Hoag SG. Dean's Column. *The Ampul*. 1990;Winter:2.

11. Ohio Northern University, College of Pharmacy Deans' Profiles (Stephen G. Hoag). Heterick Memorial Library Archives. Ada, Ohio. June 20, 2008.

12. Hoag SG. Dean's Column. *The Ampul*. 1988;Spring:2.

13. Anon. Pharm.D. program is up and running. *The Ampul*.1994;Summer:1.

14. Anon. *Ohio Northern Alumnus*. 50(4):2–3.

15. Anon. Pharm.D. program approved. *The Ampul*. 1993;Summer:1.

16. Ohio Northern University. Catalog for 1996–97. Accessed online July 17, 2008.

17. Anon. College enrolling students in its non-traditional Pharm.D. degree program. *The Ampul*. 1997;Summer:1.

18. Anon. Non-traditional Pharm.D. degree program inaugurated. *The Ampul*. 1998;Winter/Spring:7.

19. Gossel TA. Dean's Corner. *The Ampul*. 1996/97;Winter:2.

20. Anon. Advances in the pharmacy curriculum. *The Ampul*. 1998;Winter/Spring:8.

21. Ohio Northern University. Catalog for 1998–99. Accessed online July 17, 2008.

22. Ohio Northern University. Catalog for 1972–73. Accessed online July 7. 2008.

23. Ohio Northern University. Catalog for 1979–80. Accessed online July 9, 2008.

24. Ohio Northern University. Catalog for 1991–92. Accessed online July 17, 2008.

25. Ohio Northern University. Catalog for 2012–13. Bound copy.

26. Anon. Ribbon cutting ceremony marks beginning for construction of addition to pharmacy building. *The Ampul*. 1994/95;Winter:9.

27. Ohio Northern University, College of Pharmacy Deans' Profiles (Louis D Vottero).

Heterick Memorial Archives. Ada, Ohio. July, 2008.

28. Louis D. Vottero. Office of Public Information. Ohio Northern University. Ada, Ohio. July, 2008.

29. Anon. The Pellegrino Medal. Available at www.samford.edu/heal/pellegrino.html. Accessed June 1, 2010.

30. Anon. New pharmacy dean named: Dr. Stephen G. Hoag. *The Ampul.* 1987;Spring:1.

31. Ohio Northern University. College of Pharmacy: Stephen G. Hoag. Available at www. pharmacy.umn.edu/faculty/hoag_stephen/home.html. Accessed June 1, 2010.

32. Anon. Hoag leaves legacy of leadership. Available at www.pharmacy.umn.edu/prod/groups/cop/@pub/.../cop_88491.pdf. Accessed April 11, 2013.

33. Anon. Pharmacy, law deans named. *Ohio Northern Alumnus.* 1986;47(3):14.

34. Anon. College of pharmacy welcomes Dean Bryant. *The Ampul.* 2000;Winter:1.

35. Penna RP. Report of the Executive Vice President: a year in review. *American Journal of Pharmacy Education.* 1999;63(Winter Supplement):19.

36. Anon. Samford names Ohio Northern's Bobby Bryant as Dean of McWhorter School of Pharmacy. Available at www.Samford.edu/pubs/belltower/May2006.1/bryant.html. Accessed November 6, 2011.

CHAPTER ELEVEN, PREPARING FOR TOMORROW: 2000 AND BEYOND

1. Ohio Northern University, Catalog for 2012–13. Bound copy.

2. Goldberg IB. Clinical clerkship and the ONU program. *The Ampul.* 1991; Spring:1.

3. Burke-Wadsworth Act. Available at www.ohiohistorycentral.org/w/Burke-Wadsworth_Act?rec=1500. Accessed May 15, 2015.

4. Ohio Northern University, Catalog for 2011–12. Accessed online November 28, 2011.

5. Tachikawa S. Semester reception mixed at term end. *The Northern Review.* 2011;12(10):1–2.

6. Sprague JE. Ohio Northern University: Maintaining core values while implementing pharmacy educational and practice changes. *Ohio Society of Health-System Pharmacy.* 2011;31(1):6.

7. Ohio Northern University. Faculty and staff. Available at www.onu.edu/pharmacy. Accessed April 15, 2013.

8. Sprague JE. Message from the dean. Available at www.onu.edu/pharmacy. Accessed April 15, 2013.

9. Smith AC. Personal notes on the college and university. Data unknown.

10. Sprague JE. From the dean. *The Ampul.* Spring, 2011.

11. Ohio Northern University. Catalog for 1974–75. Accessed online July 7, 2013.

12. Anon. Pharmacy Skills Center. *The Ampul.* Fall, 2007.

13. Anon. Ribbon cutting ceremony marks beginning for construction of addition to pharmacy building. *The Ampul.* 1994–95:Winter:9.

14. Anon. The Hakes-Pierstorf Family Pharmacy Education Center. *The Ampul.* Spring;2005.

15. Anon. Groundbreaking of the Hakes-Pierstorf Family Pharmacy Education Center. *The Ampul.* Fall;2005.

16. DiPietro NA, Rush MJ, Bright DR, et al. Strategies to engage pharmacy students and residents in worksite-based health and wellness programs. *Current Pharmacy Teaching and Learning.* 2013;5:68–74.

17. Bright DR, Terrell SL, Rush MJ, et al. Employee attitudes toward participation in a work site-based health and wellness clinic. *Journal of Pharmacy Practice.* 2012;25:530–536.

18. Baicker K, Cutler D, Song Z. Workplace wellness programs can generate savings. *Health Affairs (Millwood).* 2010;29(2):304–311.

19. Murphy BL, Rush MJ, Kier KL. Design and implementation of a pharmacist-directed preventive care program. *Am J Health-System Pharm.* 2012;69:1513–1518.

20. Lippert A. Opening remarks 2001. Accessed online April 3, 2013.

21. Lippert A. Opening talk 2003. Accessed online April 3, 3013.

22. Anon. ONU At a glance. Available at www.onu.edu/pharmacy. Accessed April 15, 2013.

23. Anon. ONU Curriculum,. Available at www.onu.edu/pharmacy. Accessed April 15, 2013.

24. Martin, SJ. Flipping the script. *The Ampul.* 2015; Spring:8–9.

25. Anon. Ohio Northern University to establish community mobile health clinic to provide health care in Hardin County. Available at www.onu.edu/node/65617. Accessed May 21, 2015.

26. Ohio Northern University, College of Pharmacy Deans' Profiles (Jon E. Sprague). Heterick Memorial Library Archives. Ada, Ohio. June 20, 2008.

EPILOGUE

1. Boyd EE. Pharmacists in Ohio leading the way. *Ohio Pharmacist.* 2013;62(6):6.

2. Buerki RA. Recent Trends in American Pharmacy: An Introduction. *Journal of Pharmacy History.* 2009;51:91–93.

APPENDIX 2

Ohio Northern University. Summary of diplomas and degrees awarded by year, college, and gender. Accessed online July 2, 2008.

APPENDIX 3

Ohio Northern University. Catalog for 1926–27. Accessed online July 3, 2008.

APPENDIX 4

Lee CO. The Ohio Northern University College of Pharmacy. *The Ampul.* 1971;22(3):3.

APPENDIX 5

Ohio Northern University. Catalog for 1959–60. Accessed online July 7, 2008.

Ohio Northern University. Catalog for 1960–61. Accessed online July 3, 2008.

APPENDIX 7

Ohio Northern University. Catalog for 1972–73. Accessed online July 7, 2008.

APPENDIX 8

Ohio Northern University. Curriculum. Available at www.onu.edu/pharmacy. Accessed April 15, 2013.

APPENDIX 10

Benton LC, Lee CO. The early years of the Ohio Northern University College of Pharmacy II. *The Ampul.* 1964;14(3):10.

Lee CO. The early years of Ohio Northern University College of Pharmacy III. *The Ampul.* 1964;15(1):3.

Lee CO. The early years of Ohio Northern University College of Pharmacy IV. *The Ampul.* 1965;15(3):7.

Lee CO. Early years of Ohio Northern University College of Pharmacy V. *The Ampul.* 1966;16(3):5.

INDEX